HEAT
and
TEMPERATURE
MEASUREMENT

|||||||||||||||||||||||

HEAT
and
TEMPERATURE
MEASUREMENT

|||||||||||||||||||||||

ROBERT L. WEBER

Associate Professor of Physics

THE PENNSYLVANIA STATE COLLEGE

NEW YORK

PRENTICE-HALL, INC.

1950

PRENTICE-HALL PHYSICS SERIES
Donald H. Menzel, *Editor*

PRINTED IN THE UNITED STATES OF AMERICA

Preface

▮▮▮▮▮▮▮▮▮▮▮▮▮▮▮▮▮▮▮▮▮▮▮▮

Many natural phenomena and many industrial processes involve transformations which are associated with heat. Measurements of heat and temperatures are of fundamental importance. Experience in this branch of physics is valuable in the training of students in physics, chemistry, engineering, metallurgy, and ceramics.

This book describes methods of heat and temperature measurement and includes the theoretical principles necessary for their appreciation, intelligent use, and extension. The material will appropriately follow an introductory physics course and is suitable for a one-semester college course in which lecture-recitation and laboratory work are integrated. The emphasis is on experimental methods rather than on thermodynamic theory.

Part I presents the physical principles which serve as a basis for thermal measurements. Numerical examples, solved in the text, illustrate these principles quantitatively. Superscript numbers in the text refer to the bibliographies at the ends of the chapters. These references are suggested for supplementary reading to introduce the student to scientific journals through papers he can understand. The concise chapter summaries emphasize fundamental ideas and encourage systematic reviewing.

The discussion questions are designed to test the student's ability to apply and extend the text material, rather than his memory. For the same purpose, many numerical problems are presented. Answers are given to the even-numbered problems.

Part II outlines the procedures for twenty-nine laboratory experiments. Brief discussions of the theory and photographs of typical arrangements of apparatus should be helpful in planning experiments and in setting up the apparatus.

The Appendix contains chiefly tables, several aids to study, and a list of relevant motion picture films. The student will find help in the economical use of his study time and in data taking through use of the concise chapter summaries, the solved numerical examples, the procedures suggested for solving physical problems (p. 363), the form recommended for laboratory reports (p. 368), and consistent observance of rules governing the use of significant figures in experimental data (p. 365).

The sources of many illustrations are indicated through references in the text. Acknowledgment is made with thanks to the following individuals and firms for illustrations not otherwise identified: Arthur D. Little, Inc., 13.7; Frank A. Benford, 6.8; The Bristol Company, 9.5, 9.6; The Brown Instrument Company, 5.12; The Carborundum Company, 13.9; Central Scientific Company, 5.10, 10.1, 2, 4, 24, 25, 37, 38; Corning Glass Works, 7.6; General Electric Company, Lamp Department, 7.8, 9.8; J. G. Horn, 9.9, 9.11, 9.12, 9.13, 9.14, 9.15, 9.16; Leeds & Northrup Company, 7.3b, 7.5, 7.7, 9.2, 9.3, 9.4, 9.17, 9.18, 9.19, 9.20, 9.21, 10.12, 18; Humbolt W. Leverenz, 6.2; National Bureau of Standards, 5.9, 5.11, 16, 17; Parr Instrument Company, 30; Precision Scientific Company, 32, 33; Pyrometer Instrument Company, 7.9; Rubicon Company, 5.7; W. M. Welch Scientific Company, 11.3; Weston Electrical Instrument Corporation, 2.6.

The author is sincerely grateful to colleagues who in their teaching of the Heat and Temperature Measurement course have helped to improve it, especially to Dr. Kenneth V. Manning; to those whose critical reading of the manuscript has resulted in improvements, especially Dr. Donald H. Menzel and Marion Fleming Weber; to Frances M. Boldereff for her styling of the book; to the editors of Prentice-Hall, Inc., for considerate help in the production of the book; and to The Haddon Craftsmen, Inc., for careful and fitting typography.

The author will be grateful for suggestions or criticisms that will make the book more useful, or for corrections that will make it more accurate.

ROBERT L. WEBER

State College, Pa.

Contents

||||||||||||||||||||||||||||

vii

PART II

LABORATORY EXPERIMENTS

PART I

PRINCIPLES OF
HEAT AND
TEMPERATURE
MEASUREMENT

Chapter 1

||||||||||||||||||||||||||||

TEMPERATURE SCALES

EVOLUTION OF CONCEPT OF HEAT AND TEMPERATURE |||||||| *DEVELOPMENT OF MEASURING INSTRUMENTS* ||||||||

HEAT

Heat is a form of energy.   This fact was demonstrated in experiments performed by Joule, Rumford, Davy, Mayer, Helmholtz, and Colding, each of whom measured the heat produced by the performance of definite amounts of mechanical work.   In each case the quotient of the energy expended and the heat produced was found to be a constant. This observation led to the acceptance of a conservation-of-energy principle, explicitly stated by Helmholtz in 1847, which, by gradual extension, has become a basic part of all theory in the physical sciences.

We may think of heat as energy that is transferred from one body to.another by a thermal process.   A thermal process means conduction, convection, or radiation-absorption—or a combination of these processes.

Heat is an extensive quantity.   It follows the law of addition just as do length and mass.

TEMPERATURE

Our fundamental concept of temperature is obtained from the sensation of warmth or cold which we experience upon touching any object.   Such expressions as ice-cold, cool, tepid, lukewarm, warm, hot, etc., indicate that our qualitative appreciation of temperature precedes our use of numbers to characterize it.   Our experience further tells us that when two similar bodies at different temperatures are placed in thermal communication (and cut off from such communication with all other bodies) the hot body becomes colder and the cold body becomes warmer, until the two reach a thermal state or temperature that, judged by our senses, is the same.

Our observations then, plus the concept of heat exchange as an energy transfer, enable us to say that in the equalization of temperature heat passes from the hotter to the colder body.   In seeking for a definition of temperature, therefore, we find it difficult to improve on the one given by Maxwell, which is: "The temperature of a body is its thermal state considered with reference to its ability to communicate heat to other bodies."

Of two bodies having different temperatures, the one that communicates heat to the other is said to be at the higher temperature. In a temperature scale its temperature is customarily, though not necessarily, assigned the greater number.

Heat has been identified with the internal molecular energy of a body.   It is then natural to try to devise a measure of heat in terms of, say, average molecular kinetic energy.   But attempts to assign dimensions to temperature on the usual mass-length-time system of dimensions have not been successful.   Hence it may be expedient to define temperature as one of the (arbitrary) fundamental dimensions.   Another viewpoint is possible.   According to it, temperature is dimensionless, since the operation of measuring temperature always reduces to a dimensionless ratio of lengths, pressures, etc.   Either viewpoint implies that when the statement "heat is energy" is written as an equation, it includes a dimensional constant

$$W = JQ$$

COMMON TEMPERATURE SCALES

Two thermometer scales are in common use.   One, the *centigrade* scale, divides the standard interval between the freezing point and the boiling point of water into 100 equal parts called *centigrade degrees*. The other, the *Fahrenheit* scale, divides the standard interval into 180 equal parts called *Fahrenheit degrees* (Fig. 1.1).   The older scale was devised about 1724 by Gabriel Fahrenheit, a manufacturer of meteorological instruments in Danzig. Fahrenheit arbitrarily chose the zero for his scale at the temperature of a mixture of ammonium chloride and ice. The centigrade scale also has an arbitrarily chosen

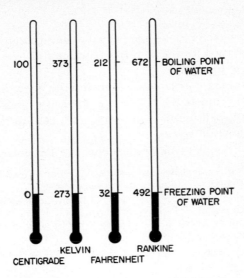

FIG. 1.1.   Fixed points on various temperature scales.

zero. Initially, as planned in 1742 by the Swedish astronomer Andreas Celsius, the 0 reading referred to the boiling point of water and the 100 reading to the temperature of melting ice. A year later, Linné and Strömer reversed this designation and established our present centigrade scale.

Temperatures may be converted from one scale to another by means of a simple proportion

$$\frac{C - 0°}{F - 32°} = \frac{100° - 0°}{212° - 32°} = \frac{5}{9} \tag{1}$$

This may be solved for either C or F to give

$$C = \tfrac{5}{9}\,(F - 32°) \tag{2}$$

$$F = \tfrac{9}{5}\,C + 32° \tag{3}$$

From the manner in which the standard interval is subdivided in the two scales (Fig. 1.1), it is evident that $100 \text{ C}° = 180 \text{ F}°$. Dividing each side of this equation by $180 \text{ F}°$ and $100 \text{ C}°$ in turn, we obtain

$$\frac{5 \text{ C}°}{9 \text{ F}°} = 1 = \frac{9 \text{ F}°}{5 \text{ C}°} \tag{4}$$

These conversion factors, which are equal to unity, as are all conversion factors, may be used for the convenient transfer of temperatures from one type of scale to another.

When expressing *a temperature* we shall write after the number one of the common symbols °C, °F, etc.; and when expressing *a difference of temperature* we shall use the symbols C°, F°, etc., or the words *centigrade degrees, Fahrenheit degrees,* etc.

Numerical examples will serve to illustrate the process.

EXAMPLE: A Fahrenheit thermometer indicates a temperature of 5°F. What is the corresponding reading on the centigrade scale?

The temperature of 5°F is $32° - 5° = 27 \text{ F}°$ below the freezing point of water. A temperature interval of $27 \text{ F}°$ is equivalent to $\frac{5}{9} (27 \text{ F}°) = 15 \text{ C}°$. Hence the reading on the centigrade scale is 15° below the freezing point of water, or $-15°\text{C}$.

$$5°\text{F} = 32°\text{F} - 27 \text{ F}°\left(\frac{5 \text{ C}°}{9 \text{ F}°}\right) = 0°\text{C} - 15 \text{ C}° = -15°\text{C}$$

EXAMPLE: A comfortable room temperature is 70°F. What is this temperature expressed on the centigrade scale?

$$\text{C} = \frac{5}{9}(70° - 32°) = \frac{5}{9}(38°) = 21°\text{C}$$

EXAMPLE: Over a period of 50 years, the extremes of temperature in New York differ by 116 Fahrenheit degrees. Express this range in centigrade degrees.

$$116 \text{ F}° = \frac{5}{9}(116) \text{ C}° = 64.4 \text{ C}°$$

Absolute temperature scales are a consequence of the establishment of certain thermodynamic principles (Chap. 12). They start from the absolute zero, below which no temperature is possible. The Kelvin scale, named after the English physicist Lord Kelvin (1824–1907), uses the same unit of temperature difference as the centigrade scale and is often called the centigrade absolute scale. The Rankine scale, named after William John Rankine (1820–1872), a Scottish engineer, uses the same unit of temperature difference as the Fahrenheit scale and is often called the Fahrenheit absolute scale.

Conversions to the Kelvin and Rankine scales are made from the relations

$$K = 273.16° + C \qquad (5)$$

$$R = 459.69° + F \qquad (6)$$

Certain corresponding temperatures on the four common types of temperature scales are indicated in Fig. 1.1 and in Table 1.1.

TABLE 1.1. COMMON THERMOMETER SCALES

Temperature	Centigrade	Kelvin	Fahrenheit	Rankine
Steam point.......	100.000°C	373.16°K	212.000°F	671.69°R
Ice point.........	0.000	273.16	32.000	491.69
Absolute zero.....	−273.16	0.00	−459.69	0.00

INSTRUMENTS FOR TEMPERATURE MEASUREMENT

In principle, any physical property which changes in a known and reproducible manner with temperature may serve as the basis for a temperature measuring device. Some of the more common practical instruments are listed in Table 1.2 with their usable ranges.

TABLE 1.2. RANGES OF COMMON TEMPERATURE MEASURING METHODS

Method	Approximate Ranges
Mercury-in-glass thermometer......................	−38°C to 350°C
Alcohol-in-glass thermometer......................	−80°C 100°C
Constant-volume gas thermometer..................	4°K 1850°K
Bimetallic thermometer...........................	−40°C 500°C
Thermocouple....................................	−250°C 1600°C
Resistance thermometer...........................	0.8°K 1600°C
Optical pyrometer................................	600°C up
Total-radiation pyrometer.........................	100°C up
Speed of sound..................................	No limits
Thermodynamic..................................	No limits

TEMPERATURE SCALES

Temperature can be measured only by indirect methods. We generally transfer heat to an instrument designed to respond to the energy so transferred. Changes in the properties listed in Table 1.3

TABLE 1.3. Temperature-Measuring Substances and Properties

Thermometric Substance	Thermometric Property	Symbol
Gas or vapor at constant volume...........	Pressure	P
Mercury in glass capillary................	Volume	V
Platinum wire...........................	Electrical resistance	R
Thermocouple..........................	Thermal emf	E
Dilatometer or bimetal strip..............	Length	L

have been found most useful for practical temperature measurement.

The process of assigning numbers to temperatures is partly analogous to the process of marking divisions on a tape measure. The zero is arbitrary. The scale is continuous, that is, an infinity of thermal states can be represented between the arbitrarily-chosen fixed points.

To assign numbers to temperatures we select (*a*) some suitable substance, then (*b*) some property of this selected thermometric substance, and finally (*c*) some function relating the temperature to this property. The temperature scale so defined will be only one of a large number of possible ones. It will depend in general on all three selections—the thermometric substance, the property, and the function. To be useful for defining a temperature scale, the thermometric property of any such device must change smoothly with changing temperature and must return to its original reading when the device returns to its original thermal state.

Suppose we select as basic fixed points the melting point of ice and the boiling point of water, each at a pressure of one standard atmosphere, and assign to them the numbers 0 and 100, respectively. We can define a scale by making equal increments on the scale correspond to equal increases in length of a tungsten rod. Thus 50° would be the temperature at which the length of the rod is halfway between its length at 0° and its length at 100°, or in general

$$t = 0° + \frac{L_t - L_0}{(L_{100} - L_0)/100} \tag{7}$$

Are the degree intervals on this scale equal? Experience shows that the length of a rod of *copper* will be halfway between its length at 0° and its length at 100° at a temperature that on our *tungsten* rod expansion centigrade scale is 54°. If we divide the interval 0 to 100 in proportion to *electrical resistance* (rather than length) we find that the *resistance* scale based on copper agrees well (fortuitously) with the *expansion* scale based on tungsten. But the resistance scale based on tungsten agrees with none of the other three. These observations raise important practical questions. How can different experimenters make temperature measurements which are reproducible and comparable? We see that the results of temperature measurements depend on the arbitrary choices of thermometric materials and properties. Even the form of calibration relation is arbitrary, being taken as linear in Eq. (7) merely for simplicity.

This illustrates a fundamental property of temperature that is often lost sight of, namely that temperature is an *intensive* and not an extensive quantity. There can be no unit temperature interval that can be successively applied to measure any other temperature interval, as can be done in the measurement of such a quantity as length. The size of a degree on one part of a scale, no matter how defined, can bear no relation to the size of a degree on any other part of the scale.

The various temperature scales differ in the thermometric substance employed, the thermometric property utilized, or in the function selected to represent the relation between the property and the temperature. Scales that differ in either of the first two features are *fundamentally* different. The difference between two scales, which differ only in the function chosen, is only *superficial*, because conversion from one scale to the other is merely a matter of the calculation and can be made with mathematical precision. Changing the numbers assigned to the fixed points makes no real change in the character of the scale and is perhaps the simplest way by which the interpolation function can be changed.

It is sometimes convenient to increase all the numbers for temperatures on these scales by a suitable constant amount, in order that the lower limit of temperature ("absolute zero") shall be designated as 0°. The amount by which a scale should be increased to accomplish this result depends upon the thermometric property and cannot be known exactly, since it must be experimentally determined. However, since the amount by which a scale has been shifted in any given case is known, this shift can be taken care of with mathematical precision.

In contrast, two scales that employ either different thermometric substances or different thermometric properties differ by an amount that can be determined only by experiment. If the same basic fixed points are employed, the scales will necessarily agree at these points, but not at other points. Two scales, both based on the apparent expansion of mercury in glass, will differ unless the kind of glass used is the same. The scale based on the change in pressure, at constant volume, of a definite mass of nitrogen differs from the scale based on the change in volume of the same gas at constant pressure. The constant-volume nitrogen scale with initial pressure (at the ice point) of 500 mm of mercury differs from the constant-volume nitrogen scale with 1000 mm initial pressure.

The ideal temperature scale would be one which made use of a property so selected that the scale would not depend on the thermometric substance. Such a scale would serve throughout the entire temperature range, since no limitations due to failure or breakdown of any substance would be met. The only scales of this kind that have so far been devised will be described in Chap. 12.

SUMMARY

Heat is the kinetic energy of the random motions of the ultimate particles of which bodies are composed.

The *temperature* of a body is the property that determines the direction of flow of heat between the body and its surroundings.

A *thermometer scale* is established by selecting as *fixed points* two easily reproducible temperatures (ice point and steam point), dividing this interval into a number of equal subintervals, and assigning an arbitrary zero.

Conversions between centigrade and Fahrenheit scale readings are made by the relations

$$C = \tfrac{5}{9} (F - 32°)$$
$$F = \tfrac{9}{5} C + 32°$$

Temperature scales based upon different thermometric substances or thermometric properties are fundamentally different.

Temperature scales which differ only in the equation used to relate temperature to thermometric property are only superficially different, and conversions from one scale to the other can be made with mathematical precision.

GENERAL REFERENCES FOR SUPPLEMENTARY READING

1. Allen, H. S., and R. S. Maxwell, *A Textbook of Heat*, Macmillan and Co., Ltd., 1944.
2. American Institute of Physics, *Temperature—Its Measurement and Control in Science and Industry*, Reinhold Publishing Corp., 1941.
3. Cork, J. M., *Heat*, 2d ed., John Wiley & Sons, Inc., 1942.
4. Edser, E., *Heat for Advanced Students*, rev., Macmillan and Co., Ltd., 1936.

5. Griffiths, Ezer, *Methods of Measuring Temperature*, 3d ed., Charles Griffin & Co., Ltd., 1947.
6. The Physical Society (London), *Reports on Progress in Physics*, Vols. I-, 1935-..., sections on *Heat*.
7. Roberts, J. K., *Heat and Thermodynamics*, Blackie and Son, Ltd., 1940.
8. Saha, M., and B. N. Srivastava, *Textbook of Heat*, Indian Press, 1931.
9. Weld, LeRoy D., *A Textbook of Heat for Upperclassmen*, The Macmillan Co., 1948.
10. Wood, W. P., and J. M. Cork, *Pyrometry*, 2d ed., McGraw-Hill Book Co., Inc., 1941.
11. Worthing, A. G., "The Temperature Concept," *Am. J. Physics*, **8,** 28 (1940).
12. Worthing, A. G., and D. Halliday, *Heat*, John Wiley & Sons, Inc., 1948.
13. Zemansky, M. W., *Heat and Thermodynamics*, 2d ed., McGraw-Hill Book Co., Inc., 1943.

QUESTIONS AND PROBLEMS

1. What is temperature?

2. What is the distinction between temperature and quantity of heat?

3. Outline clearly the logical steps in the definition of a practical temperature scale.

4. Explain the statement, "Temperature is an intensive property."

5. List several methods of measuring temperatures and mention the factors that limit the range of each.

6. Let X_0 and X_{100} be the values of a thermometric property at the ice and steam points, and X_t the value at temperature t. Then the temperature may be determined on the centigrade scale from $t = 100(X_t - X_0)/(X_{100} - X_0)$. Write the corresponding equation for the Fahrenheit scale.

7. How is a temperature scale based on the expansion of mercury fundamentally different from a temperature scale based on the pressure of nitrogen? What should be the characteristics of an ideal temperature scale?

8. Since temperature as defined by Eq. (7) depends on the thermometric property, how can we justify using mercury thermometers, thermocouples, gas thermometers, etc., interchangeably?

9. What factors need to be considered in the design of a sensitive thermometer?

10. Which can generally be measured more accurately, a temperature or a temperature difference?

11. Convert $-40°C$, $20°C$, and $37°C$ to Fahrenheit readings. Convert $-5°F$, $10°F$, and $1000°F$ to centigrade readings.

12. Express $444°C$, $96°C$, and $-219°C$ on the Fahrenheit scale. Express $-10°F$, $2651°F$, and $3227°F$ on the centigrade scale.
    Ans. $831°F$, $1760°F$, $-362°F$, $-23°C$, $1455°C$, $1775°C$.

13. (a) At what temperature does a Fahrenheit thermometer read the same as a centigrade thermometer? (b) Half as much? (c) Twice as much?

14. (a) Change $444°C$ and $-78.5°C$ to the Kelvin scale. (b) Change $68°F$ and $212°F$ to the Rankine scale. *Ans.* $717°K$, $194.7°K$, $528°R$, $672°R$.

15. Liquid oxygen freezes at $-218.4°C$ and boils at $-183.0°C$. Express these temperatures (a) on the Kelvin scale, and (b) on the Fahrenheit scale.

16. The average temperature of healthy persons is $98.6°F$. Express this on the centigrade scale, the Kelvin scale, and the Rankine scale.

Ans. $37.0°C$, $310.2°K$, $558.3°R$.

17. Express the temperature interval between the ice point and the steam point in (a) centigrade degrees, (b) Fahrenheit degrees, (c) Kelvin degrees, and (d) Rankine degrees.

18. Express a change in temperature of $36 \, C°$ in terms of Fahrenheit degrees.

Ans. $65 \, F°$.

19. The extremes of temperature recorded in New Orleans differ by $109 \, F°$. Express this range in centigrade degrees.

20. A common type of centigrade thermometer is graduated from -10 to $110°C$ and thus covers a range of $120 \, C°$. Express this range in Fahrenheit degrees.

Ans. $216 \, F°$.

Chapter 2

||||||||||||||||||||||||

EXPANSION THERMOMETERS

THERMAL EXPANSION COEFFICIENTS |||||||
DIFFERENTIAL EXPANSION ||||||| *LIQUID-IN-*
GLASS THERMOMETERS ||||||| *GAS THERMOM-*
ETER ||||||| *BIMETALLIC THERMOMETER* |||||||

COEFFICIENT OF LINEAR EXPANSION

Nearly all materials expand with an increase in temperature. A solid changes all its linear dimensions and thus its volume. Liquids and gases have no shapes of their own, and therefore only volume expansion has meaning. For solids we are concerned primarily with linear expansion.

The *coefficient of linear expansion* (or the linear expansivity), α, is the change in length per unit length per degree rise in temperature. In symbols

$$\alpha = \frac{L_t - L_0}{L_0 \, \Delta t} \tag{1}$$

where L_0 and L_t are the initial and final lengths, respectively, and Δt is the change in temperature.

Measurements of the length and the change in length are expressed in the same unit of length; hence the value of α will be independent of the length unit used, but it will depend on the temperature unit used. The linear expansivity must be specified as "per centigrade

13

degree" or "per Fahrenheit degree" as the case may be. If we let ΔL represent the change in length of a bar, then

$$\Delta L = \alpha L_0 \, \Delta t \tag{2}$$

The final length will be

$$L_t = L_0 + \Delta L = L_0 + \alpha L_0 \, \Delta t = L_0(1 + \alpha \, \Delta t) \tag{3}$$

TABLE 2.1 LINEAR EXPANSIVITIES (AVERAGE)

Material	Per C°	Per F°
Aluminum	0.000022	0.000012
Brass	0.000019	0.000011
Copper	0.000017	0.0000094
Glass, ordinary	0.0000095	0.0000053
Glass, pyrex	0.0000036	0.0000020
Invar (nickel-steel alloy)	0.0000009	0.0000005
Iron	0.000012	0.0000067
Oak, along grain	0.000005	0.000003
Platinum	0.0000089	0.0000049
Fused quartz	0.00000059	0.00000033
Steel	0.000011	0.0000061
Tungsten	0.0000043	0.0000024

EXAMPLE: The steel tire of a locomotive is 3.980 ft in inside diameter at 70°F. What is the minimum temperature to which it must be heated to slip over a wheel that is 4.000 ft in outside diameter?

$$\Delta L = L_0 \, \alpha \, \Delta t$$

$$\Delta t = \frac{4.000 \text{ ft} - 3.980 \text{ ft}}{(3.980 \text{ ft})(0.0000061/\text{F}°)} = 820 \text{ F}°$$

$$t = 70°\text{F} + 820 \text{ F}° = 890°\text{F}$$

The coefficient α as used in Eqs. (1) to (3) represents the average linear expansivity for the specified temperature interval. For all materials α varies somewhat with temperature, and these equations are not sufficient for exact purposes. An empirical equation may be obtained by introducing terms with higher powers of Δt in the right-hand member of Eq. (3) and including enough terms in the power series for the accuracy required. Thus Eq. (3) becomes

$$\frac{L - L_0}{L_0} = a_1(t - t_0) + a_2(t - t_0)^2 + a_3(t - t_0)^3 + \cdots \tag{4}$$

where a_1, a_2, etc., are constants characteristic of the material and of the reference temperature t_0 at which the length is L_0. In the limiting case, for the region about t_0 we may rewrite Eq. (1) in calculus notation

$$\alpha_{t_0} = \left(\frac{1}{L}\frac{dL}{dt}\right)_{t_0} = a_1 \tag{5}$$

showing that the constant a_1 is the linear expansivity at t_0. The terms containing a_2 and a_3 in Eq. (4) we may regard as representing second- and third-order corrections to the length at t_0 to obtain the length at t.

In theories developed by Debye and Grueneisen, α is related to the specific heat and the elastic constants of a material. Extremely accurate interferometer measurements have been made of the variation of α with temperature to test the applicability of these theories. Figure 2.1 represents the data for copper of high purity (99.979 per cent). Dots represent experimental values of $1/L(dL/dt)$. The curve is the one predicted by the Grueneisen theory.[8]

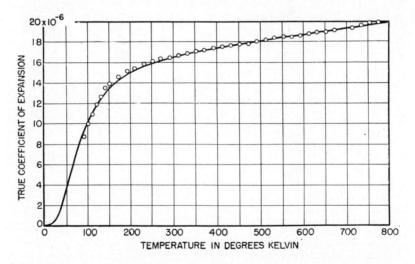

FIG. 2.1. True coefficient of thermal expansion *vs.* temperature for copper.

Many industrial problems arise from the facts that different solids have different expansivities and that the expansivity for a given material may vary appreciably with temperature. If a structure, for example a furnace, can be made of materials that expand equally over wide ranges in temperature, the structure will hold together much

better than if such materials cannot be found.   When it is impossible
to find suitable materials with approximately equal expansivities,
allowance must be made for the large forces that arise owing to the
fact that the different parts of the structure expand at different rates.
Some materials that go together well at one temperature may be
unsatisfactory at other temperatures owing to change of their expansivities with temperature.

The sealing of metal electrodes through the glass of electric-light
bulbs, radio tubes, X-ray tubes, and the like requires the matching of
the expansion characteristics of metal and glass.   Tungsten, platinum,

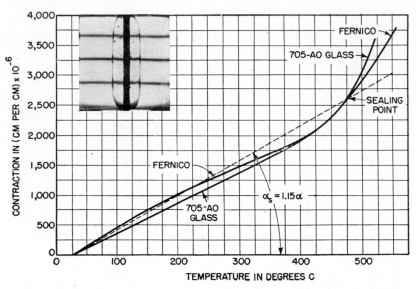

F_IG. 2.2.   Contraction of Fernico and 705–AO glass.   The average expansion
coefficient between room temperature and sealing temperature is represented by α_s.

Dumet (a nickel-steel alloy covered with a sheath of copper), and
Fernico (an iron-nickel-cobalt alloy) are often used for this purpose
since their expansions can be matched with that of appropriate glasses.
Figure 2.2 shows the close agreement of the cooling curves of Fernico
and 705-AO glass from the annealing temperature down to room
temperature.[5]   This means that glass and metal if joined together at
the annealing temperature will contract at the same rate as they cool,
and be free from strain both during cooling and after reaching room

temperature. The insert gives the photoelastic stress pattern of a test seal made with these materials. The lines are straight within one hundredth of a fringe, showing that the stress is less than 0.02 kg/mm².

COEFFICIENT OF VOLUME EXPANSION

The volume expansivity of a material is the change in volume per unit volume per degree rise in temperature. In symbols

$$\beta = \frac{V_t - V_0}{V_0 \, \Delta t} \tag{6}$$

where β is the volume expansivity, V_0 and V_t are the initial and final volumes, and Δt is the temperature change.

We may write relations for volume expansion similar to those of Eq. (4)

$$\frac{V - V_0}{V_0} = b_1(t - t_0) + b_2(t - t_0)^2 + b_3(t - t_0)^3 + \cdots \tag{7}$$

$$\beta_{t_0} = \left[\frac{1}{V} \frac{dV}{dt} \right]_{t_0} = b_1 \tag{8}$$

When the temperature of a solid is raised, the body expands in all directions. Certain crystals are found to have different linear expansivities along different axes. Many common materials, however, have the same properties in all directions. These are called isotropic substances.

TABLE 2.2 VOLUME EXPANSIVITIES OF LIQUIDS

Substance	Per C°	Per F°
Alcohol (ethyl)................................	0.0011	0.00061
Mercury..	0.00018	0.00010
Water (15 to 100°C)........................	0.00037	0.00020

There is a simple approximate relation between the linear expansivity of an isotropic solid and the corresponding volume expansivity

$$\beta = 3\alpha \quad \text{(approx)} \tag{9}$$

This relation can be derived by consideration of the expansion of a cube of the material.

To determine the expansivity of a liquid, a correction generally must be made for expansion of the container.   However, in the method of balanced columns (Exp. 2) the expansivity of a liquid may be measured quite independently of changes in dimensions of the container.

Generally a liquid expands when its temperature is raised.   Water is an important exception to this rule, since in the region from 0 to 4°C water contracts as its temperature is raised.   Above 4°C water expands with increasing temperature.

EXAMPLE: A pyrex glass flask of volume 1000 cm³ is full of mercury at 20°C. How many cubic centimeters will overflow when the temperature is raised to 50°C? The change in volume of the flask is given by

$$\Delta V = \beta V \,\Delta t$$
$$\beta = 3\alpha = 3(3.6 \times 10^{-6}/\ C°) = 10.8 \times 10^{-6}/C°$$
$$\Delta V = (10.8 \times 10^{-6}/C°)(1000\ cm^3)(50°C - 20°C) = 0.32\ cm^3$$

The change in volume of mercury is given by

$$\Delta V_{Hg} = \beta_{Hg} V \,\Delta t$$
$$\Delta V_{Hg} = (0.00018/C°)(1000\ cm^3)(50°C - 20°C) = 5.4\ cm^3$$
$$\text{Overflow} = \Delta V_{Hg} - \Delta V = (5.4 - 0.32)\ cm^3 = 5.1\ cm^3$$

LIQUID-IN-GLASS THERMOMETERS

The most common of all thermometers depend for their readings on the relative expansion of a comparatively large quantity of mercury, or other liquid, in the bulb.   This expansion indicates the temperature by the position of the end of a column of the liquid in the capillary bore of the graduated stem.   For ease in reading, the expansion per degree may be made large either by increasing the size of the bulb or by decreasing the cross section of the bore.

In addition to the liquid-in-glass thermometers for general or laboratory use, there are special types designed for definite uses. Among these we shall describe later clinical, industrial, calorimetric, Beckmann, and maximum-minimum thermometers.   But first let us examine general characteristics which should be taken into account in the intelligent use of thermometers.

TOTAL AND PARTIAL IMMERSION THERMOMETERS

Most common and inexpensive thermometers are factory calibrated under conditions of complete immersion at 0°C and 100°C.   The standard interval between corresponding marks on the scale is subdivided evenly on the assumption that the bore is exactly uniform.

If a thermometer standardized for total immersion is used at partial immersion a portion of the liquid column will be at a temperature different from that of the bath. The reading will be too low or too high, depending upon whether the surrounding temperature is lower or higher than that of the bath. For a total immersion thermometer so used an emergent stem correction may be computed from the formula

$$\text{Stem correction} = Kn(t_b - t_s) \tag{10}$$

in which K is the differential expansivity of the liquid in the thermometer in the particular kind of glass of which the thermometer is made, n is the number of degrees emergent from the bath, t_b is the temperature of the bath, and t_s is the average temperature of the liquid column of n degrees. The value of t_s is determined by means of an auxiliary thermometer. When lacking information about the thermometer glass, one may take K as 0.00016 for centigrade mercurial thermometers and 0.00009 for Fahrenheit thermometers. For centigrade thermometers containing organic liquids, it is often sufficient to use the approximate value of $K = 0.001$.

EXAMPLE: A reading of 86.74°C is observed with a thermometer immersed to the 20° mark on the scale so that 67° of the column project into the air. The mean temperature of the emergent column is found to be 39°. What is the corrected value of the temperature?

$$\text{Stem correction} = 0.00016 \times 67(87°C - 39°C) = +0.51 \ C°$$
$$t = 86.74°C + 0.51 \ C° = 87.25°C$$

There has been an increasing tendency to use partial immersion thermometers, graduated and standardized for definite depths of immersion, thus eliminating the need for a correction for the emergent stem. The appropriate depth of immersion is indicated by a mark on the thermometer. Thermometers made for 76-mm or 3-in. immersion for no specified stem temperature are available for general use. Such organizations as the American Society for Testing Materials have standardized the specifications for many types of industrial thermometers to be used in tests where the design of the apparatus requires short immersion lengths.

CHANGES IN THERMOMETER CALIBRATION

Thermometers change with time and use. Progressive changes in bulb volume may result in more or less permanent changes in calibra-

tion.   These will not exceed 0.1 C° for good grades of thermometric
glass, provided the thermometer has not been heated above 150°C.

Temporary changes that result from heating may require consideration in thermometers graduated in 0.1° or 0.2° intervals and
not intended for use above 150°C or 300°F.   Upon heating, the bulb
will, within a few minutes, assume the volume corresponding to the
higher temperature.   If the bulb is then cooled to the original temperature, it does not at once return to the original volume but remains
somewhat larger.   There is a consequent "depression" in reading.
This depression is usually somewhat less than 0.01° for each 10 C° that
the bulb is heated above the original temperature and disappears
almost entirely in a few days.

Mercury-in-glass thermometers graduated for use above 100°C
should have the capillary above the mercury column filled with a
dry inert gas, such as nitrogen, under pressure, to retard vaporization
of the mercury.   About 1 atm is required at 300°C, up to 20 atm at
550°C.   When a thermometer is subjected to temperatures approaching the softening range of the glass the high internal pressure enlarges
and permanently injures the bulb.

For initially well-annealed thermometers not subjected to excessive
temperatures, further changes (contraction) due to annealing of the
bulb are small and can be allowed for by initial and subsequent determinations of the reference-point reading and application of the
necessary corrections.

THERMOMETRIC LAG

When a thermometer is placed in a medium of temperature T',
the temperature T indicated by the thermometer approaches that of
its surroundings at a rate dT/dt given by the equation

$$dT/dt = \frac{-1}{\lambda}(T - T') \tag{11}$$

The lag coefficient λ is a constant which depends upon the type of
thermometer, the medium, and the speed with which the medium
moves relative to the thermometer.

EXAMPLE: A thermometer initially at temperature $T_i = 20°$ C is placed in an
unstirred water bath at 90°C.   Under these conditions $\lambda = 10.0$ sec.   What time
elapses before the thermometer indicates a reading within 2 per cent of the bath
temperature?

By integrating Eq. (11) we have

$$\log_e \frac{T - T'}{T - T_i} = -\frac{t}{\lambda}$$

$$\log_e \frac{2}{90 - 20} = -\frac{t}{10 \text{ sec}}$$

$$t = -(10 \text{ sec})(\log_e 0.0286) = (-10 \text{ sec})(3.55) = 36 \text{ sec}$$

TOLERANCES FOR THERMOMETERS

Table 2.3 is an excerpt from a more complete table published by the National Bureau of Standards.[1] It states the graduation intervals appropriate for the temperature ranges listed, the tolerances allowed by the NBS in issuing certificates, the accuracies which may be expected, and the decimal figure to which corrections are stated in the certificate.

TABLE 2.3 NBS TOLERANCES FOR TOTAL IMMERSION
(Mercurial Thermometers Not Graduated above 150°C)

Temperature Range in Degrees	Graduation Interval in Degrees	Tolerance in Degrees	Accuracy in Degrees		Corrections Stated to
0 up to 100............	0.1	0.3	0.01 to 0.3		0.01
0 150............	0.2	0.4	0.02	0.05	0.02
0 150............	1 or 0.5	0.5	0.1	0.2	0.1

Tolerance is the maximum error which may reasonably be allowed for a thermometer made in accordance with good manufacturing practice. Accuracy here refers to the best values attainable in the use of the instrument when all the corrections are applied.

The tolerance (scale error) requirements for American Society for Testing Materials thermometers are smaller than those given in Table 2.3, being 0.03, 0.05, and 0.2° respectively. ASTM requirements are based on the expectation that the readings will be used *without* corrections; the corrections are assumed to be small enough to be negligible. Greater accuracy can be obtained, however, with a thermometer requiring appreciable corrections, with those corrections applied, than with a thermometer showing smaller corrections which are not applied to the readings.

SPECIAL LIQUID-IN-GLASS THERMOMETERS

Clinical or fever thermometers (Fig. 2.3) are small maximum-reading instruments used in measuring body temperatures. The range of scale is usually from about 96 to 106°F. The capillary is constricted above the bulb. The opening permits mercury to be forced through when the bulb is being warmed but it is sufficiently small to prevent cohesive forces from withdrawing the thread into the bulb after the warming ceases. To return the mercury thread to the bulb after a reading, the inertia of the mercury is used, either by shaking it down by hand or else by swinging the thermometer rapidly in a curved path.

Industrial or metal-protected liquid-in-glass thermometers are adapted for plant use where ruggedness is more necessary than high precision. These thermometers cover a range from about −40 to 500°C and are graduated for partial immersion of the liquid column. The thermometers are often fitted into separable sockets which permit their removal without interfering with the functioning of the apparatus.

The Beckmann thermometer is a difference thermometer so constructed that a portion of the mercury may be removed from the bulb in order that the scale, about 30 cm long, may be used for differential measurements over a 5 or 6 C° range, reading directly to 0.01 C°. The reservoir for storing mercury in excess of that used for any particular temperature range is located at the top of the scale. The setting temperature of the thermometer refers to the temperature of the bulb when the reading is 0° on the scale. This temperature is ordinarily obtained with the aid of a less sensitive thermometer.

For different setting temperatures there are different amounts of mercury in the bulb. Whenever the thermometer is used at a setting different from the one (usually 20°C) at which it was calibrated, setting factors are used to convert the temperature differences read into true temperature differences. These setting factors, tabulated by the NBS, combine corrections for the different changes in volume of different quantities of mercury during equal temperature changes, and the difference between the mercury-in-glass scale and the International Temperature Scale.

In calorimetric thermometers, designed chiefly for use with the gas calorimeter (Exp. 23), the accuracy at any one temperature is of less importance than the accuracy of the temperature intervals.

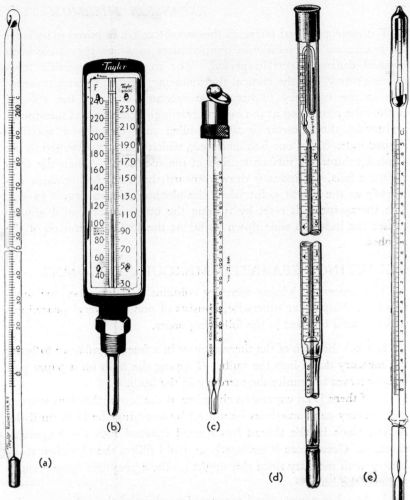

Fig. 2.3. Types of mercury-in-glass thermometers: (a) nitrogen-filled, (b) industrial, (c) clinical, (d) Beckmann differential, (e) Philadelphia differential, (f) meteorological maximum-and-minimum.

(f)

For meteorological purposes thermometers are required to indicate the maximum and minimum temperatures to which they have been exposed during a certain period. The maximum-registering thermometer may, like the clinical thermometer, depend upon a constriction in the capillary to break the mercury column, the column in the tube remaining at the highest reading. One type of minimum-registering thermometer is alcohol-filled and contains a specially shaped index about one-half inch long, which is kept submerged in the alcohol column by surface tension of the meniscus. When the temperature falls, the index is drawn toward the bulb, but remains stationary at the lowest point when the alcohol column begins to rise. The thermometer is reset by tipping the bulb upward until gravity causes the index to slide down as far as the surface meniscus of the alcohol.

REUNITING SEPARATED MERCURY COLUMNS

The process of joining mercury columns that have become separated, in shipping or otherwise, consists of one or several procedures which should be tried in the following order.

1. Cool the bulb of the thermometer in a freezing mixture to bring the mercury down into the bulb. Tapping the bulb on a paper pad usually serves to reunite the mercury in the bulb.

2. If there is an expansion chamber at the top of the thermometer the mercury can sometimes be united by warming the bulb until the broken place in the thread has moved upward into the expansion chamber. Great care is necessary to avoid filling the chamber completely with mercury since this might produce pressures large enough to burst the bulb.

3. As a last resort, small separated portions of the column can be warmed to disperse them into droplets tiny enough to leave space for the gas to by-pass, and these droplets can then be collected by a rising mercury column. Alternatively, one may hold the thermometer in a slanting position with the bulb upward and by gently heating the detached thread, distill the mercury from it to unite it with the main portion of the mercury column.

It is advisable to make a check of the ice point or some other reference point on the scale after carrying out one of these procedures.

EXPANSION OF GASES

The behavior of a gas when its temperature is changed can be examined in the apparatus shown in Fig. 2.4. It is convenient to keep either the pressure or the volume constant in order to study the variation in the other factor with change in temperature. To restore the level of mercury in the left-hand column to the index 0, one raises the reservoir R. The gas then occupies its original volume. Its pressure P_t can be found by measuring the difference in levels of the mercury columns and adding to it the atmospheric pressure.

The coefficient of pressure change β_v at constant volume is defined as

$$\beta_v = \frac{P_t - P_0}{P_0 \, \Delta t} \qquad (12)$$

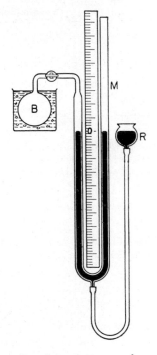

Substitution of observed values for the pressure P_0 at the ice point and the pressure P_t at the temperature t gives the value of β_v for the particular gas used. The interesting result is that the value of β_v is roughly the same for all gases, providing the pressure of the gas is not too high. The value found for β_v is $\frac{1}{273}$ per C° or 0.00366 per C°. That is, the pressure of any gas at constant volume will change by $\frac{1}{273}$ of its pressure at 0°C for each degree change in temperature.

In a suitable apparatus a gas may be held at constant pressure while its change in volume is read from the displacement of mercury. The volume expansivity β_p at constant pressure may then be obtained from Eq. (6). It is found that, when the pressure of the gas is not too high, the value of β_p is approximately the same for all gases and is the same as the value for β_v.

FIG. 2.4. Apparatus for measuring expansion of a gas.

CONSTANT-VOLUME GAS THERMOMETER

It is apparent from their behavior that gases can be used as thermometric substances. Constant-volume thermometers (Fig. 2.5), being less difficult to manipulate, are used almost to the exclusion of constant-pressure ones. Even the constant-volume thermometer usually is employed only to determine accurately the temperatures of certain boiling, melting, and transformation points. These then serve as calibration points for other more convenient temperature-measuring devices.

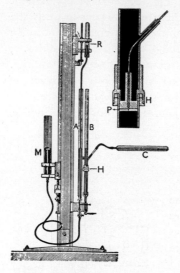

At sufficiently low pressures, many gases follow the relation

$$PV = MRT \qquad (13)$$

with rather high precision. It follows that

$$\frac{T - T_0}{T_{100} - T_0} = \frac{P - P_0}{P_{100} - P_0} \qquad (14)$$

from which $T - T_0$, the centigrade temperature corresponding to pressure P, may be found in terms of the pressures P_0 and P_{100} at the ice and steam calibration temperatures.

FIG. 2.5. Constant-volume gas thermometer: one-liter bulb C, manometer AB, barometer R. By adjusting mercury reservoir M, mercury surface in lower part of B is set at index P in sleeve H, thus keeping volume of gas constant. The difference in mercury levels in B and R measures the pressure.

The temperature agreement obtained by using different gases becomes progressively better as the pressure P_0 is reduced, suggesting that as the pressure approaches zero all gases become ideal and follow Eq. (13). Advantage is taken of this fact by rewriting the equation in the form

$$PV = A + BP + CP^2 + DP^3 + \cdots$$

The constants A, B, C, and D are complicated functions of the temperature but they are independent of pressure. They are found by noting the volume occupied by the gas at different pressures. Experiments on a number of gases in the range from -183 to $400°C$ have shown that the C term and those following are negligible. Thus the equation simplifies to

$$PV = A + BP \qquad (15)$$

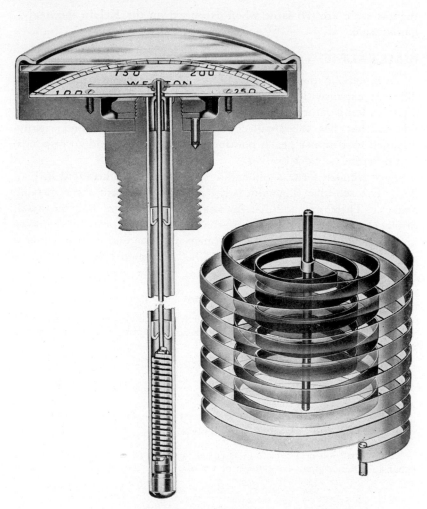

FIG. 2.6.   Weston bimetallic thermometer: (a) Sectional view is shown on left,
(b) enlarged view of bimetallic coil on right.

For low pressures the gas obeys Boyle's law, $PV = A$.   Hence in order
to obtain temperature readings corrected to the ideal gas scale, observations of the unknown temperature T are made using successively
smaller pressures P_0 in the thermometer, and the results for T are
extrapolated to zero pressure.   Absolute temperatures determined on

the gas scale are the same when expre.sed on the Kelvin thermodynamic scale.

BIMETALLIC THERMOMETERS

A bimetallic thermometer consists of strips of two metals with different expansivities, riveted, soldered, or welded together. With a rise in temperature, the composite strip will bend toward the component that has the smaller expansivity. With one end rigidly attached to a support, each position of the deflecting end corresponds to a different temperature.

A convenient form of bimetallic thermometer is illustrated in Fig. 2.6. The sensitive bimetallic strip is wound to form three coaxial helixes. These are additive in rotational deflection, but the axial displacements are mutually counterbalanced. With proper immersion an accuracy of ½ per cent of the range over the entire scale is guaranteed by the maker of a common laboratory-model bimetallic thermometer.

SUMMARY

A *coefficient of expansion* (*expansivity*) is the fractional change (in length or in volume) per degree change in temperature. The units, per $C°$ or per $F°$, must be expressed

$$\alpha = \frac{L_t - L_0}{L_0 \, \Delta t}$$

$$\beta = \frac{V_t - V_0}{V_0 \, \Delta t}$$

$$\beta = 3\alpha \text{ (approx)}$$

The expansion of a substance is equal to the product of its coefficient of expansion, the original size (length or volume), and the temperature change

$$\Delta L = \alpha L_0 \, \Delta t \qquad \text{and} \qquad \Delta V = \beta V_0 \, \Delta t$$

When a thermometer standardized for total immersion is used at partial immersion, an emergent-stem correction may be computed from the formula

$$\text{Stem correction} = Kn(t_b - t_s)$$

In measuring temperature with a mercury-in-glass thermometer, one should immerse the thermometer properly, provide adequate circulation, allow sufficient time for thermometer to reach equilibrium, make sure that liquid column is not separated, and avoid parallax by keeping eye level with top of column when reading the thermometer. For high accuracy one should apply any necessary corrections for scale errors and for length of emergent stem, and check the thermometer occasionally against a standard to detect changes in calibration.

A *differential thermometer* provides a means of enlarging a 5° interval in the region of the anticipated temperature to permit direct reading to 0.01 C°.

The pressure and volume coefficients of expansion, β_v and β_p, of all gases are approximately equal to $\frac{1}{273}$ per C°, and become more nearly identical as the pressure is reduced.

REFERENCES FOR SUPPLEMENTARY READING

1. Am. Inst. Physics, *Temperature—Its Measurement and Control in Science and Industry*, pp. 228–255, "Liquid-In-Glass Thermometers," by Johanna Busse, Reinhold Publishing Co., 1941.
2. Dowden, J. B., "Increasing Sensitivity of Bimetal Thermometers," *Product Engineering*, **6**, 388 (1935).
3. Eskin, S. G., and J. R. Fritze, "Thermostatic Bimetals," *Trans. Am. Soc. Mech. Eng.*, No. 17 (1939).
4. Harper, D. R., "Thermometric Lag," *Bull. Bur. Standards*, **8**, 659 (1912).
5. Hull, A. W., E. E. Burger and L. Navias, "Glass-to-Metal Seals II," *J. App. Phys.*, **12**, 698 (1941).
6. Morley, E. W., and W. A. Rogers, "On the Measurement of the Expansion of Metals by the Interferential Method," *Phys. Rev.*, **4**, 1, 6 (1896).
7. Mueller, E. F., and R. M. Wilhelm, "Methods of Testing Thermometers," *Proc. Am. Soc. Testing Materials*, **38**, 1, 493 (1938).
8. Nix, F. C., and D. MacNair, "The Thermal Expansion of Pure Metals: Copper, Gold, Aluminum, Nickel, and Iron," *Phys. Rev.*, **60**, 597 (1941).
9. Stanton, L. R., "A Recording Dilatometer for Metal Specimens," *J. Iron Steel Inst.*, **147**, 95 (1943).
10. Tool, A. Q., D. B. Lloyd, and G. E. Merritt, "Dimensional Changes Caused in Glass by Heating Cycles," *Bur. Standards J. Research* **5**, 627 (1930).

QUESTIONS AND PROBLEMS

1. Why do solids and liquids generally expand when heated? How do you account for the fact that some crystals have different expansivities along different axes?

2. Would the numerical value of a coefficient of linear expansion be different if the inch were used as the unit of length rather than the centimeter? If the Fahrenheit scale were used rather than the centigrade scale? Explain.

3. Show that the coefficient of area expansion is approximately twice that of linear expansion and that the coefficient of volume expansion is approximately three times that of linear expansion.

4. A steel pin fits into a hole in a brass plate. What will be the effect on the closeness of fit if the pin alone is heated? If the plate alone is heated? If both are heated equally?

5. In the early manufacture of light bulbs platinum wire was sealed through the glass. By reference to Table 2.1, show why this was feasible.

6. Suggest some practical uses of differential expansion of two different materials. In what cases is differential expansion undesirable?

7. Explain why an observation of the apparent expansion of a liquid contained in a bulb or tube does not give the true expansion of the liquid.

8. What precautions should be observed in the selection and use of a liquid-in-glass thermometer in order to attain the best accuracy?

9. Suggest a simple form of apparatus which could be used to determine the volume expansivity of alcohol, independent of changes in dimensions of the container.

10. Would the error introduced by the expansion of the container be larger for a liquid thermometer or for a gas thermometer? Explain.

11. A centigrade thermometer placed in a steam point apparatus indicates 98.0°C. The barometric pressure is 720.2 mm of mercury. Find the boiling-point error of the thermometer. (Consult Table 24 in the Appendix.)

12. A steel tape correct at 68°F is used to measure land when the temperature is −20°F. What percentage error will result in length measurements due to contraction of the tape?   *Ans.* 0.054 per cent.

13. A section of steel tape is 100,000 ft long at 68°F. Find its length (a) at 38°F, and (b) at 98°F.

14. A barometer having a brass scale indicates a pressure of 724.0 mm of mercury when the temperature is 22°C. What would be the reading if the barometer were subjected to the same atmospheric pressure at 0°C?   *Ans.* 711.5 mm.

15. In general the reading of a mercury barometer must be corrected to 0°C for the altered density of the mercury due to expansion and for expansion of the brass scale. (a) Show that the correction for altered density of the mercury is effected by multiplying the observed height by $(1 - \beta_{Hg} t)$. (b) Show that the observed height must be multiplied by $(1 + \alpha_{Br} t)$. (c) Show that the barometric height P_0 corrected for both expansion of mercury and scale is given in terms of the observed height P by the relation $P_0 = P [1 + (\alpha_{Br} - \beta_{Hg}) t]$ approximately.

16. A mercury barometer indicates a pressure of 29.92 in. of mercury when the temperature is 80°F. What is the barometric pressure when corrected to 32°F for expansion of the mercury and the brass scale?   *Ans.* 29.79 in. of mercury.

17. Measurements are made at 25°C of a brass tube by a steel scale correct at 0°C. The result is 64.50 cm. Find the length that would have been obtained if tube and scale were at 0°C.

18. A 30.0-gal steel drum is filled with acetone (volume expansivity 13.1 × $10^{-4}/C°$) when the temperature is 50°F. How much acetone will overflow when the temperature becomes 110°F?   *Ans.* 1.3 gal.

19. Benzene is placed in two vertical glass tubes which are open at the top and which are connected by a horizontal capillary tube at the bottom. When one tube is kept at 11°C and the other at 81°C, the levels of the benzene are observed to be 49.0 and 70.0 cm, respectively, above the capillary. Find the average coefficient of volume expansion for the benzene.

20. Ethyl alcohol is placed in two vertical glass tubes which are open at the top and which are connected by a horizontal capillary tube at the bottom. When one tube is kept at 0°C and the other at 60°C, the levels of the alcohol are observed to be 50.0 and 53.3 cm, respectively, above the capillary. (a) Find the average volume expansivity of the alcohol. (b) Show that the expansivity determined in this way is independent of expansion of the container.   *Ans.* 0.0011 per C°.

21. (a) A thermometer contains 250 mm³ of mercury. The diameter of the bore is 0.20 mm. If the volume coefficients of expansions for the mercury and the glass are 0.000182 per C° and 0.000022 per C° respectively, how long are the degree intervals on the stem?   (b) What does this problem illustrate regarding the dependence of sensitivity on bulb size, bore diameter, and glass expansivity?

22. A spherical pyrex glass bulb has an inside diameter of 20.0 cm.   Find its change in volume when heated from 20 to 180°C.   Linear expansivity of pyrex is 0.0000036 per C°.   *Ans.* 7.25 cm³.

23. A reading of 785°F is observed with a thermometer immersed to the 200° mark on the scale so that 585° of the column project into the air.   The average temperature of the emergent column is found to be 172°F.   Find the corrected temperature (a) by applying Eq. (10) and (b) by using the result from (a) for t_b, applying Eq. (10) a second time to get a better approximation.

24. A mercury-in-glass thermometer calibrated for total immersion is inserted for part of its length in a boiler.   It indicates a temperature of 98.0°C.   There are 40° of emergent mercury column, the average temperature of which is 50°C.   What is the boiler temperature corrected for emergent stem?   *Ans.* 98.3°C.

25. A certain thermometer has a coefficient of lag of 15 sec.   The thermometer, initially at 70° F, is inserted into an oven at 400°F.   What time will elapse before the thermometer indicates a temperature in excess of 395°F?

26. A certain thermometer has a coefficient of lag of 0.60 min.   The thermometer is transferred from a bath at 100°C to one at about 20°C.   How long should an observer wait before reading the thermometer in order that the temperature indicated for the bath be in error by not more than 5 per cent due to lag?
                                                                            Ans. 2.6 min

Chapter 3

HEAT TRANSFER

STEADY CONDUCTION THROUGH PLATES,
SPHERICAL AND CYLINDRICAL WALLS serverID
HEAT FLOW IN THREE DIMENSIONS serverID
VARIABLE FLOW serverID *CONVECTION* serverID

TYPES OF HEAT TRANSFER

We regard heat as the internal energy associated with the molecular activity in a body. The simplest mode of transfer of heat, which we call *conduction*, is the direct communication of molecular disturbance through a substance by molecular or atomic collisions. In the case of metals the movements of valence electrons may be predominantly responsible for conduction of heat as well as conduction of electricity.

Convection transfers heat by actual motion of the hot material.

Heat transfer is accomplished also by a combination of *radiation* and *absorption*. In the process of radiation heat is transformed into radiant energy, consisting of vibratory electric and magnetic disturbances which move through space in phase. The radiant energy may travel a great distance before being absorbed and changed back into heat.

THIN PARALLEL PLATE

As a simple example of the conduction of heat, consider a thin slice of material having parallel faces, one at temperature T_1, the other at temperature T_2, as in Fig. 3.1. Intuition suggests, and

32

experiment confirms, that when the temperature at every point has become steady, the amount of heat Q transferred across the plate is directly proportional to the temperature difference $T_1 - T_2$, the area A, the time t, and is inversely proportional to the thickness L, and also depends upon the material

$$Q = \frac{kAt(T_1 - T_2)}{L} \tag{1}$$

The coefficient k is called the thermal conductivity of the material.

Rewriting Eq. (1) in the form

$$k = \frac{Q}{At}\ \frac{\Delta L}{\Delta T} \tag{2}$$

will help clarify the units in which thermal conductivity is expressed. The temperature change per unit distance, $\Delta T/\Delta L$, is called the *temperature gradient*. This term appears in the denominator of Eq. (2). Thus we may say that the *thermal conductivity* of a material represents the heat it transfers per unit area per unit time per unit temperature gradient. In the metric system k is expressed in cal/(cm^2 sec C$°$/cm). In the British system thermal conductivity is usually expressed in Btu/(ft^2 hr F$°$/in.).

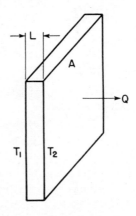

The quantity $1/k = n$ is called the *thermal resistivity*, or the thermal resistance of a unit cube. Thermal resistances of insulators in "series" or "parallel" may be computed from formulas analogous to those used for electrical resistances. An equation, analogous to Ohm's law, may be written for the thermal current, $dQ/dt = \Delta T/n$.

FIG. 3.1. Heat conduction through a thin plate.

There are three convenient steady-state conditions often employed in the precise measurement of thermal conductivity. These are: the unidirectional flow of heat along a rod whose sides are thermally insulated, the flow of heat radially outward from the axis of a cylinder, and the flow of heat radially outward from the center of a sphere.

Although a bar can never have its sides perfectly insulated, in practice longitudinal heat flow along parallel lines can be assured by a guard-ring heater.[6] In the apparatus of Fig. 3.2, sections of the test specimen are placed symmetrically on each side of an electrically heated plate. The heat passes from the hot plate through the specimen and into plates cooled by flowing water. A guard-ring heater eliminates losses from the edges of the specimen so that for an area equivalent to that of the hot plate the equitemperature surfaces are sensibly plane. Thermocouples serve to measure the fall in temperature $T_1 - T_2$ across a measured thickness L of the specimen. The thermal conductivity is calculated from

$$k = \left(\frac{VI}{2\mathcal{J}}\right)\frac{L}{A(T_1 - T_2)} \tag{3}$$

where V is the potential difference across the electric heater and I the current. Dividing the product VI (joules/sec) by the mechanical equivalent of heat, $\mathcal{J}$, (4.18 joules/cal) we have the heat per unit time

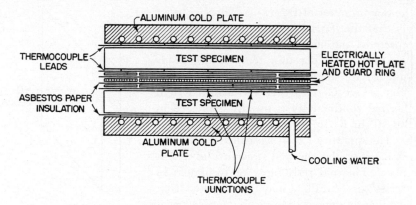

Fig. 3.2.   Hot-plate method for measuring thermal conductivity.

corresponding to Q/t in Eq. (2). The factor 2 in the denominator of Eq. (3) takes care of the fact that half the heat is conducted through each of the two specimens.

EXAMPLE: A 3.0-in. wall of fire brick, $k = 8.0$ Btu/(ft^2 hr F°/in.), has one surface at 335°F, the other at 80°F. Find (a) the temperature gradient in the brick, and (b) the heat conducted through an area of 1.0 ft^2 in 1 day.

(a) Temperature gradient $\Delta T/\Delta L = \dfrac{335°F - 80°F}{3.0 \text{ in.}} = 85$ F°/in.

(b) Heat transferred $Q = \dfrac{kA(T_1 - T_2)t}{L}$

$= \dfrac{8 \text{ Btu}/(\text{ft}^2 \text{ hr } F°/\text{in.}) \; 1 \text{ ft}^2 \; 255°F \; 24 \text{ hr}}{3.0 \text{ in.}} = 1\bar{6},320 \text{ Btu}$

In expressing the result of a physical measurement a vinculum is often used over the first doubtful digit, here the 6. Alternatively, the answer could be written 1.6×10^4 Btu.

EXAMPLE: A storage chamber has walls made of a 3.0-in. thickness of insulating brick $k = 0.0004$ cal/(cm² sec C°/cm) lined with a 1.0-in. layer of cork ($k = 0.0001$). How much heat is transmitted each hour per square foot of wall when the temperature is 10°F inside and 80°F outside?

The heat flow through the brick is

$$\frac{Q}{t} = \frac{k_1 A (T_1 - T_x)}{L_1}$$

The heat flow through the cork is

$$\frac{Q}{t} = \frac{k_2 A (T_x - T_2)}{L_2}$$

In the steady state these flows must be equal. (Why?)

Hence
$$\frac{k_1 A (T_1 - T_x)}{L_1} = \frac{k_2 A (T_x - T_2)}{L_2}$$

Solving for T_x and substituting in either of the first two equations, we find

$$Q = \frac{A(T_2 - T_1)t}{(L_1/k_1) + (L_2/k_2)}$$

Since 1 cal/(cm² sec C°/cm) = 2900 Btu/(ft² hr F°/in.), $k_1 = 1.16$ and $k_2 = 0.29$ Btu/(ft² hr F°/in.) and

$$Q = \frac{1 \text{ ft}^2 \; 70 \; F° \; 1 \text{ hr}}{\left(\dfrac{3.0}{1.16} + \dfrac{1.0}{0.29}\right) \dfrac{\text{in.}}{\text{Btu}/(\text{ft}^2 \text{ hr } F°/\text{in.})}} = 58 \text{ Btu}$$

CONDUCTION THROUGH SPHERICAL SHELL

Consider a spherical shell (Fig. 3.3) having a heater at its center. The flow of heat will be radially outward. Equation (2) may be applied to the flow through an element in the form of a spherical shell of radius r and thickness dr

$$\frac{dQ}{dt} = -kA\frac{dT}{dr} \tag{4}$$

where the minus sign indicates that the temperature gradient is negative in the direction of heat flow. When steady conditions have been attained the rate of flow of heat is constant, and Eq. (4) becomes

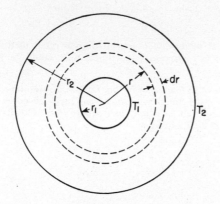

$$-4\pi r^2 k \frac{dT}{dr} = B' \quad \text{(a constant)}$$

(5)

The variables r and T are separable

$$dT = -\frac{B'}{4\pi k}\frac{dr}{r^2} = -B\frac{dr}{r^2}$$

(6)

and integration gives

Fig. 3.3. Conduction through spherical shell.

$$T = \frac{B}{r} + C$$

(7)

where B and C are constants which we can determine from the boundary conditions. At the inner surface $r = r_1$ and $T = T_1$, while at the outer surface $r = r_2$ and $T = T_2$. By substitution of these pairs of values in turn in Eq. (7) we get two simultaneous equations from which we find

$$B = \frac{r_1 r_2}{r_2 - r_1}(T_1 - T_2)$$

(8)

Equation (7) becomes

$$T = \frac{T_1 - T_2}{r_2 - r_1} \times \frac{r_1 r_2}{r} + C$$

(9)

which represents the temperature T in the shell at any distance r from the center. Differentiating Eq. (9) we get

$$\frac{dT}{dr} = -\frac{T_1 - T_2}{r_2 - r_1} \times \frac{r_1 r_2}{r^2}$$

(10)

and when this is substituted for the temperature gradient in Eq. (4) we have the heat flow expressed in terms of readily measured quantities

$$\frac{dQ}{dt} = k4\pi r^2 \frac{T_1 - T_2}{r_2 - r_1} \times \frac{r_1 r_2}{r^2} = \frac{4\pi k r_1 r_2(T_1 - T_2)}{r_2 - r_1}$$

(11)

The thermal conductivity of a material may be determined by forming it in a spherical shell, placing an electric heater in the cavity, and applying Eq. (11) to the measurements made under steady conditions. The product of the potential difference V and the current I gives the rate (in joules/sec) at which energy is supplied. In place of

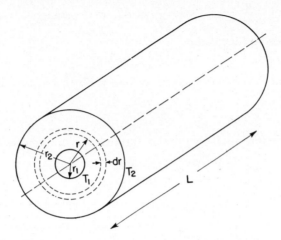

FIG. 3.4.   Conduction through cylindrical shell.

dQ/dt in Eq. (11) we can write $VI/\mathcal{J}$ where $\mathcal{J}$ is the mechanical equivalent of heat (4.18 joules/cal), and solve for the thermal conductivity

$$k = \frac{VI(r_2 - r_1)}{4\pi \mathcal{J} r_1 r_2 (T_1 - T_2)} \qquad (12)$$

EXAMPLE: The spherical-shell method (Fig. 3.3) is used to measure the thermal conductivity of mineral wool. The central metal sphere is 12.0 cm in diameter, and the outer metal shell has a 15.0-cm inside diameter. When a steady state has been reached for an input of 3.40 watts, the temperature of the inner sphere is 45.0°C and the outer shell is at 28.0°C. What is the thermal conductivity of the mineral wool (a) in metric units, and (b) in British units?

$$k = \frac{3.40 \text{ joules/sec } (7.5 \text{ cm} - 6.0 \text{ cm})}{4\pi (4.18 \text{ joules/cal}) \times 6.0 \text{ cm} \times 7.5 \text{ cm} (45.0°C - 28.0°C)}$$

$k = 0.000127 \text{ cal}/(\text{cm}^2 \text{ sec C}°/\text{cm})$

$$k = \frac{0.000127 \text{ cal}}{\text{cm}^2 \text{ sec C}°/\text{cm}} \times \frac{\text{Btu}}{252 \text{ cal}} \times \frac{(2.54 \times 12)^2 \text{ cm}^2}{\text{ft}^2} \times \frac{3600 \text{ sec}}{\text{hr}} \times \frac{5/9 \text{ C}°}{\text{F}°} \times \frac{\text{in.}}{2.54 \text{ cm}}$$

$k = 0.368 \text{ Btu}/(\text{ft}^2 \text{ hr F}°/\text{in.})$

RADIAL CONDUCTION IN TUBES

It is frequently convenient to measure the thermal conductivity of a sample in the shape of a cylindrical shell, as in the case of pipe insulation. From Fig. 3.4 it is apparent that the heat leaving the cylindrical surface per second, under steady conditions, is

$$\frac{dQ}{dt} = -2\pi r k L \frac{dT}{dr} = B' \quad \text{(a constant)} \tag{13}$$

This becomes on integration

$$T = B \log_e r + C \tag{14}$$

The constant B is determined, as before, from boundary conditions

$$B = \frac{T_1 - T_2}{\log_e r_1/r_2}$$

The equation for radial conduction through a cylindrical wall becomes

$$\frac{dQ}{dt} = \frac{2\pi k L (T_1 - T_2)}{\log_e r_2/r_1} \tag{15}$$

EXAMPLE: A steel pipe 5.0 cm in inside diameter and 6.0 cm in outside diameter which carries steam at 400°C is covered by a magnesia insulating sleeve 5.0 cm thick, whose outer surface is at 150°C. The thermal conductivity of magnesia is 0.00030 cal/(cm² sec C°/cm) and that for steel 0.11. (a) At what rate is heat lost from the pipe per meter of length? (b) Compute the temperature drops expected in the steel and in the magnesia covering.

Since the conductivity of steel is several hundred times that of magnesia, we may assume first that the entire temperature drop (250 C°) occurs across the insulation. Then, applying Eq. (15) to the layer of magnesia, we get

$$\frac{1}{L} \frac{dQ}{dt} = \frac{2\pi \times 0.00030(400°C - 150°C)}{\log_e 8.0/3.0} \frac{\text{cal}}{\text{sec cm C}°} = 0.48 \frac{\text{cal}}{\text{sec cm}}$$

For a 1.0-m length

$$\frac{dQ}{dt} = 480 \text{ cal/sec}$$

Of course there must be some temperature drop in the steel, for otherwise there would be no heat flow. We can now apply Eq. (15) to find ΔT for the steel

$$\frac{1}{L} \frac{dQ}{dt} = \frac{2\pi \times 0.11 \, \Delta T}{\log_e 3.0/2.5} \frac{\text{cal}}{\text{sec cm C}°} = 0.48 \frac{\text{cal}}{\text{sec cm}}$$

$$\Delta T = 0.13 \text{ C}°$$

THREE DIMENSIONAL FLOW

We have limited our discussion of heat flow thus far to several conditions which, while they are of considerable practical importance, nevertheless represent very special cases. The nature of the general problem of heat conduction may be better appreciated by examining a differential equation which will describe the conduction of heat in three dimensions inside an isotropic body.

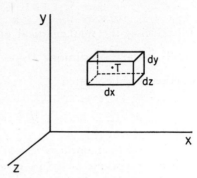

Taking rectangular coordinates, consider a small parallelepiped (Fig. 3.5) with its edges parallel to the axes. Let T be the temperature at the center of the element. The temperature at the left face is then $T - \frac{1}{2}(\partial T/\partial x)$ dx and that of the right face $T + \frac{1}{2}(\partial T/\partial x)dx$. The rate at which heat enters the element through the left face is

FIG. 3.5. Conduction in three dimensions.

$$-k\frac{1}{x}\left(T - \frac{1}{2}\frac{\partial T}{\partial x}\right)dxdydz \qquad (16)$$

The rate at which heat leaves through the opposite face is

$$-k\frac{1}{x}\left(T + \frac{1}{2}\frac{\partial T}{\partial x}\right)dxdydz \qquad (17)$$

Hence the net rate of gain of heat in the volume element due to the x component of the flow is the difference of Eqs. (16) and (17) or

$$k\frac{\partial^2 T}{\partial x^2}\,dxdydz \qquad (18)$$

When we add similar expressions for the flow through the remaining two pairs of faces, we see that the net rate at which heat accumulates in the element is

$$k\left(\frac{\partial^2 T}{\partial x^2} + \frac{\partial^2 T}{\partial y^2} + \frac{\partial^2 T}{\partial z^2}\right)dxdydz \qquad (19)$$

This will produce a rise in the temperature of the element and hence must be equal to $cd\frac{\partial T}{\partial t}dxdydz$ where d is the density of the material and c its specific heat

$$k \left(\frac{\partial^2 T}{\partial x^2} + \frac{\partial^2 T}{\partial y^2} + \frac{\partial^2 T}{\partial z^2} \right) = cd \frac{\partial T}{\partial t} \tag{20}$$

Introducing the mathematical operator ∇ for the expression $\frac{\partial^2}{\partial x^2} +$ $\frac{\partial^2}{\partial y^2} + \frac{\partial^2}{\partial z^2}$, and substituting $D = \frac{k}{cd}$ the general equation for heat conduction may be written

$$D \nabla^2 T = \frac{\partial T}{\partial t} \tag{21}$$

Kelvin gave the name *diffusivity* to the constant D. It is apparent that D is an important factor in determining the velocity of a thermal disturbance through the medium.

A problem in thermal conduction often consists of finding a solution of this differential equation for the given boundary conditions. The French mathematician Jean Fourier (1768–1830) devised a method of solution which has been generally used since. As considered here, Eq. (20) relates the rate of transfer of heat and the rate of storage of heat per unit of volume. But this relation (Poisson's equation) finds important application in the fields of electricity, magnetism, sound, gravitation, and radiation, with appropriate changes in the meanings of the different symbols.

PERIODIC FLOW OF HEAT IN ONE DIMENSION

A problem of practical interest is the flow of heat in one direction that takes place in a body when the surface of the body, normal to the direction of flow, has simply periodic variations in temperature. The surface of the earth, for example, is subjected to daily and annual changes of temperature that are nearly simply periodic. It is desirable to know at what time a maximum or a minimum of temperature will be attained at any point below the surface, and the actual value of this temperature. Such knowledge would be useful in the case of the earth's surface in determining the depth necessary for water pipes to avoid freezing.

In the steady-state flow of heat in one dimension the temperature gradient $\Delta T / \Delta x$ is constant. If T_0 is the temperature at the heated end of a uniform rod (Fig. 3.6), then at any other position x the temperature is $T_0 - (\Delta T / \Delta x) x$.

We now superpose upon this distribution a periodic heating at the end where x is zero, representing the variation by a sine or a cosine function. A thermal disturbance will travel along the bar. Equation (21) may be rewritten for the case of flow in one direction as

$$\frac{\partial^2 T}{\partial x^2} = \frac{1}{D}\frac{\partial T}{\partial t} = \frac{cd}{k}\frac{\partial T}{\partial t} \tag{22}$$

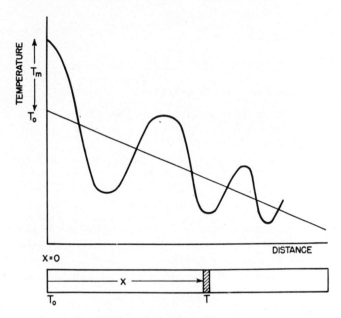

Fig. 3.6. Instantaneous temperature distribution in unidirectional periodic flow of heat.

The solution of Eq. (22) must fit the boundary condition

$$T = T_0 + \Delta T = T_0 + T_m \sin \omega t \qquad \text{at} \quad x = 0 \tag{23}$$

where T_m is the maximum amplitude of the variation in temperature and ω is 2π times the frequency f of the periodic heating.

Since Eq. (22) is linear and homogeneous with constant coefficients, it would be reasonable to try a solution of the form

$$T = T_0 = \frac{\Delta T}{\Delta x}x + T_m e^{ax} \sin (\omega t + bx) \tag{24}$$

where a and b are constants, T is the temperature at time t at a distance x from the boundary, T_m is the amplitude of the thermal disturbance, and e is the base of the natural logarithms.

We obtain the derivatives needed for Eq. (22) by differentiating Eq. (24)

$$\frac{\partial T}{\partial t} = T_m \omega e^{ax} \cos (\omega t + bx) \tag{25}$$

$$\frac{\partial T}{\partial x} = -\frac{\Delta T}{\Delta x} + a T_m e^{ax} \sin (\omega t + bx) + b T_m e^{ax} \cos (\omega t + bx) \tag{26}$$

$$\frac{\partial^2 T}{\partial x^2} = a^2 T_m e^{ax} \sin (\omega t + bx) - b^2 T_m e^{ax} \sin (\omega t + bx)$$

$$+ 2ab T_m e^{ax} \cos (\omega t + bx) \tag{27}$$

When we substitute the expressions from Eqs. (25) to (27) for the corresponding derivatives in Eq. (22), we find that the constants must be related as follows

$$a^2 = b^2$$
$$2ab = \omega / D$$

or
$$a = \pm b = \pm \sqrt{\omega / 2D}$$

By choosing the negative sign for a, we can represent the physical fact that the amplitude of the variations in temperature decreases with distance from the boundary surface.

The temperature in the one-dimensional periodic flow of heat thus is represented by the equation

$$T = T_0 - \frac{\Delta T}{\Delta x} x + T_m e^{-x\sqrt{\omega/2D}} \sin (\omega t - x \sqrt{\omega/2D}) \tag{28}$$

The sort of distribution of temperature represented by Eq. (28) at a particular instant is shown in Fig. 3.6.

The temperature at any point x will have a maximum value when the value of the sine term in Eq. (28) is unity. At any instant

$$(\omega t - x \sqrt{\omega/2D}) - [\omega t - (x + \lambda) \sqrt{\omega/2D}] = 2\pi = \sqrt{\omega/2D} \tag{29}$$

where λ is the wavelength, that is the distance between successive maxima. It follows that

$$D = \frac{\omega \lambda^2}{8\pi^2} = \frac{f\lambda}{4\pi} = \frac{k}{cd} \tag{30}$$

Hence, we may calculate the diffusivity D from measurements of the distance between successive temperature maxima and the period of the variation. From D the value of the thermal conductivity k may be calculated by

$$k = cdD \tag{31}$$

where c is the specific heat of the material and d is its density.

EXAMPLE: The diffusivity of a sandy loam soil is 0.0047 cm²/sec. (a) Find the speed of propagation of the diurnal wave into the surface. (b) What time is required for a maximum to travel to a depth of 1.0 meter?

(a) $$v = \lambda f = \sqrt{4\pi \, Df}$$

$$v = \sqrt{\frac{4\pi (0.0047) \text{ cm}^2/\text{sec}}{86,000 \text{ sec}}} = 8.3 \times 10^{-4} \text{ cm/sec}$$

(b) $$t = \frac{x}{v} = x\sqrt{\frac{1}{4\pi \, Df}}$$

$$t = 1.0 \text{ m}\sqrt{\frac{86,000 \text{ sec}}{4\pi (0.0047) \text{ cm}^2/\text{sec}}} = 32 \text{ hr}$$

In the simplest cases of steady conduction of heat considered earlier in this chapter, the temperature at any point has been constant. In the special case of periodic flow in one dimension the temperature at any point in the body varies in a simply periodic manner with the time, and although the temperature condition is not steady it duplicates itself in each complete period. The more general cases of variable heat flow can be treated only when one has acquired familiarity with Fourier's series. In the more general cases the temperature is a more or less complicated function of time and rarely reaches the same value twice at a given point.

CONVECTION

The transfer of heat by convective circulation in a liquid or a gas is associated with pressure differences, most commonly brought about by local changes in density. In most fluids the existence of a temperature gradient in which temperature decreases upwards results in instability, with layers of more dense fluid above the less dense. Relative motion ensues, with the more dense cool fluid displacing the less dense warm fluid. Heat transfer accompanies this motion, called *natural convection.* The primary circulation of the earth's atmosphere is an example of natural convection, as is also the circulation of water in an ordinary hot-water house heating system. Sometimes the pressure differences are produced mechanically by a pump or blower, in which case the heat transfer is said to occur by *forced convection.* In all cases of convection heat is transferred into or out from the fluid stream somewhere in its path.

There are two types of fluid motion. In laminar or *streamline flow* successive particles of fluid follow a path in an orderly procession. At higher speeds a second kind of motion called *turbulent flow* occurs. The flow is unsteady, there are eddies and whirlpools and the paths of the particles are continually changing.

Laminar flow can be treated theoretically, but, in general, problems involving turbulent flow are too difficult for exact analysis. They are dealt with by approximate and empirical methods. The method of dimensional analysis has been valuable in extending data on convective heat transfer to conditions not specifically covered by experiment.

CONDUCTION THROUGH FLUID FILMS

When a cool fluid flows along a heated wall heat is transferred from the wall to the fluid. Langmuir (1912) dealt with this situation by assuming that heat is transferred by conduction through a thin layer of fluid close to the wall, comprising roughly the laminar-flow region, to a region in which the ambient temperature is maintained by turbulent flow. A convective heat transfer of this type is treated approximately in the same manner as heat conduction using the relation

$$\frac{dQ}{dt} = Ah\,\Delta T \tag{32}$$

where ΔT is the temperature difference between the wall and the fluid at some distance from it, and h is called a *film coefficient* and represents the conductivity of the fluid divided by the effective thickness of the conducting layer.

The conducting layer is assumed to extend from the wall to the region where the temperature of the main body of fluid is reached, assuming that the temperature gradient across the conducting layer is constant and is equal to that actually existing at the wall. The thickness of the conducting layer is somewhat greater than the thickness of the laminar-flow region. The film coefficient h is found experimentally to vary with the speed of the fluid, the nature of the fluid-wall surface, and other factors.

SUMMARY

Heat is the most common form of energy, being associated with the molecular activity in a body.

Conduction is heat transfer from molecule to molecule through a body, or through bodies in contact.

Convection is heat transfer due to motion of matter caused by change in density.

In the process of *radiation*, energy is transferred as an electromagnetic wave from one body to another where, upon *absorption*, it again becomes energy of thermal motion.

Temperature gradient is temperature difference per unit distance along the direction of heat flow. Its units may be centigrade degrees per centimeter, Fahrenheit degrees per inch, etc.

Thermal conductivity, k, is a quantity characteristic of a substance that expresses how well it conducts heat. It may have units of calories per square centimeter per second for a gradient of 1 $C°/cm$ or Btu per square foot per hour for a gradient of 1 $F°/in$.

$$k = \frac{Q}{At(\Delta T/L)}$$

For conduction through a spherical shell

$$Q = \frac{4\pi k r_1 r_2 (T_1 - T_2)t}{r_2 - r_1}$$

For conduction through a cylindrical wall

$$Q = \frac{2\pi k L (T_1 - T_2)t}{\log_e r_2/r_1}$$

Conduction through a fluid film is described by the relation

$$\frac{dQ}{dt} = Ah \, \Delta T$$

where the *film coefficient h* represents the conductivity of the fluid divided by the effective thickness of the conducting layer.

REFERENCES FOR SUPPLEMENTARY READING

1. Allcut, E. A., "Properties of Heat Insulating Materials," *Eng. J. Canada* **24**, 514 (1941).
2. Babcock, R. W., "Thermal Convection," *Phys. Rev.*, **35** (2), 1008 (1930)
3. Ede, A. J., "A New Form of Chart for Determining Temperatures in Bodies of Regular Shape During Cooling," *Phil. Mag.*, **36**, 845 (1945).
4. Fourier, J., *The Analytical Theory of Heat*, Cambridge University Press, 1878.
5. Gard, J. S. F., "The Thermal Insulation of Structures," *Fuel Econ. Rev.*, **24**, 37 (1945).
6. Griffiths, E., "Heat Insulating Materials," *J. Sci. Instruments*, **15**, 117 (1938).
7. Griffiths, E., R. W. Powell, and M. J. Hickman, "Thermal Conductivity of Some Industrial Materials," *J. Inst. Fuel*, **15**, 107 (1942).
8. Henderson, G. H., "A New Method of Determining the Temperature Variation of the Thermal Conductivity of Gases, I.," *Phys. Rev.*, **15** (2), 46 (1920).
9. Ingersoll, L. R., "Methods of Measuring Thermal Conductivity," *J. Optical Soc. Am.*, **9**, 495 (1924).
10. Ingersoll, L. R., O. J. Zobel, and A. C. Ingersoll, *Heat Conduction*, McGraw-Hill Book Co., Inc., 1948.
11. Jacob, M., "Some Investigations in the Field of Heat Transfer," *Proc. Phys. Soc. (London)*, **59**, 726 (1947).
12. Johnston, R. M., and C. B. Ruehr, "Effect of Radiation upon Thermal Conductivities Determined by Hot Plates," *Heating, Piping, Air Conditioning*, **13** (5), 325 (1941).
13. Lauder, C. H., "Review of Recent Progress in Heat Transfer," *J. Proc. Instn. Mech. Eng. (London)*, **148**, 81 (1943).
14. McAdams, W. H., *Heat Transmission*, McGraw-Hill Book Co., Inc., 1933.
15. O'Day, M. D., "A New Application of the Bar Method for the Measurement of Thermal Conductivity," *Phys. Rev.*, **23** (2), 245 (1924).
16. Olson, F. C. W., and J. M. Jackson, "Heating Curves, Theory and Practical Application," *Ind. Eng. Chem.*, **34**, 337 (1942).
17. Olson, F. C. W., and O. T. Schultz, "Temperatures in Solids during Heating or Cooling," *Ind. Eng. Chem.*, **34**, 874 (1942).
18. Osborn, R. H., "Thermal Conductivities of Tungsten and Molybdenum at Incandescent Temperatures," *J. Optical Soc. Am.*, **31**, 428 (1941).
19. Schack, A., *Industrial Heat Transfer*, John Wiley & Sons, Inc., 1933.
20. Taylor, T. S., "Heat Transfer by Convection," *J. Optical Soc. Am.*, **9**, 693 (1924).
21. White, W. P., "Heat Convection in Air, and Newton's Law of Cooling," *Phys. Rev.*, **10** (2), 743 (1917).
22. Wohlenberg, W. J., "Heat Transfer by Radiation," *Eng. Bull. Purdue Univ.*, **24**, No. 4a (1940).

QUESTIONS AND PROBLEMS

1. What concepts and quantities are analogous in describing the flow of heat and the flow of electricity?

2. What kinds of materials are good thermal insulators? Why?

3. Why is a hollow wall filled with rock wool a better insulator than when filled with air alone?

4. A piece of paper wrapped tightly on a brass rod may be held in a gas flame without being burned. If wrapped on a wooden rod, it burns quickly. Explain.

5. Can you design apparatus to demonstrate the differences in thermal conductivities of various metals, which would give results that would not depend also on differences in the specific heats?

6. Derive an equation for converting a conductivity expressed in cal/(cm² sec C°/cm) to its value when expressed in Btu/(ft² hr F°/in.).

7. A certain thermal conductivity is expressed in the units Btu/(ft² sec F°/in.). Derive expressions for expressing its value (a) in cal/(cm² sec C°/cm) and (b) in joules/(cm² sec C°/cm).

8. What is the role of molecular action in convection and in conduction?

9. To insure proper draft in a fireplace chimney one sometimes burns a sheet of newspaper in the flue before lighting the fire on the hearth. Is this effective? Why?

10. How do each of the following factors affect heat transfer by convection in the tubes of a boiler or other heat exchanger: specific heat of fluid, conductivity, velocity of circulation, density, viscosity, tube diameter, and length?

11. How much heat is conducted in 1.0 hr through a brass plate [$k = 0.26$ cal/(cm² sec C°/cm)] which is 0.50 cm thick and 400 cm² in area, the temperatures of the two sides being kept at 15.0 and 20.0°C?

12. A certain window glass, 24 by 32 in., is ⅛ in. thick. One side has a uniform temperature of 68°F and the second face a temperature of 50°F. What is the temperature gradient? *Ans.* 144 F°/in.

13. A window 3.0 by 4.0 ft is made of glass ³⁄₁₆ in. thick which has a thermal conductivity 0.40 Btu/(ft² hr F°/in.). On a cold day, the inner and outer surfaces of the glass differ by 2.5F°. (a) How much heat is lost through the window in 8.0 hr? (b) Using coal which has a heat of combustion of 12,000 Btu/lb and a heating system 75 per cent efficient, what is the day's consumption of coal that results on account of this window?

14. An insulating wall is to be designed so that the thermal leakage is not more than 96 Btu/(ft² day) when the temperatures of the two surfaces differ by 40 F°. What is the minimum thickness of glass wool needed, if its conductivity is 0.30 Btu/(hr ft² F°/in.)? *Ans.* 3.0 in.

15. A block of Foamglas is placed in a conductivity apparatus similar to that of Fig. 3.2. From electrical measurements it is computed that 0.786 Btu/hr pass through an effective area of 16.0 in.² of the block. Thermometers inserted in the Foamglas 2.0 in. apart, in the line of heat conduction, read 80.0°F and 50.0°F. (a) What is the temperature gradient in the specimen? (b) What is the thermal conductivity of Foamglas?

16. The apparatus of Fig. 3.2 is used to measure the thermal conductivity of cork. The heater has faces of 200 cm² area and takes a current of 0.46 amp from a 6.0-volt battery. Thermocouples in the cork indicate a temperature difference of 50 C° between points 5.0 cm apart in the direction of heat flow. Calculate the conductivity.   *Ans.* 1.65 × 10⁻⁴ cal/(cm² sec C°/cm).

17. The thermal conductivity of ice is 1.27 Btu/(ft² hr F°/in.) and its density is 57.5 lb/ft³. At what rate will pond ice increase in thickness when the upper surface is kept at 0°F and the thickness is 2.0 in.?

18. Heat is conducted through a compound wall composed of parallel layers of two different conductivities, 0.32 and 0.14 cal/(cm² sec C°/cm), and of thicknesses 3.6 and 4.2 cm respectively. The temperatures of the outer faces of the wall are 96°C and 8°C. Find (a) the temperature of the interface, and (b) the temperature gradient in each section of wall.   *Ans.* 72°C, 6.9 C°/cm, 15.0 C°/cm.

19. The walls of a refrigerating chamber are made of concrete 3.0 in. thick, $k = 5.0$ Btu/(ft² hr F°/in.), lined with a 3.0-in. layer of corkboard ($k = 0.27$). The temperature inside the refrigerator is −10°F, and the temperature outside 76°F. (a) Find the temperature gradient in cork and in concrete. (b) How much heat is conducted per day through each square foot of wall?

20. The space between two thin concentric copper shells of radii 5.0 cm and 15.0 cm is filled with charcoal. When energy is supplied at the steady rate of 2.58 watts to a heater at the center, a temperature difference of 50 C° is observed between the spheres. Find the thermal conductivity of the charcoal.
                                                     Ans. 1.31 × 10⁻⁴ cal/(cm² sec C°/cm).

21. The spherical-shell method (Fig. 3.3) is used to measure the thermal conductivity of mineral wool. The central metal sphere is 12.0 cm in diameter. The hollow metal shell is 15.0 cm in inside diameter and 16.0 cm in outside diameter. When a steady state has been attained, the temperatures of inner sphere and outer shell are 45°C and 28°C, respectively. The input rate of energy is 3.40 watts. What is the thermal conductivity of the mineral wool expressed (a) in metric units, (b) in British engineering units?

22. A steam pipe has an outer diameter of 10.0 cm and a surface temperature of 150°C. It is covered with a layer of asbestos 2.5 cm thick whose outer surface is at 25°C. If the thermal conductivity of the asbestos is 0.00040 cal/(cm² sec C°/cm), how much heat is lost per minute from a 1.0-m section of the pipe?
                                                                                    Ans. 4660 cal.

23. A steel pipe of 4.6 cm inside diameter and 5.8 cm outside diameter, which carries steam at 350°C, has a magnesia insulating sleeve 5.0 cm thick, whose outer surface is at 80°C. Thermal conductivity for magnesia is 0.00030 cal/(cm² sec C°/cm) and for steel 0.11. (a) Compute the temperature drops expected in both the steel and the magnesia covering. (b) At what rate is energy lost from the pipe per foot of length?

24. A wire 1.0 mm in diameter having a resistance of 0.10 ohm/cm forms the axis of a gas-filled tube 4.0 cm in diameter. A current of 0.25 amp produces a 30 C° difference in temperature between wire and tube. Calculate the thermal conductivity of the gas.   *Ans.* 1.83 × 10⁻⁵ cal/(cm² sec C°/cm).

25. A steel steam pipe 1.0 in. in outside diameter is covered by a cylindrical glass wool insulating sleeve of wall thickness 5.0 in. The thermal conductivity of the glass wool is 0.30 Btu/(hr ft² F°/in.). The temperature of the inside surface of the sleeve is 350°F and that of the outer surface 80°F. How much heat is conducted through a 5.0-ft section of the insulation in one day?

Chapter 4

||||||||||||||||||||||||||

THERMOELECTRICITY

SOURCES OF THERMAL EMF'S """" *THERMO-*
DYNAMIC RELATIONS FOR A THERMOCOUPLE
"""" *THERMOELECTRIC COEFFICIENTS* """"

THERMAL EMF

In 1821, Thomas Seebeck discovered that an electric current is
maintained in a circuit of two dissimilar metals when their junctions
are held at different temperatures.

A pair of dissimilar electrical conductors, so joined as to produce
a thermal emf when the junctions are at different temperatures, is
called a *thermocouple* or thermel. The emf developed by typical
thermocouples varies from about 1 to 7 millivolts when the temperature
difference between the junctions is 100 C°. Thus a thermocouple is
not an important industrial source of electrical energy. The dependence of the thermal emf upon temperature gives the thermocouple
practical importance, however, as a device for accurate electrical
measurement of temperature over a wide range.

PELTIER EFFECT

In 1834, Jean Peltier made the fundamental discovery that when
a current exists in one direction across the junction of two dissimilar
metals heat is absorbed and the junction cooled, and that when the
current is maintained in the opposite direction the junction is heated
(Fig. 4.1). The Peltier effect, as this phenomenon is called, is *reversible.*

The same amount of heat is absorbed when the current is in one direction as is evolved when the current is reversed. The heat developed is proportional to the *first power* of the current. The Peltier heat depends on the pair of metals chosen but is independent of the form

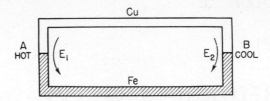

FIG. 4.1. Two dissimilar metals connected as a thermocouple.

and dimensions of the metals at the junction.   In contrast, the ordinary Joule heating effect is irreversible and, being proportional to I^2R, depends upon the dimensions of the conductor and does not change sign when the current is reversed.

The fact that energy is absorbed at A (Fig. 4.1) when the current is from Cu to Fe suggests that at the junction there is an emf E_1, directed from Cu to Fe.   Also, the release of energy at B is evidence that at B an emf is directed from Cu to Fe.   When charge flows in the direction of the electric field, work E_1' per unit charge is done on the current, heat is consequently absorbed, and the junction A cools.   The charges crossing junction B do work against E_2', developing heat and warming this junction.

The values of E_1' and E_2' depend on the metals that form the junctions, and also on the absolute temperatures of the junctions. If, therefore, one junction is held at a higher temperature than the other, the net emf $(E_2' - E_1')$ will maintain a current in the circuit.

A simple picture of the Peltier effect assumes that the conduction electrons in a metal behave like an electron gas.   In different metals these electrons have different concentrations and different average velocities of thermal agitation.   If two metals are placed in contact (Fig. 4.2), there is a diffusion of electrons across the interface, which continues until an electric field is established that opposes the transfer of more electrons and brings about equilibrium.

If metals A and B are brought into contact at another point to form a complete circuit, and if the two junctions are held at the same temperature, the thermal emf's at the junctions are equal in magnitude but opposite in direction. No net flow of electrons occurs. If, however, the junctions are maintained at different temperatures, the electron concentrations (and pressures) differ, and steady flow occurs. Heat is transformed into electrical energy.

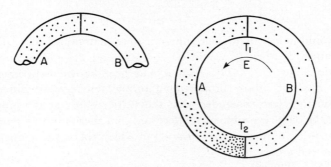

FIG. 4.2. Difference in electron density as the source of thermal emf.

THOMSON EFFECT

In 1851, William Thomson (later Lord Kelvin) concluded from thermodynamic reasoning and the then known characteristics of thermocouples that the reversible absorption of heat at the junctions of dissimilar metals was not the only reversible heat effect in a thermoelectric circuit. In brief he reasoned as follows:

Assuming that the Peltier emf's represent the only reversible effects in a simple thermoelectric circuit, the resultant emf E in the circuit is given by

$$E = E_2' - E_1' \tag{1}$$

where E_1' is the Peltier emf of the junction that is at temperature T_1 and E_2' is the Peltier emf of the junction that is at temperature T_2.

Neglecting the effect of thermal conduction (an irreversible process) the thermocouple can be considered as a reversible heat engine with a source at temperature T_2 and sink at temperature T_1. We have an expression for the efficiency based on the second law of thermodynamics (Chap. 12)

$$\frac{E_2' - E_1'}{E_1'} = \frac{T_2 - T_1}{T_1} \tag{2}$$

Combining Eqs. (1) and (2) we have

$$E = \frac{E_1'(T_2 - T_1)}{T_1} \tag{3}$$

It would follow that if one junction were maintained at a constant temperature T_1, then E_1' would be constant and the emf E would be proportional to $(T_2 - T_1)$. But it had been shown experimentally that E was not simply proportional to the temperature difference. Thomson therefore concluded that the Peltier effect at the junctions was not the only reversible heat effect and that there must be a reversible absorption of heat in the *conductors* in which there is a temperature gradient and a current.

In 1854, Thomson succeeded in showing experimentally that in certain homogeneous metals heat is absorbed when there is an electric current from colder to hotter parts. In certain other metals the opposite of this effect occurs, and in still other metals the effect is too small to be detected. This heating or cooling, called the Thomson effect, is reversible and occurs only where there is a temperature gradient in a metal. It is entirely distinct from the irreversible Joule heating.

The reversible absorption of heat in a homogeneous conductor has the same effect as if an emf existed in the temperature gradient. The direction and magnitude of this emf $\mathcal{E}$ between any two points depend upon the metal, the average temperature, and the temperature difference between the two points, and may be written

$$d\mathcal{E} = \sigma \, dT \tag{4}$$

The Thomson coefficient σ is characteristic of the material of the conductor and depends on the temperature. The Thomson emf $\mathcal{E}$ of the conductor between any two points at temperatures T_1 and T_2 is given by

$$\mathcal{E} = \int_{T_1}^{T_2} \sigma \, dT \tag{5}$$

SEEBECK EMF

In a simple thermoelectric circuit of two metals A and B (Fig. 4.3) there exist four separate and distinct emf's: the Peltier emf's at the two junctions and the Thomson emf's along the part of each wire that lies

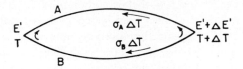

FIG. 4.3. The two Peltier emf's and two Thomson emf's in a thermocouple.

in the temperature gradient. The identity of the individual emf's can be established only by observations of the reversible heat effects. The net emf E_{AB} in the circuit is then the algebraic sum of the two Peltier emf's and the two Thomson emf's

$$E_{AB} = (E'_{AB})_{T_2} - (E'_{AB})_{T_1} + \int_{T_1}^{T_2} (\sigma_A - \sigma_B) \, dT \qquad (6)$$

The net emf, called the Seebeck emf, is in general not zero and hence a current will be maintained in the circuit as long as the junctions are held at different temperatures.

SIGN CONVENTIONS

The Thomson emf is positive, by definition, if heat is generated when the current is from the hotter to the colder parts of the conductor. Metal A will be considered positive with respect to metal B if the Seebeck emf in an AB thermocouple is from A to B at the *reference* junction, usually held at 0°C. According to this convention, the polarity of a thermocouple reverses as the temperature of the measuring junction passes through the reference temperature.

THERMODYNAMIC RELATIONS

Thomson applied the laws of thermodynamics to the thermoelectric circuit of two metals, A and B (Fig. 4.3). Let the temperatures of the two junctions differ by the small amount ΔT and let the corresponding Peltier emf's differ by $\Delta E'$. The net emf ΔE in the circuit is given by

$$\Delta E = \Delta E' + (\sigma_A - \sigma_B) \, \Delta T \qquad (7)$$

If we allow ΔT to become small, approaching zero, Eq. (7) becomes in the limit

$$\frac{dE}{dT} = \frac{dE'}{dT} + (\sigma_A - \sigma_B) \tag{8}$$

By virtue of the second law of thermodynamics, $\Sigma(Q/T) = 0$ where Q represents a quantity of heat transferred by a reversible process at temperature T. We regard the thermocouple as a reversible heat engine. When a unit charge of electricity q passes around the circuit, we obtain by considering only the reversible effects

$$q\,\frac{(E' + \Delta E')}{T + \Delta T} - q\,\frac{E'}{T} + q\,\frac{\sigma_A\,\Delta T}{T + \dfrac{\Delta T}{2}} - q\,\frac{\sigma_B\,\Delta T}{T + \dfrac{\Delta T}{2}} = 0 \tag{9}$$

The numerator of each term represents energy, the product of charge and emf (work per unit charge). Hence, Eq. (9) states $\Sigma(Q/T) = 0$. It may be rewritten in the form

$$\Delta\left(\frac{E'}{T}\right) + \frac{(\sigma_A - \sigma_B)\,\Delta T}{T + \dfrac{\Delta T}{2}} = 0 \tag{10}$$

which becomes in the limit

$$\frac{d}{dT}\left(\frac{E'}{T}\right) + \frac{1}{T}(\sigma_A - \sigma_B) = 0 \tag{11}$$

or

$$\sigma_A - \sigma_B = \frac{E'}{T} - \frac{dE'}{dT} \tag{12}$$

Eliminating $(\sigma_A - \sigma_B)$ between Eq. (8) and (12) we have

$$E'_T = T\frac{dE}{dT} \tag{13}$$

Substituting Eq. (13) in Eq. (11) we get

$$\sigma_A - \sigma_B = -T\frac{d^2E}{dT^2} \tag{14}$$

The Peltier emf at the junction of any two dissimilar metals at any temperature can be calculated from Eq. (13) and measurements of the variation in the thermal emf with temperature. For metals commonly used in temperature measurement the Peltier emf is 0.1 volt or less.

The difference between the Thomson coefficients in two metals can be calculated from Eq. (14) and measurements of the variation in thermal emf with temperature. Various types of experiments indicate that the Thomson effect in lead is extremely small, if not zero, at ordinary atmospheric temperatures. Consequently, some information regarding the magnitude of the Thomson coefficients in other metals can be determined if it is assumed that this coefficient is zero for lead. On this basis it is found that the Thomson coefficient (in microvolts per degree) at 0°C is -9 for platinum, -8 for iron, $+2$ for copper, -23 for constantan, -8 for Alumel, -2 for .90 Pt-.10Rh alloy, and $+2$ for Chromel-P.

DEPENDENCE OF EMF ON TEMPERATURE

We cannot integrate Eq. (13) or (14) and obtain a general relation between E and T without some information on the manner in which ε or σ varies with T. Experiments indicate that P and σ both depend upon T, but the manner in which they vary with T has not been established either theoretically or experimentally with much accuracy.

A number of hypotheses have been made as to the manner in which σ varies with temperature. P. Q. Tait and others have suggested, on the basis of limited experimental evidence, that σ is proportional to T. If so, the rate of change of thermal emf with temperature dE/dT, called (for no good reason) the *thermoelectric power*, may be expressed as a linear equation. From Eq. (14)

$$\frac{dE}{dT} = b' + 2cT \tag{15}$$

If the temperature t is expressed on the centigrade scale, the equation for thermoelectric power becomes

$$\frac{dE}{dt} = b + 2ct \tag{16}$$

We can integrate Eq. (16) to obtain an equation for the emf of a thermocouple

$$E = a + bt + ct^2 \tag{17}$$

where t is the centigrade temperature of the measuring junction, the reference junction being kept at some constant temperature. If this junction is held at 0°C then $a = 0$ in Eq. (17). For other reference junction temperatures, a represents the reference junction correction, the emf that the thermocouple would develop between 0°C and the reference temperature employed.

Whereas Eq. (17) is applicable to most thermocouples of practical importance, there are many materials whose emf-temperature curves cannot be represented so simply. Equations relating E and T, based on any particular hypothesis regarding the relation between σ and T, represent experimentally determined values over limited temperature ranges. Consequently, the relation between E and T for any pair of metals must be determined experimentally and the thermocouple calibration is given by a table or an empirical equation for the temperature range of interest.

Values for the constants in the expression for the thermoelectric power Eq. (16), called the *thermoelectric coefficients*, are frequently tabulated to facilitate calculation of the thermoelectric power or the thermal emf for various combinations of metals (Table 4.1). The coefficients were formerly given with reference to lead. They are now more often stated with respect to platinum, with which measurements can be made over a wider range of temperature.

TABLE 4.1 THERMOELECTRIC COEFFICIENTS

The table gives the thermoelectric power in microvolts per centigrade degree when the reference junction is at 0°C.

$$\frac{dE_{AB}}{dt} = b + 2ct \times 10^{-2} + 3dt^2 \times 10^{-5}$$

$$E_{AB} = bt + ct^2 \times 10^{-2} + dt^3 \times 10^{-5}$$

A	B	t_1	t_2	b $\mu v/\mathrm{deg}$	$2c$ $\mu v/\mathrm{deg}^2$	$3d$ $\mu v/\mathrm{deg}^3$
Ag	Pb	0°C	100°C	2.50	1.15	
Bi	Pb	0	100	74.42	3.2	
Cu	Pb	0	100	2.76	1.22	
Pt	Pb	0	100	−1.788	−3.460	
Fe	Cu	0	100	13.7	−7.80	6.60
Ni	Pb	0	200	−19.067	−3.022	
Constantan (.60 Cu−.40 Ni)	Cu	0	400	−38.105	−8.884	+8.568
.90Pt−.10Rh	Pt	0	1600	7.048	0.5896	−0.1284

Note: These figures are illustrative only. Small amounts of impurities, or variations in heat treatment, may produce large changes in thermoelectric coefficients.

The temperature t_n at which $dE/dt = 0$ is called the *neutral temperature*. From Eq. (16)

$$t_n = -\frac{b}{2c} \qquad (18)$$

From Eq. (17) it is seen that the emf is zero when the measuring junction has the same temperature t_o as the reference junction and also when the measuring junction has the temperature

$$t_i = -\frac{b}{c} - t_o \qquad (19)$$

where t_i is called the *inversion temperature*.

For most metals and alloys used in thermocouples the operating range is sufficiently far removed from the neutral temperature so that the calibration, Eq. (17), is essentially linear.

THERMOELECTRIC LAWS

Accurate experimental measurements on many thermoelectric circuits have established certain facts. These facts or laws may be reduced to three fundamentals.

(a) *The law of the homogeneous circuit.* An electric current cannot be sustained in a circuit of a single homogeneous metal, however varying in section, by the application of heat alone.

(b) *The law of intermediate metals.* If in any circuit of solid conductors the temperature is uniform from point P through all the conductors to point Q, the algebraic sum of the thermal emf's in the entire circuit is totally independent of these intermediate conductors and is the same as if P and Q were put in contact (Fig. 4.4)

$$E_{ABC} = E_{AB} \qquad \text{(both ends of C at same temperature)} \qquad (20)$$

An alternative statement of this same law is: The thermal emf generated by any thermocouple AB with its junctions at temperatures T_1 and T_2 is the algebraic sum of the emf of a thermocouple composed of A and any metal C and that of one composed of C and B, both with their junctions at T_1 and T_2, or

$$E_{AB} = E_{AC} + E_{CB} \qquad \text{(for a given temperature difference)} \qquad (21)$$

(c) *The law of successive or intermediate temperatures.* The thermal emf developed by any thermocouple of homogeneous metals with its junctions at any two temperatures T_1 and T_3 is the algebraic sum of the emf of the thermocouple with one junction at T_1 and the other at any other temperature T_2 and the emf of the same couple with its junctions at T_2 and T_3.

$$E_{T_1}^{T_3} = E_{T_1}^{T_2} + E_{T_2}^{T_3}$$ (22)

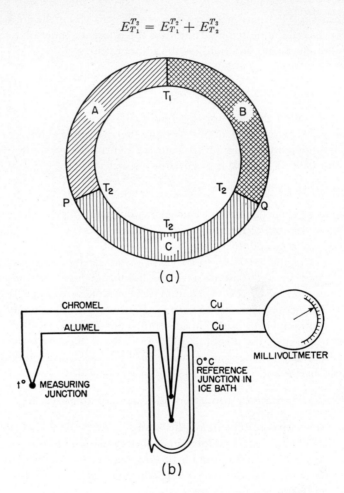

(a)

(b)

FIG. 4.4.   (a) The emf is independent of third metal C, provided both its terminals are at same temperature.   (b) Application in connecting a thermocouple to a meter with copper extension wires.

SUMMARY

An *emf* is produced in a circuit of two or more dissimilar metals, a *thermocouple*, when one junction is heated or cooled relative to the rest of the circuit.

A *Peltier emf* represents the rate (joules/sec) at which heat is generated or absorbed per unit current (coulomb/sec) at a junction of dissimilar metals.

A *Thomson coefficient* σ represents the emf developed per unit temperature gradient in a conductor.

The thermocouple sign convention used in this book is that metal A is considered positive with respect to metal B if the current (positive) is from A to B at the *reference* junction, usually held at 0°C.

Thermodynamic relations for a thermocouple give the Peltier emf as

$$E'_T = T\frac{dE}{dT}$$

and the net Thomson coefficient as

$$\sigma_A - \sigma_B = -T\frac{d^2E}{dT^2}$$

Practical thermocouples have empirical calibration relations between emf and temperature of the form

$$E = a + bt + ct^2$$

The thermoelectric power is the rate of change of thermal emf with temperature

$$\frac{dE}{dT} = b + 2ct$$

The *neutral temperature* t_n is the temperature at which $dE/dt = 0$.

The *inversion temperature* t_i is the temperature of the measuring junction for which the thermocouple emf is zero for a given reference-junction temperature, $t_i = {}_2t_n - t_0$.

Three thermoelectric laws of practical importance are

$$E_{ABC} = E_{AB} \qquad \text{(both ends of } C \text{ at same temperature)}$$

$$E_{AB} = E_{AC} - E_{BC} \qquad \text{(for a given temperature difference)}$$

$$E_{T_1}^{T_3} = E_{T_1}^{T_2} + E_{T_2}^{T_3} \qquad \text{(for a given thermocouple)}$$

REFERENCES FOR SUPPLEMENTARY READING

1. Barker, H. C., "A Method of Measurement of the Peltier E.M.F. in Absolute Units," *Phys. Rev.*, **31**, 321 (1910) and **34**, 224 (1912).
2. Bridgman, P. W., *The Thermodynamics of Phenomena in Metals*, Macmillan and Co., Ltd., 1934.

3. Emmons, H., "Theory and Application of Extended Surface Thermo-couples," *J. Franklin Inst.*, **229,** 29 (1940).
4. Fagan, H. D., and T. R. D. Collins, "Peltier and Thomson Effects for Bismuth Crystals," *Phys. Rev.*, **35** (2), 421 (1930).
5. Thomson, W., "On the Dynamical Theory of Heat . . .," *Trans. Roy. Soc.*, *Edinburgh*, **21,** 123 (1854).

QUESTIONS AND PROBLEMS

1. List the chief experimental discoveries and theories of thermoelectricity in proper historical order.

2. Distinguish between the Peltier heat and the Joule heating in a thermocouple circuit. Suggest an experimental procedure for measuring the Peltier heat that would not be effected by the Joule (I^2R) heating.

3. What is meant by the term "specific heat of electricity," sometimes applied to σ?

4. Draw a typical graph of thermoelectric power *vs.* temperature for a thermocouple. Identify the Peltier emf's, the Thomson emf's, and the net (Seebeck) emf in terms of areas on this thermoelectric diagram.

5. How are the Peltier and Thomson coefficients represented on the thermoelectric diagram?

6. Why was lead commonly used as a reference material in tabulating thermoelectric constants? Why is platinum now so used? What is the practical value of such tables?

7. List the three thermocouple laws, Eqs. (20) to (22), in order of their practical importance. Justify your selection.

8. Define "neutral temperature" in several ways.

9. Under what circumstances might it be advantageous to use a reference junction temperature other than 0°C for a thermocouple?

10. Show how a current-carrying wire with a small thermocouple welded to it might be adapted to measure (a) an alternating current, (b) the standard current for a potentiometer, (c) the pressure of gas in a vacuum system, (d) the extent of eddying currents in a wind tunnel, or (e) the wind speed outdoors.

11. Using the data of Table 4.1, construct a thermoelectric diagram for iron-lead and constantan-lead. Show how the amounts of heat absorbed or evolved in the different parts of an iron-constantan thermocouple with junctions of 0°C and 100°C and current 0.01 amp are represented in the diagram.

12. The ends of a 30-cm metal rod 1.0 cm² in cross section are maintained at 30°C and 0°C. The resistivity of the metal is 150 microhm cm. For a current of 0.050 amp from the warm end to the cool end, the temperature gradient in the rod is unchanged. Find the Thomson coefficient for the metal.   *Ans.* 7.5 $\mu v/\text{C}°$.

13. A chromel-alumel thermocouple has the labels for the individual wires missing. It is connected at random to a millivoltmeter, and a lighted match is held under the thermocouple junction. If the millivoltmeter deflects in the negative sense, which wire is connected to its positive terminal?

14. An iron-constantan thermocouple is to be used to measure the temperature of an oven. Which wire should be connected to the positive terminal of the millivoltmeter?   *Ans.* Iron.

15. What is the neutral temperature of a silver-bismuth thermocouple? Does this temperature lie outside the range of use of the thermocouple? Is this an advantage or disadvantage?

16. What is the neutral temperature for a copper-nickel thermocouple?
Ans. $-516°C$ (Significance?).

17. What emf is developed by a copper-constantan thermocouple whose junctions are at $-80°C$ and $200°C$, respectively? (Use Table 11 in Appendix.)

18. A chromel-alumel thermocouple with reference junction at $70°F$ develops an emf of 5.25 mv. What is the temperature of its measuring junction? (Use Table 10 in Appendix.) *Ans.* $300°F$.

19. A copper-constantan thermocouple has its reference junction at $0°C$. Find (a) the neutral temperature, (b) the inversion temperature, and (c) the emf, when the other junction is at $200°C$. Comment on (a) and (b).
Ans. $-405°C$, $-810°C$, 10.19 mv.

20. One junction of an iron-copper thermocouple is kept at $0°C$, the other at $100°C$. Find (a) the neutral temperature, (b) the inversion temperature, and (c) the emf. *Ans.* $176°C$, $252°C$, 1.01 mv.

21. Compute the Peltier and Thomson emf's of an iron-copper thermocouple whose junctions are at $100°$ and $0°C$.

22. Compute the Peltier and Thomson emf's of a copper-constantan thermocouple whose junctions are at $100°$ and $0°C$. *Ans.* 19.0 mv, 11.2 mv, 0.326 mv.

Chapter 5

⁗⁗⁗⁗⁗⁗⁗⁗⁗⁗⁗

THERMOELECTRIC TEMPERA-
TURE MEASUREMENTS

TYPES OF THERMELS AND THEIR CHARAC-
TERISTICS ⁗⁗ *THERMOCOUPLE MILLI-*
VOLTMETERS AND POTENTIOMETERS
⁗⁗ *MEASURING PROCEDURES* ⁗⁗

THERMOELECTRIC THERMOMETERS

Becquerel used Seebeck's discovery of the thermoelectric effect as early as 1830 in his measurement of flame temperatures. With the development of suitable thermocouple materials, thermoelectric pyrometry has attained a degree of precision inferior only to that of resistance thermometry below 900°C, while for higher temperatures it is the only sensitive and convenient electrical method.

In its simplest form a thermoelectric thermometer consists of a thermocouple, or *thermel*, of two dissimilar metals that develop an emf when the junctions are at different temperatures, and an instrument for measuring the emf, connected as shown in Fig. 5.1. As long as the instrument and its terminals are at a uniform temperature the presence of the instrument does not modify the thermal emf developed in the circuit. If the reference junction is held at some known reference temperature, such as 0°C, the emf of the thermocouple can be determined as a function of the temperature of its measuring junction.

The calibration usually can be expressed by assigning values to the constants a, b, and c in an equation of the form

$$E = a + b\,\Delta t + c(\Delta t)^2 \tag{1}$$

where Δt is the difference in temperature between the measuring junction and the reference junction. If the latter is maintained at 0°C, then Eq. (1) becomes

$$E_0 = a + bt + ct^2 \tag{2}$$

Its calibration having been determined, the thermoelectric thermometer can then be used to measure temperatures.

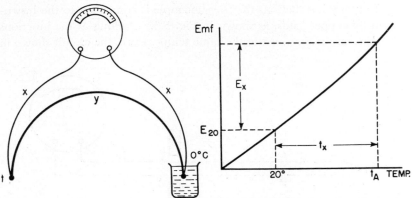

FIG. 5.1.   A thermocouple circuit.   FIG. 5.2.   Calibration curve for a thermocouple with reference junction at 0°C.

REFERENCE JUNCTION CORRECTIONS

It is not necessary that the reference junction be maintained at the same temperature during use as during calibration. The temperature of the reference junction must be known, however, in each case. Assume, for example, that Fig. 5.2 represents the relation between emf E and temperature t for a certain thermocouple whose reference junction is at 0°C. Suppose we now use this thermocouple to measure some temperature, and we observe an emf E_x when the reference junction is held at 20°C. We may add the observed emf E_x to E_{20} (the emf given by the curve when one junction is at 0°C and the other at 20°C) and obtain from the curve the true temperature t_A of the measuring junction.

A thermocouple calibration generally is not a linear relation between emf and temperature. Hence, equal increments in temperature do not correspond to equal increments in emf.

EXAMPLE: A copper-constantan thermocouple develops an emf of 16.43 mv when one junction is at 20°C and the other is in a furnace at temperature t. Find the temperature of the furnace.

From the copper-constantan table in the Appendix, $E_{20} = 0.79$ mv. Adding this reference-junction correction to the observed emf, 0.79 mv $+$ 16.43 mv $=$ 17.22 mv. The corresponding temperature read from the table is 340°C, which is the temperature of the furnace.

LEAD WIRES

In many installations the thermocouple is connected to the instrument by copper leads, as shown in Fig. 5.3. As long as the junctions C and C' are maintained at the same temperature, the circuit shown in

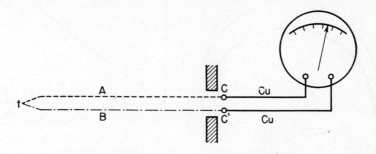

Fɪɢ. 5.3.   Thermocouple with extension lead wires.

Fig. 5.3 is equivalent to that shown in Fig. 5.1. If the junctions C and C' are not maintained at the same temperature, the net emf in the circuit will depend not only on the AB thermocouple and the temperature of its measuring junction, but also upon the temperatures of junctions C and C' and the thermoelectric properties of copper against each of the individual wires. Such a condition is usually avoided.

TYPES OF THERMOCOUPLES

Of the many possible types of thermocouples only a few have been found suitable for use in the measurement of temperatures (Fig. 5.4). They have the following desirable characteristics:

(1) The thermal emf increases continuously with increasing temperature over the range of use. The neutral temperature is remote from the temperature range of use.

(2) The thermal emf is large enough to be measured with reasonable accuracy.

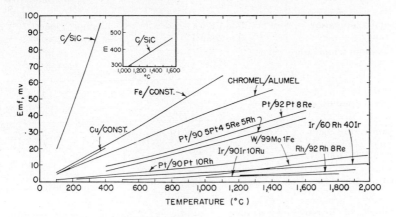

Fig. 5.4. Characteristics of typical thermocouples

(3) The thermoelectric characteristics are not appreciably altered during calibration and use either by internal changes, such as recrystallization, or by chemical contamination in the environment in which the thermocouple is used.

(4) The metals have melting points above any temperature at which the thermocouple is to be used and are resistant to any action such as oxidation, corrosion, etc., which destroys the wire.

(5) The thermocouples are reproducible and readily obtainable in uniform quality. This is an important consideration in industrial uses to permit replacement of the thermocouple without recalibrating the temperature scale of the indicating instrument.

The combinations of metals and alloys extensively used as thermocouples for the measurement of temperatures are listed in Table 5.1, with some of their characteristics. The Pt *vs.* .90 Pt–.10 Rh thermocouple introduced by Le Chatelier (1886) is widely used to measure temperatures in the range 0 to 1450°C. It is used to define the international temperature scale in the range 660 to 1063°C. These thermocouples are not suitable for temperature measurements below

TABLE 5.1 THERMOCOUPLE CHARACTERISTICS

Type	Pt–PtRh		Chromel P–Alumel	
Composition, Per Cent	100 Pt	.90 Pt–.10 Rh	.90 Ni–.10 Cr	.95 Ni–.02 Al–.02 Mn–.01 Si
Usual temperature range	0 to 1450°C 0 to 2650°F		−200 to 1200°C −300 to 2200°F	
Maximum temperature	1700°C 3100°F		1350°C 2450°F	
Resistivity, microhm per centimeter cube	9.8	18.3	69.4	28.6
Temperature coefficient of resistivity, $1/C°$, (0–100°C)	0.0039	0.0018	0.000349	0.000125
Melting temperature	1773°C	1830°C	about 1430°C	
Influence of environment	Resistance to oxidizing atmosphere good; poor for reducing atmosphere. Susceptible to chemical alteration by As, Si, P vapor in reducing gas (CO_2, H_2, H_2S, SO_2). Pt corrodes easily above 1000°C. Used in a gas-tight protecting tube.		Resistance to oxidizing atmosphere good; poor for reducing atmosphere. Affected by reducing or sulfurous gases, SO_2 and H_2S.	
Particular applications	International standard 630 to 1063°C		Used in oxidizing atmosphere in electric furnaces, ceramic kilns, tube stills.	
Emf (mv) at various temperatures (°C) with reference junction at 0°C	100°C 200 400 600 800 1000 1200 1400 1600	0.643 mv 1.436 3.251 5.222 7.330 9.569 11.924 14.312 16.674	4.1 mv 8.13 16.39 24.90 33.31 41.31 48.85 55.81	

TABLE 5.1 (*Continued*)

Iron–Constantan		Copper-Constantan		Chromel P–Constantan	
.999 Fe	.55 Cu–.45 Ni	.999 Cu	.55 Cu–.45 Ni	.90 Ni–.10 Cr	.55 Cu–.45 Ni
−200 to 750°C −300 to 1400°F 1000°C 1800°F		−200 to 350°C −300 to 650°F 600°C 1100°F		0 to 800°C 0 to 1500°F 1100°C 2000°F	
10	49	1.71	49	70	49
0.005	0.00002	0.0039	0.00002	0.00035	0.0002
1535°C	1190°C	1081°C	1190°C		1190°C
Oxidizing and reducing gases have little effect on accuracy. Protect from moisture and sulfur. Resistance to oxidation good up to 400°C but poor above 700°C.		Subject to oxidation and alteration above 400°C due Cu, above 600°C due constantan wire. Required protection from acid fumes obtained by nickel-plating Cu tube. Resistance to oxidizing and reducing atmospheres good.		Resistance to oxidizing atmosphere good; poor for reducing atmosphere.	
Industrial uses up to 800°C, especially for reducing atmospheres. Steel annealing, boiler flues, tube stills.		Industrial uses, as a tube element in steam lines, internal combustion engines, low temperature measurements.			
100°C 200 400 600 800 1000	5.28 mv 10.78 21.82 33.16 45.48 58.16	4.28 mv 9.29 14.86		6.3 mv 13.3 28.5 44.3	

$0°C$ because the thermoelectric power (dE/dt) is only about 5 $\mu v/C°$ at $0°C$ and decreases to zero at about $-138°C$.

Some American thermocouples are made with an .87 Pt–.13 Rh alloy, which gives a somewhat greater emf (see Table 7, Appendix), chiefly to provide replacement thermocouples for calibrated instruments already in use.

Both platinum and rhodium can be obtained with high purity. The Pt–PtRh thermocouples have the primary advantages of reproducibility and long temperature range. High cost limits their use. The cost of long leads from the measuring junction of a Pt–PtRh thermocouple may be reduced by the use of compensating leads of dissimilar metals which together have the same thermoelectric properties as the thermocouple, in the temperature range used. A copper wire is attached to the PtRh alloy wire, and a nickel-copper alloy wire to the platinum, for extension leads.

The Pt–PtRh thermocouples are extremely sensitive to contamination by metallic vapors in a reducing atmosphere. They must be suitably protected if their calibration is to remain valid.

Pt–PtRh thermocouples are the only rare-metal thermocouples in common use in this country. Other types have been used in Germany to secure higher emf, or higher temperature range, or lower cost. They do not appear to surpass the Pt–PtRh thermocouple in reliability, and in some cases are inferior to base-metal thermocouples.

The four types of thermocouples listed after Pt–PtRh in Table 5.1 are base-metal thermocouples extensively used for temperature measurement and control in the laboratory and in industrial processes. They are characterized by relatively high emf (four to seven times that of Pt–PtRh) which permits the use of more rugged and less expensive indicators. They are comparatively inexpensive thermocouples. Their emf-temperature curves are nearly straight lines. Thus, the calibration can be determined by emf measurements at only a few known temperatures. Reference-junction corrections involve merely the addition or subtraction of a temperature interval. Further, when one rechecks a calibrated couple after use, the per cent correction determined at one temperature applies to the whole range.

Several types of base-metal thermocouples are used for high temperature measurements. A .99Mo–.01Fe *vs.* W thermocouple gives an emf of 16 mv at $2000°C$ and can be used to $2200°C$. A .75W–.25Mo *vs.*

W thermocouple produces an emf of 5.8 mv at 2570°C and can be used to 3000°C.

Of the nonmetallic thermocouples, the carbon-graphite combination is the oldest. Its emf, less than 1 mv, is too small for practical use. Constantan–SiC and TaC–C thermocouples have been used. The C–SiC thermocouple is useful, particularly in the measurement of steel temperatures. It has the advantage of large emf and a long temperature range, but unfortunately has high electrical resistance.

THERMOCOUPLE MILLIVOLTMETERS

Instruments for measuring the emf generated by a thermocouple, or for indicating the corresponding temperature directly, may be divided into four classes: (a) galvanometers or millivoltmeters, (b) potentiometers, (c) deflection potentiometers, which combine features of the first two, and (d) electron tube potentiometers.

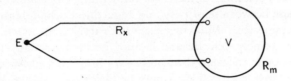

FIG. 5.5. Ohm's law applied to a thermocouple circuit: $E = IR_x + IR_m$.

A millivoltmeter consists of a coil of wire suspended between the poles of a permanent magnet and free to rotate. A pointer is attached to the coil and moves over a scale graduated in millivolts or degrees. Leads from a thermocouple are connected to the coil, usually through a series resistor. The emf of the thermocouple maintains a current in the coil causing it to deflect in the magnetic field until the electromagnetic torque is balanced by the opposing torque of a small control spring.

Consider a thermocouple connected to a millivoltmeter (Fig. 5.5). The current I in the circuit is given by

$$I = \frac{E}{R_x + R_m} \qquad (3)$$

where E is the resultant emf in the circuit, R_m the resistance of the meter, and R_x the resistance of the thermocouple and leads. The potential difference V across the terminals of the instrument is given by

$$V = \frac{R_m}{R_m + R_x} E \tag{4}$$

For ordinary use, a millivoltmeter is calibrated to indicate the potential difference across its own terminals. A reading obtained from such an instrument will be less than E, the emf developed by the thermocouple, by Eq. (4).

A millivoltmeter may be specially calibrated to indicate E correctly when connected to a thermocouple and leads of specified resistance R_x. Any change then in either R_m or R_x causes a change in the indications of the instrument. Inasmuch as the millivoltmeter may be used with more than one thermocouple, and inasmuch as R_x changes with the temperature of the wire and the length heated, it is desirable to have R_m large compared to R_x.

The choice of a millivoltmeter for use with thermocouples is usually a compromise between sensitivity and ruggedness, which largely determines the resistance. Millivoltmeters with resistances much over 600 ohms are extremely delicate and cannot be used in many locations. In order to obtain the ruggedness necessary for portability or use under conditions of severe vibrations it may be necessary to make R_m as low as 10 or 15 ohms. This means that variations in R_x will have a larger effect on the indications of the instrument, as shown in Table 5.2 for a millivoltmeter calibrated to indicate E correctly when $R_x = 2$ ohms.

TABLE 5.2   ERROR DUE TO CHANGE IN LINE RESISTANCE
(Chromel-alumel Thermocouple)

Line Resistance R_x (Ohms)	Error in Indicator Reading (Per Cent)		Error, in Degrees, at 1000°C	
	$R_m = 300$ ohms	$R_m = 10$ ohms	$R_m = 300$ ohms	$R_m = 10$ ohms
1	+0.33	+9.1	+3.3 C°	+91.0 C°
2	±0.00	±0.0	±0.0	±0.0
3	−0.33	−7.7	−3.3	−77.0
4	−0.66	−14.3	−6.6	−143.0

Variation in line resistance may be caused by oxidation of the wires, poor contacts, temperature variations in the line, and by partial fracture of the lead wires. If a millivoltmeter, particularly a low-resistance instrument, is to be used where there is considerable variation in line resistance, the meter may be provided with a variable resistor in series with the moving coil. The meter is initially calibrated with this resistance at its maximum. In service the resistance is repeatedly adjusted (with the aid of a potentiometer) to compensate for changing (increasing) line resistance.

The scale of a millivoltmeter may be calibrated either in millivolts or in degrees of temperature for a particular type of thermocouple. To correct for changes in reference junction temperature, one can set the pointer of the indicator to read the reference-junction temperature on open circuit. In some instruments this is accomplished auto-matically by a properly adjusted bimetallic spring attached to the control spring of the moving coil.

THE POTENTIOMETER PRINCIPLE

Precise laboratory measurements of thermal emf's and most industrial thermocouple measurements are made with potentiometers. The fundamental principle of the potentiometer, that of balancing

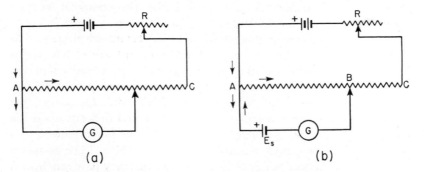

(a)   (b)

Fig. 5.6.   (a) A potential divider.   (b) A simple slide-wire potentiometer.

one voltage against another in parallel with it, should be clear from an examination of the circuits in Fig. 5.6. In Fig. 5.6a a branched circuit is shown in which the deflection of the galvanometer indicates a current, due to the potential difference along the slide-wire AC to which it is connected. In Fig. 5.6b a cell has been introduced into the lower branch. Depending upon the emf of this cell, the current in the lower branch may now be in either direction as indicated by the arrows. As a special case the current in the lower branch may be zero when the emf of the cell just equals the potential difference between A and B and the positive terminal of this cell is connected to the same end of the slide-wire as the positive terminal of the service battery.

Preparatory to measuring an unknown emf, a standard cell of known emf E_s is placed in series with the galvanometer. The sliding contact is set so that the reading on the scale at B is equal to the emf of the cell. For example, an emf $E_s = 1.018$ volts might be represented by 1018 scale divisions between A and B. By means of the rheostat R the current in the slide-wire is then adjusted so that the potential difference between A and B is just equal to E_s, this condition being indicated by zero deflection of the galvanometer. The potential difference per scale division is then 1 mv. A cell or thermocouple of unknown emf is now inserted in place of the standard cell and the contact B is adjusted until the potentiometer is balanced. Since the potentiometer has been made to read directly, the emf of the unknown is read on the scale, in millivolts.

The voltage of the service cell may change during prolonged use. Hence, it is desirable to restandardize the potentiometer current occasionally during use, by the method just outlined.

The potentiometer method has several important advantages. As there is no current in the galvanometer circuit when balance is obtained, the reading of the potentiometer is independent of the characteristics of the galvanometer, since the meter serves solely to indicate zero current in its branch of the circuit. Of course, the precision with which a balance can be determined depends upon the sensitivity of the galvanometer. The scale of the potentiometer can be made very open, thus permitting precise readings. The accuracy of these readings does not depend upon the constancy of magnets, coil springs, or jewel bearings nor upon the level of the instrument, factors which may influence the indications of a millivoltmeter.

The resistors between A and C frequently are made up of fixed coils and a slide-wire in series, as shown in Fig. 5.7. A separate resistor DA is used to standardize the battery current. With switch S closed, the current is adjusted until the potential drop across resistor DA is equal to the emf of the standard cell. The emf of the thermocouple can then be determined by closing the X switch and moving contacts A' and B until the potential drop from A' to B is

equal to the emf of the thermocouple.   This is read as the sum of the
settings on the fixed coils and on the slide-wire.

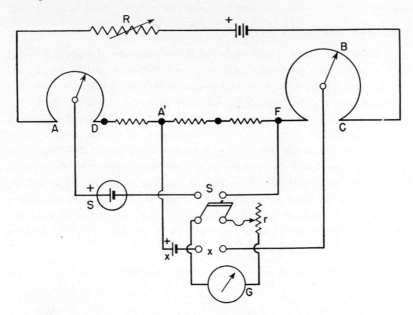

Fig. 5.7.   Wiring diagram of a commonly used type of potentiometer.

REFERENCE JUNCTION COMPENSATION

Potentiometers designed for industrial use with thermocouples are
usually provided with either a hand-operated or an automatic reference-junction compensator.   The former is an adjustable resistor,
having a scale graduated in millivolts, which the operator sets to
correspond to the observed reference-junction temperature.   Its effect
is to add a corresponding potential difference to that indicated on the
scale $A'B$.   For use with any one type of thermocouple the compensator
may include a copper-nickel coil which varies in resistance as the
temperature changes and thus compensates automatically for change
in reference-junction temperature.   An instrument so designed is
usually calibrated directly in degrees of temperature.

An automatic compensator can be located wherever desired,
although it is usually at the instrument.   In that case the lead wires
are of the same materials as the thermocouple or of materials having

essentially the same emf-temperature relationship. The couple is in effect extended up to the instrument so that the reference junction is exposed to the same ambient temperature as is the compensating coil.

PROTECTION TUBES

Closed-end tubes of porcelain, of pyrex glass, or of materials listed in Table 5.3 are generally used to protect thermocouples from contamination, which usually results from the thermocouple wires coming in contact with other metals or metallic vapors or from the action of reducing gases at high temperatures. In the latter case, the silica of the insulating or protecting tube is reduced to silicon which alloys with the thermocouple wires. For temperatures above 600°C the wires should be insulated by porcelain tubing and protected from contamination by glazed porcelain tube. For temperatures below 600°C, pyrex tubes are very satisfactory for both protecting and insulating the wires. An additional sheath of metal, alundum, or quartz is used when mechanical strength is required, as in measurements in molten metals.

TABLE 5.3 RECOMMENDED MAXIMUM OPERATING TEMPERATURE OF THERMO-
COUPLE PROTECTION TUBES

Type of Tube	Maximum Temperature	Type of Tube	Maximum Temperature
Monel (.70 Ni–.30 Cu)	500°C	Inconel (.78 Ni–.13 Cr)	1100°C
Seamless steel	550	Fused quartz (SiO_2)	1000–1400
Wrought iron	700	Porcelain	1300
Cast iron	700	Fire clay	1400
Calorized (Al–Al_2O_3-coated) wrought iron	800	Mullite base refractory	1300
14 per cent Chrome iron	800	Silica	1500
28 per cent Chrome iron	1100	Sillimanite (.37 SiO_2–.63 Al_2O_3)	1600–1800
Stainless steel (.18 Cr–.8 Ni)	850	Mullite (3 $Al_2O_3 \cdot 2 SiO_2$)	1650
Nichrome (.38 Ni–.20 Cr–.42 Fe)	1100	Silicon carbide (SiC)	1650
Chromel	1100	Rare-earth oxides (ThO_2, BeO, or ZrO_2)	2000
Nickel	1100		

Tests on the permeability of various protection tubes to gas leakage have shown very refractory porcelain, mullite, or sillimanite to be especially suitable.[12] Calorized wrought iron is superior to most other metals. Nichrome is generally more gas tight than other alloys.

Gas often enters the tubes through tiny pinhole imperfections rather than by diffusion through the walls. Ceramic tubes become less permeable to gas at higher temperature, possibly owing to increased gas viscosity.

When a thermocouple is used for measurements in molten metal at high temperatures, it is customary to increase the thickness of the protection tube. This practice has certain disadvantages: the long time required for preheating to avoid fracture of the sheath, and for attaining equilibrium on immersion; the risk of damage to the sheath in the bath; and the danger of contamination of the couple by reducing gases.

An alternative "quick-immersion" technique has been developed[17] enabling the Pt–PtRh thermocouple to be used for regular measurements in liquid steel up to 1700°C. It consists essentially in lightly sheathing the couple in silica thus allowing its sudden immersion in the steel, the taking of readings in a few seconds, and the withdrawal of the thermocouple intact. The arrangement of the end of the apparatus to be immersed in steel is shown in Fig. 5.8. To reduce the lag, one may dispense with the steel jacket *B* and the lower portion of the two-bore insulator *C*. The time necessary to get a temperature reading ranges from 4 to 15 seconds according to circumstances. If necessary the short inexpensive silica sheath is replaced after each insertion. The thermocouple will stand from 10 to 20 immersions without appreciable contamination, and the full emf

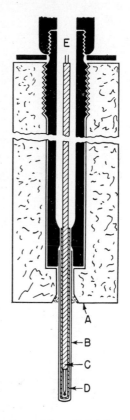

Fig. 5.8. Quick-immersion thermocouple.

can readily be restored by cutting off an inch or two from the heated end.

THERMOCOUPLE CALIBRATION AT FIXED POINTS

A thermocouple is calibrated by measurement of its emf at fixed points whose temperatures are assigned, or by comparison with a previously calibrated couple placed in good thermal contact with it. Calibration of a thermocouple at a few selected fixed points will yield a working standard that is accurate to a few tenths of a degree in the range 0 to 1100°C. Fixed points are also conveniently used with varying degrees of accuracy ranging from 0.1 to 5C° in the calibration

TABLE 5.4 FIXED POINTS AVAILABLE FOR CALIBRATING THERMOCOUPLES

Thermometric Fixed Point	Values on the International Temperature Scale				Temperature of Equilibrium (t_p) in °C as a Function of the Pressure (p) Between 680 and 780 mm of Hg
	Assigned (Primary Points)		Determined (Secondary Points)		
	°C	°F	°C	°F	
Boiling point of oxygen ..	−182.97	−297.35	. . . .	. . . .	$t_p = t_{760} + 0.0126(p − 760)$ $= 0.0000065(p − 760)^2$
Sublimation point of carbon dioxide.	. . . .	. . . .	−78.5	−109.3	$t_p = t_{760} + 0.1443(t_p + 273.2)$ $\log \left(\dfrac{p}{760}\right)$
Freezing point of mercury	. . . .	. . . .	−38.37	−37.97	
Melting point of ice.	0.000	32.000	. . . .	. . . .	
Boiling point of water . . .	100.000	212.000	. . . .	. . . .	$t_p = t_{760} + 0.0367(p − 760)$ $−0.000023(p + 760)^2$
Boiling point of naphthalene.	. . . .	. . . .	217.96	424.33	$t_p = t_{760} + 0.208(t_p + 273.2)$ $\log \left(\dfrac{p}{760}\right)$
Freezing point of tin[1]. . . .	. . . .	. . . .	231.9	449.4	
Boiling point of benzophenone.	. . . .	. . . .	305.9	582.6	$t_p = t_{760} + 0.194(t_p + 273.2)$ $\log \left(\dfrac{p}{760}\right)$
Freezing point of cadmium	. . . .	. . . .	320.9	609.6	
Freezing point of lead[1]. . .	. . . .	. . . .	327.3$_5$	621.2$_3$	
Freezing point of zinc[1]. . .	. . . .	. . . .	419.4$_8$	787.0$_6$	
Boiling point of sulfur ..	444.60	832.28	. . . .	. . . .	$t_p = t_{760} + 0.0909(p − 760)$ $−0.000048(p − 760)^2$
Freezing point of antimony	. . . .	. . . .	630.5	1166.9	
Freezing point of aluminum[1].	. . . .	. . . .	660.1$_5$	1200.2$_7$	
Freezing point of Cu-Ag eutectic alloy[2].	. . . .	. . . .	778.8	1433.8	
Freezing point of silver ..	960.5	1760.9	. . . .	. . . .	
Freezing point of gold. . . .	1063.0	1945.4	. . . .	. . . .	
Freezing point of copper[1].	. . . .	. . . .	1083.0	1981.4	
Melting point of palladium	. . . .	. . . .	1555	2831	
Melting point of platinum	. . . .	. . . .	1773	3223	

[1] Standard samples of these materials are procurable from the National Bureau of Standards with certificates giving the freezing point of the particular lot of metal. The values given in this table for these materials apply for the standard samples that are being issued as of the present date.
[2] 28.1 per cent copper and 71.9 per cent silver by weight.

and checking of various types of thermocouples in the range −190°C to the melting point of platinum (1773°C). The fixed points for which values have been assigned or determined accurately and at which it has been found convenient to calibrate thermocouples are given in Table 5.4.[16]

The emf developed by a homogeneous thermocouple at the freezing

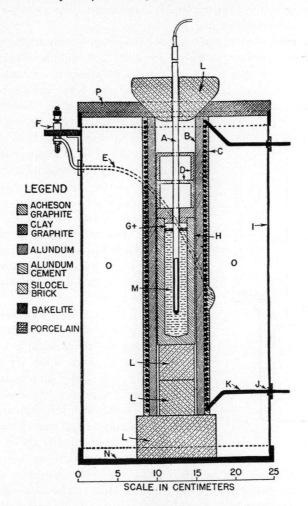

LEGEND

- ACHESON GRAPHITE
- CLAY GRAPHITE
- ALUNDUM
- ALUNDUM CEMENT
- SILOCEL BRICK
- BAKELITE
- PORCELAIN

SCALE IN CENTIMETERS

Fig. 5.9. Furnace used in calibrating thermocouples at the freezing points of metals.

point of a metal is constant and reproducible if all of the following conditions are fulfilled: (1) the couple is protected from contamination; (2) the couple is immersed in the freezing point sample sufficiently to eliminate heating or cooling of the junction by heat flow along the wires and protection tube; (3) the reference junctions are maintained at a constant and reproducible temperature; (4) the freezing point sample is pure; and (5) the metal is maintained at essentially a uniform temperature during freezing.

The temperature of the reference junctions is most easily controlled at a known temperature by an ice bath. A widemouthed thermos bottle filled with shaved ice saturated with water is very satisfactory. Electrical connection between a thermocouple wire and a copper lead wire is easily made by inserting them into a small glass tube containing

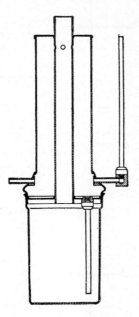

a few drops of mercury. The glass tubes are then inserted into the ice bath to a depth of about 10 cm. The lead wires should be insulated from the thermocouple wires, except where they make contact through the mercury. The glass tubes should be kept clean and dry inside. Moisture is likely to condense in the tube from the atmosphere but should not be allowed to accumulate. A little moisture and dirt at the bottom of the tube will form a galvanic cell which may vitiate the readings.

The depth of the immersion necessary to avoid heating or cooling of the junction by heat flow along the thermocouple wires and protection tube depends upon the material and size of the wires, the dimensions of the insulating and protecting tubes, and the difference between the temperature of the freezing point sample and that of the furnace and atmosphere immediately above it. The safest method of determining whether the depth of immersion is sufficient is by trial. It should be such that during the period of freezing the thermocouple can be lowered or raised at least 1 cm from its normal position without altering the indicated emf by as much as the allowable uncertainty in the calibration.

FIG. 5.10.   Hypsometer.

Figure 5.9 shows the type of furnace used in freezing point determinations. The heating element is No. 6 or 8 gauge .80Ni–.20Cr wire wound on an alundum tube and imbedded in alundum cement. The space between the heating element and the outside wall is filled with silocel powder. Acheson-graphite diaphragms are placed above the crucible in order to minimize the oxidation of the crucible and to promote temperature uniformity in the metal.

Calibrations at the steam point are made by the use of a hypsometer designed to avoid superheating and contaminating the vapor around the thermocouple.[8] A simple type of hypsometer suitable for calibrations not requiring the highest accuracy is illustrated in Fig. 5.10.

THERMOCOUPLE CALIBRATION BY COMPARISON

The calibration of a thermocouple by comparison with a working standard is sufficiently accurate for most purposes and can be done conveniently in most industrial and technical laboratories. The success of this method usually depends upon the ability of the observer to bring the junction of the couple to the same temperature as the actuating element of the standard, such as the hot junction of a standard thermocouple or the bulb of a resistance or liquid-in-glass thermometer. The accuracy obtained is further limited by the accuracy of the standard. Of course, the reference-junction temperature must be known, but this can usually be controlled by using an ice bath, as described earlier, or measured by a liquid-in-glass thermometer.

FIG. 5.11.   Arrangement to insure good thermal contact between junction of a base-metal thermocouple and that of a Pt–PtRh thermocouple.

It is important that the thermocouple being calibrated and the standard thermocouple have their junctions at the same temperature. For this purpose the two thermocouples may be inserted in holes drilled in a copper or a nickel block, or the couples may even be welded together as in Fig. 5.11. Separate potentiometers, one connected to each couple, are used to measure the emf's. To permit simultaneous readings, each potentiometer is provided with a reflecting galvanom-

eter. The two spots of light are reflected on a single scale, the galvanometers being set so the spots coincide at zero on the scale when the
circuits are open, and hence also when the potentiometers are set to
balance the emf of each couple.   One potentiometer is set to a determined value and the other adjusted so that both spots of light pass across
the zero of the scale together as the temperature of the furnace is
raised or lowered.   This method is particularly adapted to the calibration of thermocouples at any number of selected points.

METHODS OF INTERPOLATING BETWEEN CALIBRA-TION POINTS[13]

After the thermocouple has been calibrated at a number of points,
the next requirement is a convenient means of obtaining corresponding
values of emf and temperature at other points.

A curve or a table giving corresponding temperature and emf values
may be prepared. The values in such a table may be obtained by
computing an empirical equation or series of equations through the
calibration points, by direct interpolation between points, or by
drawing a difference curve from an arbitrary reference table that
closely approximates the temperature-emf relation of the couple.   The
method to be selected for a particular calibration (Table 5.5) depends
upon such factors as the type of couple, number of calibration points,
temperature range, accuracy required, and personal preference.

For the highest accuracy in the range 660 to 1063°C with Pt *vs.*
.90Pt–.10Rh thermocouples, the method is the one prescribed in the
International Temperature Scale.   An equation of the form $E = a +
bt + ct^2$ is used, where a, b, and c are constants determined by calibra-
tion at the freezing points of gold, silver, and antimony.   By calibrating the couple also at the freezing point of zinc and using an equation of the form $E = a' + b't + c't^2 + d't^3$, the temperature range can
be extended down to 400°C without introducing an uncertainty of
more than 0.1 C° in the range 660 to 1063°C.   By calibrating the
couple at the freezing points of gold, antimony, and zinc and using an
equation of the form $E = a'' + b''t + c''t^2$, a calibration is obtained
for the range 400 to 1100°C, which agrees with the International
Temperature Scale to 0.5 C°.   The freezing point of copper may be
used instead of the gold point, and the aluminum point used instead
of the antimony point without introducing an additional uncertainty
of more than 0.1 C°.

TABLE 5.5 METHODS AND ACCURACIES OBTAINABLE IN CALIBRATING THERMO-
COUPLES

Type of Thermocouple	Temperature Range (°C)	Method of Calibration	Accuracy at Observed Points (C°)	Uncertainty in Interpolated Values (C°)
Platinum *vs.* .90 Pt– .10 Rh	600 to 1063	International temperature scale. Freezing points of Sb, Ag, Au	0.2	0.2[1]
Platinum *vs.* .90 Pt– .10 Rh	0 to 1500	Freezing points of Sn, Zn, Al, and Cu (NBS standard samples)	0.2	0.5 to 1100[1] 2 to 1500[1]
Chromel-alumel	0 to 1200	Comparison with standard couple about every 100 C°	1.0	2.0[1]
Chromel-alumel } Iron-constantan }	−190 to 350	Comparison with standard resistance thermometer (about every 60 C°) or at fixed points	0.1	0.5[2]
Copper-constantan	0 to 300	Comparison with standard resistance thermometer or at fixed points about every 100 C°	0.1	0.2[3]
	0 to −190	Sublimation point of CO_2 and boiling point of O_2	0.1	0.3[2]

[1] Equation $E = a + bt + ct^2$.
[2] Difference curve from reference table (e.g. Tables 9, 11, 13 in Appendix).
[3] Equation $E = at + bt^2 + ct^3$ or difference curve from reference table.

For temperatures outside the range 660 to 1063°C, the method of drawing a smooth curve through the temperature and emf values has just as much claim to accuracy as the method of passing empirical equations through the calibration points, because an empirical equation performs the same function as a curved ruler. For the temperature range 0 to 1500°C, a curve for interpolation to 1 or 2 C° requires calibration points not more than 200 C° apart and a careful plot on a large sheet of paper, which is tedious to read. A reduction in the number of calibration points increases the uncertainty proportionately. It is preferable to plot a difference curve. For ordinates we take the difference between observed emf and that calculated from the first degree equation, $E = 10t$. The abscissas are the emf's. Then to obtain a corrected temperature, the differences may be read from the curve and added to the quantity $10t$. In this way the uncertainty in interpolated values is much less than in the case in which the emf is plotted directly against the temperature. If we go one step further and plot differences from an arbitrary reference table the values of which closely represent the form of the temperature-emf relation for the type of couple in question, the maximum differences to be plotted will be only a few degrees. In this way interpolated values are obtained in which the uncertainty in the interpolated values is not appreciably greater than that at the calibration points. The more accurately the values in the arbitrary reference table conform to the emf-temperature relation of actual couples, the fewer the number of calibration points required for a given accuracy.

The materials used in the construction of base-metal thermocouples generally are not so pure as those used for rare-metal thermocouples, nor is this necessary. Manufacturers have adopted somewhat different calibration curves for thermocouples having the same name but differing slightly in thermoelectric properties. Replacement couples having the same calibration are provided by controlling the composition of the elements or by selecting pairs of materials from different heats which will match the predetermined calibration. This also leads to the occasional use of a different composition of constantan for iron-constantan and for copper-constantan thermocouples.

Specifications for iron-constantan and copper-constantan thermocouples have been established[15] in an attempt to meet the first two essential requirements and the last three desirable conditions listed below:

(1) The calibration should be such that it can be reproduced over a large temperature range with materials readily available at present (and presumably in the future).

(2) It should be the same (within reasonable limits) as the temperature-emf relation of a large percentage of such thermocouples now in use.

(3) It should be near the mean of the extreme limits of the temperature-emf relation for thermocouples of that type.

(4) It should agree with the most widely used existing table.

(5) The constantan selected for use with copper to reproduce the relation for copper-constantan should be such that it can be used with a particular iron to reproduce the relation for iron-constantan as well. Typical tables are given in the Appendix.

SPECIAL FORMS OF THERMOCOUPLES

Thermocouples are designed in special forms for a wide variety of measurements. Operating temperatures of internal combustion engines are measured by thermocouples in the form of flat rings clamped under the spark plugs or fixed in cavities in the cylinder block. A thermocouple in the form of a hypodermic needle is used to determine the internal temperature of foods, tires, plastics, etc.

The friction between two dissimilar metal surfaces has been studied by measurement of their thermal emf. The surface temperature of a brass wire drawn through a steel die is determined by use of the die and wire as elements of a thermocouple.

One type of vacuum gauge consists of a thermocouple attached to a filament and mounted in the test chamber. A constant heating current is maintained in the filament. Its temperature depends largely on the rate at which gas molecules encountering the filament conduct heat from it. As the pressure in the chamber is reduced, the temperature of the filament rises. The deflection of the thermocouple galvanometer increases and with proper calibration this can be used to indicate pressure directly.

Thermocouples can be designed to detect minute amounts of radiant energy. A tiny thermojunction of low thermal capacity is mounted in a transparent evacuated bulb and placed where it receives and absorbs the radiant energy. Measurements are usually made with a sensitive galvanometer. Vacuum thermocouples find application in radiation pyrometers, devices for measuring stellar or solar energy, and locators which are actuated by the feeble radiant energy received from a distant airplane engine or other target.

Increased sensitivity can be secured by connecting two or more thermocouples in series and mounting them compactly with the hot junctions close together and with the cold junctions shielded from radiation that should not reach them. Such a device is called a *thermopile*. Figure 5.12 is an enlarged view of a thermopile showing the hot junctions flattened and blackened to receive incident radiation and the terminal strips attached to an annular ring of mica. As used in a radiation pyrometer, a lens concentrates radiant energy on the hot junctions through an aperture that shields the cold junctions. Fine silver and bismuth wires have been used extensively for thermo-

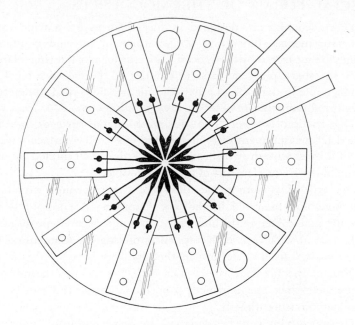

FIG. 5.12.   Thermopile of a radiation pyrometer.

piles because of their large thermal emf. Other factors such as the thermal conductivity and electrical resistivity of the wires and the area exposed are important and the construction of sensitive thermopiles requires considerable skill. Launer has described a simplified technique for constructing thermopiles using chromel and constantan wires (of No. 36 and 38 gauge, respectively) with the measuring junctions soldered to silver foil receivers. The thermoelectric power (dE/dt) of such a thermopile is more than 60 mv/C°.

SUMMARY

The emf of a thermocouple whose reference junction is at $0°C$ is commonly expressible in terms of the temperature t of the measuring junction by an equation of the form

$$E_0^t = a + b + ct^2$$

A thermocouple is calibrated at selected fixed points with a constant, known reference-junction temperature (usually $0°C$). Adequate immersion of the protected thermocouple in a pure freezing point sample and maintenance of essentially uniform temperature during freezing are precautions necessary to assure a reproducible scale.

When a thermocouple is used at a different reference-junction temperature, a *reference-junction correction*, E_r, is added to the observed emf E_x to obtain the tabulated emf E_0

$$E_0 = E_r + E_x$$

When thermal emf's are read on a millivoltmeter it is usually necessary to correct for the effects of resistance

$$V = \frac{R_m}{R_m + R_x} E$$

A potentiometer, using a balance method, permits measurement of thermal emf's independent of resistance or resistance changes in the thermocouple circuit.

The selection of a base- or rare-metal thermocouple, its size, and its protection depend upon the maximum temperature and the chemical environment to be encountered.

Temperature measurements can be obtained over the range from -200 to $3000°C$ by using thermocouples of various types.

A *thermopile* is a sensitive detector of radiation made by connecting many fine thermocouples in series.

REFERENCES FOR SUPPLEMENTARY READING

1. Am. Inst. of Phys., *Temperature—Its Measurement and Control in Science and Industry*, pp. 180–205, "Thermoelectric Thermometry" by W. F. Roeser; pp. 206–218, "The Calibration of Thermocouples at Low Temperatures" by R. B. Scott; pp. 265–278, "Potentiometers for Thermoelectric Measurements" by W. P. White, Reinhold Publishing Corp., 1941.
2. Brenner, B., "Recent Developments in Platinum Thermocouples," *Ind. Eng. Chem., Anal. Ed.,* **27,** 438 (1935).
3. Caldwell, F. R., "Thermoelectric Properties of Platinum-Rhodium Alloys," *Bur. Standards J. Research,* **10,** 373 (1933).
4. Cartwright, C. H., "General Theory, Design, and Construction of Sensitive Vacuum Thermopiles," *Rev. Sci. Instruments,* **1,** 592 (1930).

5. Dahl, A. I., "Stability of Base-Metal Thermocouples in Air from 800° to 2200°F," *J. Research Nat. Bur. Standards*, **24**, 205 (1940).
6. Fitterer, G. R., "A New Thermocouple for the Determination of Temperatures up to at Least 1800°C," *Trans. Am. Soc. Mech. Eng.*, **105**, 290 (1933). "Some Metallurgical Applications of the C-SiC Thermocouple," *Trans. Am. Soc. Mech. Eng.*, **120**, 189 (1936).
7. Launer, H. F., "Easily Constructed, Rugged, Sensitive Thermopile," *Rev. Sci. Instruments*, **11**, 98 (1940).
8. Mueller, E. F., and T. S. Sligh, Jr., "Laboratory Hypsometers," *Rev. Sci. Instruments*, **6**, 958 (1922).
9. Mueller, E. F., and F. Wenner, "Adjustable Resistance Elements," *J. Research Nat. Bur. Standards*, **15**, 477 (1935).
10. Niven, C. D., "A Gas-Tight Furnace for Thermocouple Standardization," *Can. J. Research*, **14**, 177 (1936).
11. Patton, E. L., and R. A. Feagan, Jr., "A Method of Installing Tube-wall Thermocouples," *Ind. Eng. Chem.*, *Anal. Ed.*, **13**, 823 (1941).
12. Roeser, W. F., "Passage of Gas through the Walls of Pyrometer Protecting Tubes at High Temperature," *Bur. Standards, J. Research*, **7**, 485 (1931).
13. Roeser, W. F., "Thermoelectric Temperature Scales," *Bur. Standards J. Research*, **3**, 343 (1929).
14. Roeser, W. F., "Thermoelectric Thermometry," *J. App. Phys.*, **11**, 388 (1940).
15. Roeser, W. F., and A. I. Dahl, "Reference Tables for Iron-Constantan and Copper-Constantan Thermocouples," *J. Research Nat. Bur. Standards*, **20**, 337 (1938).
16. Roeser, W. F., and H. T. Wensel, "Methods of Testing Thermocouples and Thermocouple Materials," *J. Research Nat. Bur. Standards*, **14**, 247 (1935).
17. Schofield, F. H., and A. Grace, "A 'Quick-immersion' Thermocouple for Measuring the Temperature of Liquid Steel . . .," *Iron & Steel Inst.* (*London*), *Special Report* No. **25**, sec. VII, 235 (1939).
18. Stein, I. M., "Design of Potentiometers," *Trans. Am. Inst. Elec. Eng.*, **50**, 118 (1931).
19. Weller, C. T., "Characteristics of Thermocouples," *Gen. Elec. Rev.*, **49**, 50 (1946).

QUESTIONS AND PROBLEMS

1. The calibration equation for a certain Pt–PtRh thermocouple in the range 300 to 1200°C is given as $E = -0.323 + 0.008276t + 0.000001638t^2$ for a reference junction at 0°C. Compare with Eq. (2). Why is not a equal to zero in this case? When would you expect a to be zero?

2. When is a reference junction correction needed in thermocouple measurements? How is it made?

3. Which of the common thermocouples included in Fig. 5.4 has the largest thermoelectric power at (a) 400°C, (b) 1200°C?

4. Assume that you have an uncalibrated potentiometer with uniform slide-wire. Derive an equation from which you could determine E, an unknown emf,

from the known emf E_s of a standard cell and the lengths of slide-wire L and L_s necessary to balance each.

5. Is the precision of measurements made with the potentiometer of Fig. 5.6(b) affected by variable contact resistance at B? at A or C? by variation in the emf of the battery? by a uniform change in temperature of the entire circuit?

6. Under what conditions might one appropriately choose to measure thermo-couple emf's by using (a) a millivoltmeter, (b) a potentiometer?

7. Is it highly desirable that a furnace used for the calibration of thermocouples by comparison with a Pt–PtRh standard be well-insulated thermally? Explain.

8. In determining the freezing temperature of molten metal in a crucible how could you assure yourself that you had provided sufficient immersion for the thermocouple and its protecting tube?

9. Under what conditions might one purposely use a thermocouple with insufficient immersion?

10. Assume that it is desired to measure the average temperature of a heated enclosure. Compare the advantages and disadvantages of using thermocouples in the following methods: (a) by reading the thermocouples individually and averaging the results, (b) by connecting them in series and measuring the total emf, (c) by making the thermocouples of equal resistance and connecting them in parallel so the average emf is read directly.

11. The emf-temperature relation for a certain thermocouple is
$$E = 0.041t - 0.000041t^2$$
where the temperature is in centigrade degrees and the emf is in millivolts. (a) What is the neutral temperature? (b) What is the emf at this neutral temperature?

12. What is the thermoelectric power of an iron-constantan thermocouple in the neighborhood of 500°C? (Use tables.) *Ans.* 0.055 mv/C°.

13. What is the thermoelectric power of a Pt *vs.* .90Pt–.10Rh thermocouple in the neighborhood of 0°C?

14. The temperature of a furnace is measured with an iron-constantan thermo-couple. With one junction at 20°C and the other at the temperature of the furnace, the thermocouple produces an emf of 15.51 mv. What is the temperature of the furnace? (Use tables.) *Ans.* 300°C.

15. A copper-constantan thermocouple with one junction at 25°C indicates an emf of 13.87 mv when the other junction is placed in an annealing oven. What is the temperature of the oven? (Use tables.)

16. A Pt *vs.* .90Pt–.10Rh thermocouple which with its leads has a resistance of 17 ohms is connected to a millivoltmeter having a resistance of 50 ohms. The millivoltmeter indicates 1.79 mv when one junction of the thermocouple is in an ice bath and the other is at temperature t. Find the value of temperature t. *Ans.* 590°F.

17. A chromel-alumel thermocouple which with its leads has a resistance of 3.0 ohms is connected to a millivoltmeter having a resistance of 25.0 ohms (Fig. 5.5). When the reference junction is at 0°C and the measuring junction is at temperature t, the millivoltmeter indicates a potential difference across its terminals of 10.9 mv. What is the temperature of the measuring junction?

18. The emf E (mv) of a certain copper-constantan thermocouple having its reference junction at 0°C and its measuring junction at temperature t is given by

$E = 0.0381t + 0.0000444t^2$.   (a) What emf will be developed when one junction is at 20°C, the other at 100°C?   (b) Under these conditions, what potential difference will be indicated by a 25-ohm millivoltmeter connected to the thermocouple, if the resistance of thermocouple and leads is 2.0 ohms?

Ans. 3.51 mv, 3.25 mv.

19. A thermocouple and its leads are made of 14 B & S gauge chromel and alumel wires having resistances of 0.104 and 0.0432 ohm/ft, respectively.   What is the maximum distance that a 200-ohm millivoltmeter can be placed from the measuring junction without having the line drop (IR) introduce an error greater than 2 per cent in its readings?

20. The slide-wire AC of the potentiometer shown in Fig. 5.6(b) has a resistance of 3.00 ohms and is provided with a scale graduated in 2000 equal divisions.   The potentiometer is to be standardized so each scale division corresponds to 1.0 millivolt.   What resistance R should be placed in series with the battery, which has an emf of 6.0 volts and internal resistance 0.2 ohm?   *Ans.* 5.8 ohms.

21. A simple potentiometer has a uniform slide-wire AB of 40-ohm resistance connected in series with a 6.0-volt battery of internal resistance 4.0 ohms and an adjustable resistance R.   A scale attached to AB is graduated in 2000 equal divisions.   It is desired to make the potentiometer direct-reading, one scale division corresponding to one millivolt.   What should be the value of resistance R?

Chapter 6

||||||||||||||||||||||||

RADIANT ENERGY

RADIATION TERMINOLOGY |||||| *RADIATION*
LAWS FOR AN IDEAL RADIATOR ||||||
RADIATION AND ABSORPTION BY
A NON-BLACKBODY ||||||

RADIATION

Energy may be transferred from one body to another by a process of radiation and absorption even though there is no material in the space between the bodies. The earth receives its chief supply of energy from the sun, by radiation and absorption. The solar energy that is absorbed by the earth becomes heat energy. Nearly all of this is reradiated into space, but a small part is stored by the activity of plant and animal life and is represented by the fuel value of our forests, coal, oil, and gas deposits.

Radiation and *absorption* is a universal process of energy transfer. The energy in transit through space is called *radiant energy*. It travels out from the source or radiator until it encounters some object where, in general, it is partly reflected, partly absorbed, and partly transmitted.

Radiation is a general term applied to such diverse physical phenomena as: (1) temperature radiation, which is determined by the nature of the radiator and its temperature, (2) luminescent radiation, which depends upon the kind of radiator and factors other than its temperature, (3) X-ray radiation, associated with shifts in the configuration of inner electrons in atoms, and (4) nuclear radiation which is associated with the structure of atomic nuclei and the emission of fundamental particles, X rays, and gamma rays. We are here concerned only with temperature radiation and particularly with those laws and principles that serve as a basis for methods of measuring temperature.

RADIANT ENERGY

Experiments with appropriate detectors have shown that radiant energy and light behave in a similar way. In fact, light is that par-

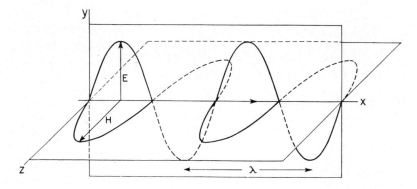

Fig. 6.1. Graph showing the values of the intensities of *E*, the electric, and *H*, the magnetic, fields in a plane electromagnetic wave at a given instant of time.

ticular kind of radiant energy capable of producing visual sensation. James Clerk Maxwell (1831–1879) conceived of radiant energy in free space as propagated by vibratory electric and magnetic disturbances (Fig. 6.1) at right angles to one another which are in phase and move through space in a direction perpendicular to those disturbances. This concept of electromagnetic waves led to experiments which showed the fundamental similarity of a number of types of radiation phenomena that superficially seem unrelated. The whole visible spectrum is now recognized as comprising a little less than one octave in the broad spectrum of electromagnetic radiation whose indeterminate extent is at least 80 octaves (Fig. 6.2).

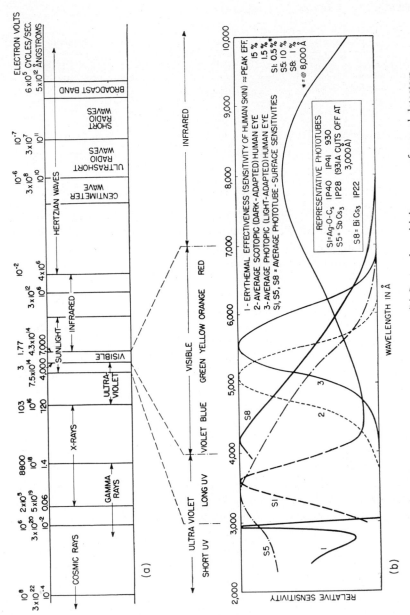

FIG. 6.2.   (a) The electromagnetic spectrum.   (b) Spectral sensitivity curves of several detectors.

91

TABLE 6.1 UNITS OF WAVELENGTH

Unit	Symbol	Equivalent to
Micron.....................................	μ	10^{-4} cm
Millimicron................................	$m\mu$	10^{-7}
Micromicron...............................	$\mu\mu$	10^{-10}
Angstrom..................................	A	10^{-8}
X-unit.....................................	XU	10^{-11}

The different units used in expressing wavelengths are given in Table 6.1.

EXCHANGE OF RADIATION

All bodies emit radiant energy at a rate which increases with the temperature and which is independent of neighboring bodies. At the same time, they absorb, at least in part, radiation originating elsewhere and incident upon them. This assumption is known as Prévost's theory of exchange after Pierre Prévost of Geneva who formulated these ideas in 1792. They are in accord with our experience that a relatively hot body cools by radiating energy to its surroundings more rapidly than it absorbs radiant energy that comes from its surroundings. Similarly, a body, initially cooler than its surroundings, warms up because its rate of emission is then less than its rate of absorption of energy. A body in a given environment eventually comes into thermal equilibrium with its surroundings; at equilibrium the rates of emission and absorption are equal.

RADIANT-ENERGY TERMS AND DEFINITIONS

Certain terms needed for a quantitative study of radiant energy are listed and defined in Table 6.2. These radiation terms refer to quantities measurable by purely physical methods and expressible in physical units. The analogous light terms, in contrast, refer to psychophysical concepts which are measurable only by reference to a standard observer.

Radiant flux is the rate of flow of energy from a radiator. We may refer to the radiant flux through a specified opening, incident on a specified surface, or emitted by a source (Fig. 6.3). Radiant flux is a power unit

$$P = \frac{dU}{dt}$$

(1)

TABLE 6.2 RADIANT-ENERGY TERMS*

Symbol	Quantity	Symbolic Definition	Common Units c.g.s.	Common Units m.k.s.
U	Radiant energy...............		erg	joule
u	Radiant density...............	dU/dV	erg/cm^3	joule/m^3
P	Radiant flux.................	dU/dt	erg/sec	watt
W	Radiant emittance (radiant flux density)..................	dP/dA	e·g/sec cm^2	watt/m^2
ω	Solid angle...................	A/r^2	steradian	steradian
J†	Radiant intensity, of a source..	$dP_e/d\omega$	erg/sec ω	watt/ω
N	Radiance (steradiancy) of a source.....................	dJ/dA_p	erg/sec ω cm^2	watt/ω m^2
H	Irradiance (irradiancy) of a surface.......................	$J \cos \theta/l^2$	erg/sec cm^2	watt/m^2
R†	Radiancy of a source..........	dP_e/dA	erg/sec cm^2	watt/m^2
α	Total absorptance	P_a/P_i		
ρ‡	Total reflectance..............	P_r/P_i		
τ‡	Total transmittance	P_t/P_i		
ϵ‡	Total emittance...............	R/R_b		

* When we refer to monochromatic rather than total radiation, we shall use the word *spectral* before each term and a subscript λ (wavelength) attached to the symbol. An appropriate λ interval is included in the denominator of most units.

† Subscript e indicates that P is a flux emitted by a source.

‡ Subscript i indicates that P is a flux incident upon a specified surface. Subscripts r, a, t indicate that P is a reflected, absorbed, or transmitted flux. Subscript p indicates that dA_p is a projected area, equal to dA multiplied by the cosine of the angle between its normal and the direction considered. Subscript b refers to a blackbody source at the same temperature as the source being compared.

Solid angle refers to the opening subtended at the apex of a cone or pyramid. It is measured by the ratio of the area A which the cone or pyramid intersects on the surface of a sphere centered at the apex, to the square of the radius r of that spherical surface

$$\omega = \frac{A}{r^2} \tag{2}$$

The unit solid angle is the steradian, the solid angle subtended by one square meter of surface of a sphere having a radius of one meter. The solid angle defined by the walls and floor intersecting in the corner of a room is equal to $\pi/2$ steradian. A hemispherical solid angle is equal to 2π steradians, and a total sphere angle equals 4π steradians.

The radiant intensity $\mathcal{J}$ of a source is the emergent flux per unit solid angle in the direction of the axis of that solid angle

$$\mathcal{J} = \frac{dP_e}{d\omega} \tag{3}$$

The analogous term for light is the luminous intensity I. Except in the case of a uniform spherical source, $\mathcal{J}$ (or I) varies with the direction considered. In such cases the symbol $\mathcal{J}_\theta$ is used to represent the radiant intensity in a direction at an angle θ to the normal.

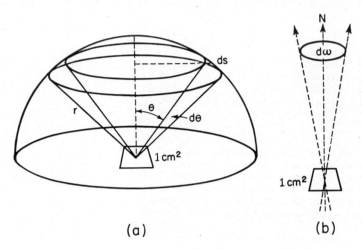

(a)   (b)

FIG. 6.3.   (a) Element of solid angle θ formed between two coaxial cones with unit area of radiator at their vertex.   (b) Radiant energy flow through unit area within solid angle $d\omega$.

The radiancy R of a source is the flux in all directions emergent per unit area

$$R = \frac{dP_e}{dA} \tag{4}$$

Radiant emittance (or radiant flux density) W represents radiant flux per unit area where that area is not part of a source

$$W = \frac{dP}{dA} \tag{5}$$

A window through which there is radiant flux from the sun is an example for which the dA in Eq. (5) represents an element of area separate from the source. If, however, we think of the window as a secondary source of radiant energy we may correctly speak of its radiancy, and R will equal W.

The radiance or steradiancy N of a source is the radiant flux per unit of area projected on a plane surface perpendicular to the direction of propagation considered

$$N = \frac{d\mathcal{J}}{dA_p} = \frac{d\mathcal{J}}{dA \cos \theta} \tag{6}$$

The irradiance or irradiancy H of a surface is the rate at which it receives radiant energy per unit area

$$H = \frac{dP_i}{dA} \tag{7}$$

The analogous light term is illuminance E, which is expressed in lumens per square meter.

When radiant energy falls on a body it is generally in part absorbed, in part reflected, and in part transmitted. The coefficients α, ρ, τ are used to indicate respectively the fractional part of the incident radiation that is absorbed, reflected, or transmitted by the body.

A *blackbody* is defined simply as a body that absorbs all radiation incident upon it (and reflects or transmits none). An equivalent definition of a blackbody which follows as a consequence of Kirchhoff's law (below) is: A blackbody is an ideal radiator which, at any specified temperature, emits in each part of the spectrum the maximum energy obtainable per unit time from any radiator as a result of temperature alone. Radiant energy from such a body is called blackbody radiation and is the standard in terms of which radiation laws are investigated. It is an idealized concept, as is a perfect gas, and can be realized only approximately in practice.

KIRCHHOFF'S RADIATION LAW

Good absorbers of radiant energy are also good radiators. This can be demonstrated with a piece of painted porcelain. Those parts of the pattern which are good absorbers and appear dark by reflected light appear brighter than their background when the porcelain is heated to incandescence. The radiancy of an actual source is related to that of a blackbody by the total emittance

$$\epsilon = \frac{R}{R_b} \tag{8}$$

The emittance ϵ of a non-blackbody is equal to its total absorptance α for radiation from a blackbody at the same temperature

$$\epsilon = \alpha \qquad (9)$$

Kirchhoff's law is equally true for each wavelength, that is the spectral emittance ϵ_λ equals the spectral absorptance α_λ

$$\epsilon_\lambda = \alpha_\lambda \qquad (10)$$

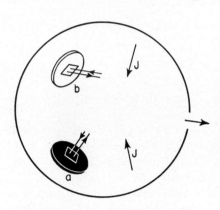

FIG. 6.4. A blackbody (a) and a non-blackbody (b) within a uniformly heated enclosure.

Kirchhoff's law is based on the experimental fact that, when a body is placed in a cavity that has opaque walls maintained at constant temperature, the body eventually attains that temperature, thus coming into equilibrium with the walls. Consider a blackbody, a, and a non-blackbody, b, in such an enclosure (Fig. 6.4) under equilibrium conditions. The rate R_b at which the blackbody radiates energy must equal the rate H_b at which it receives energy

$$H_b = R_b \qquad (11)$$

For the non-blackbody at equilibrium the irradiance H_b of its surface is equal to the radiancy R_a plus that part ρH_b of the incident radiant energy that is reflected per unit area per unit time

$$H_b = \rho H_b + R_a \qquad (12)$$

This may be rewritten by substitution from Eq. (11) as

$$R_a = (1 - \rho)R_b = \epsilon R_b \qquad (13)$$

since for an opaque body

$$\rho + \epsilon = 1$$

The non-blackbody is maintained in equilibrium with its surroundings. It must radiate energy to its surroundings at the same

rate that it absorbs energy.   The non-blackbody absorbs energy at
the rate of ϵR_b, so

$$\alpha H_b = \epsilon R_b \tag{14}$$

and from Eq. (11) $\alpha = \epsilon$

that is, the absorptance of a body is equal to its emittance.

APPROXIMATE BLACKBODIES

The concept of a blackbody would have a very limited utility if
it were not possible to realize approximate blackbody conditions
experimentally.   Actually there are no blackbody materials although
carbon black, platinum black, zinc black, and carborundum are
approximately blackbodies.

Radiation in an enclosure, say a sphere, after numerous reflections,
comes to equilibrium with its surroundings and becomes blackbody
radiation characteristic of that temperature.   Its radiant density at
each wavelength depends only on the wavelength and the temperature
and is independent of the material or shape of the enclosure.   A small
observation hole cut in the sphere does not disturb this condition

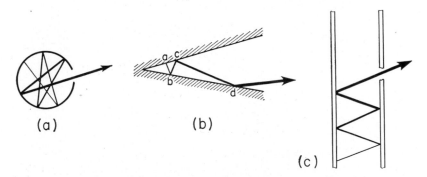

Fig. 6.5.   Non-blackbody radiation builds up in a cavity at constant temperature
to give blackbody radiation.

appreciably and the radiant flux from the opening will be very nearly
blackbody.

Figure 6.5 shows experimental blackbodies in the form of spherical
and tubular enclosures and a narrow wedge.   Miniature blackbodies
are made in the form of Fig. 6.5c by using a tubular filament of

tungsten or platinum and making a small hole in the wall. The tube is heated electrically to incandescence.

Consider the ray *abcd* sketched in Fig. 6.5. Along its path an observer receives radiant energy emitted by the surface at d, plus some originating at c and reflected at d, plus some originating at b and reflected successively at c and d, etc. The radiancy is then given by

$$R = R_a + \rho R_a + \rho^2 R_a + \cdots = \frac{R_a}{1 - \rho} \qquad (15)$$

where R_a is the radiancy of the wall and ρ the coefficient of reflection. The radiancy R_b of a blackbody is related to R_a by the equations

$$R_a = \epsilon R_b = (1 - \rho)R_b \qquad (16)$$

Hence, after a large number (strictly, an infinite number) of reflections the radiation will be blackbody radiation

$$R = R_b \qquad (17)$$

EXAMPLE: The total emissivity ϵ_t for tungsten at 2400°K is 0.296. After what number n of reflections will the radiation in a tungsten cavity at 2400°K be 99.5 per cent blackbody radiation?

$$R = (\epsilon + \epsilon\rho + \epsilon\rho^2 + \cdots + \epsilon\rho^n)R_b$$

For any opaque body $\qquad\qquad \rho = 1 - \alpha$

From Kirchhoff's law $\qquad\qquad \alpha = \epsilon$

Substituting $1 - \rho$ for ϵ in the first equation gives

$$R = (1 - \rho + \rho - \rho^2 + \rho^2 + \cdots - \rho^{n+1})R_b = (1 - \rho^{n+1})R_b$$

$$\frac{R}{R_b} = 0.995 = 1 - 0.704^{n+1}$$

$$n + 1 \log 0.704 = \log 0.005$$

$$n + 1 = 15$$

LAMBERT'S COSINE LAW

The brightness B and the radiance N of a blackbody are independent of the direction from which it is observed. For all wavelengths the radiant intensity J from a blackbody varies as the cosine of the angle of emission

$$J = J_0 \cos \theta \qquad (18)$$

This can be shown to be a consequence of Kirchhoff's law. Non-blackbody sources, however, may show large departures from the cosine law.

ABSORPTION OF RADIATION

Generally, when radiant energy falls on a surface, a part is absorbed, another part reflected, and the remainder transmitted. The absorptance (α), reflection (ρ), and the transmittance (τ) are defined as the fractional parts of the incident radiant energy which are, respectively, absorbed, reflected, or transmitted. It is evident that the sum of these three coefficients is unity

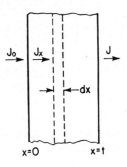

$$\alpha + \rho + \tau = 1 \qquad (19)$$

For an opaque body the coefficient of transmission is zero and Eq. (19) reduces to $\alpha + \rho = 1$.

From the assumption that the transmission coefficient of any body is independent of the intensity of radiation, it follows that each element of thickness dx in a homogeneous material (Fig. 6.6) will reduce the intensity in the same ratio

FIG. 6.6. Absorption of radiant flux.

$$-\frac{dJ}{J_x} = k\,dx$$

Here k is the coefficient of absorption and represents the decrease in intensity per unit intensity per unit path distance.

Integrating, $\log_e J_x = -kx + C$

when $x = 0$, $J = J_0$ hence $C = \log_e J_0$

and $$\log_e \frac{J}{J_0} = -kt$$

or $$\tau = \frac{J}{J_0} = e^{-kt} \qquad (20)$$

When the absorbing medium is a solution, Beer's law states

$$J = J_0 e^{-c\beta t} \qquad (21)$$

where c is the concentration of the absorbing substance, β is its specific absorptivity, and t the path length.

EXAMPLE: The absorption coefficient of a certain type of glass is 0.10 per mm. What thickness is needed to reduce the intensity of radiation to one-half its original value?

$$J/J_0 = 0.50 = e^{-0.10t}$$
$$\log_e 0.50 = -0.10t$$
$$-.694 = 0.10t$$
$$t = 6.9 \text{ mm}$$

TOTAL RADIATION

A fundamental relation which describes the total radiation of a blackbody at all wavelengths was established experimentally by Ludwig Boltzmann (1884), who also gave a theoretical derivation from thermodynamic considerations treating radiation in a blackbody cavity as analogous to a perfect gas. The blackbody radiancy R_b is found to be proportional to the fourth power of the temperature of the radiator

$$R_b = \sigma T^4 \tag{22}$$

Stefan had deduced this law earlier (1874) from meager evidence and hence the fourth-power law is usually known as the Stefan-Boltzmann total radiation law.

In experimental tests of the total radiation from a blackbody cavity the indications of the instrument receiving the radiation are never strictly proportional to the fourth power of the temperature of the blackbody, for there is always an exchange of energy between the blackbody radiator at temperature T and its surroundings at temperature T_0. The indication D of the detecting instrument depends upon both temperatures

$$D = c(T^4 - T_0{}^4) \tag{23}$$

where c is a constant depending on the instrument and the experimental arrangement. This equation is basic in the use of total-radiation pyrometers (Chap. 7).

Extensive measurements of the radiation from blackbody sources at controlled temperatures have given a value for the Stefan-Boltzmann constant σ in Eq. (22) of 5.673×10^{-12} watt/cm^2 (K$^\circ$)^4.

EXAMPLE: A tungsten filament has a length of 10 cm and a diameter of 0.010 cm (about 4 mils). It is mounted in a vacuum tube and heated electrically to 2400°K. (a) What would be the power needed assuming all heat loss occurred by radiation and that tungsten is a perfect radiator? (b) If the power actually found necessary to maintain the filament at this temperature is 18 watts, what is the emissivity of tungsten?

If the vacuum tube is at room temperature, T_0^4 is negligible compared to T^4 and Eq. (22) represents closely the net power radiated from the filament.

(a) Area $= \pi 0.010$ cm $\times 10$ cm $= 0.314$ cm^2

Power $=$ area $\times$ radiancy $= A\sigma T^4 = (0.314$ cm$^2)(5.67 \times 10^{-6}$ microwatts/cm$^2)(2400°$K$)^4 = 59.1$ watts

(b) $\epsilon = R/R_b = 18/59.1 = 0.3$

NEWTON'S LAW OF COOLING

The net rate of loss of energy dQ/dt by a blackbody at temperature T_1 on cooling in an evacuated enclosure at the temperature T_2 is the difference between its own rate of loss of energy and its rate of absorption of energy from the surroundings

$$\frac{dQ}{dt} = A(R_1 - R_2) = A\sigma(T_1^4 - T_2^4)$$
$$= (T_1 - T_2)(T_1 + T_2)(T_1^2 + T_2^2)A\sigma \qquad (24)$$

in which the first factor is the simple difference of temperatures. If the temperature difference is small

$$\frac{dQ}{dt} = k'(T_1 - T_2) \qquad (25)$$

If the specific heat of the body is constant, its rate of cooling will be proportional to the temperature difference

$$\frac{dT}{dt} = \frac{1}{mc}\frac{dQ}{dt} = k''(T_1 - T_2) \qquad (26)$$

This relation is known as Newton's law of cooling. It is an approximate relation of very limited validity. Such a first-power relation can be used for any phenomena provided the steps in variation are small enough, and hence the crude approximation has little significance as a law.

Thus far we have considered a blackbody cooling by radiation alone in an evacuated chamber. A case of more practical interest, especially in calorimetry, is that of an object cooling by convection, conduction, and radiation losses. In this more complex case, Newton's law has a much greater range of applicability. For $T_2 = 300°$K and $T_1 - T_2 = 50$ K° the predictions of Eqs. (25) or (26) may be too low by some 20 per cent when applied to a body losing energy by radiation alone, but low by less than 1 per cent when applied to a body cooling by convection and radiation.

BLACKBODY DISTRIBUTION CURVE

The spectral distribution of blackbody radiation, as determined experimentally, can be represented by such curves as are shown in Fig. 6.7. Each curve shows the distribution of power in the spectrum

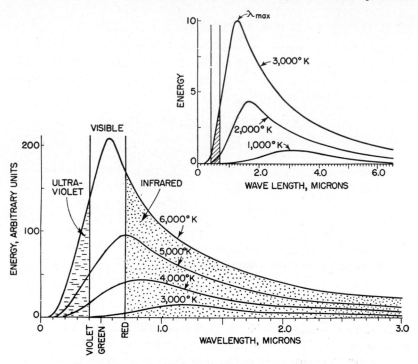

FIG. 6.7. Spectral distribution of blackbody radiation.

for unit area of perfect radiating surface at the temperature indicated.

Prior to 1900 the best representation in equation form of the distribution of power in the spectrum of a blackbody was given by Wilhelm Wien in the form

$$R_\lambda = c_1\lambda^{-5} e^{\frac{-c_2}{\lambda T}} \tag{27}$$

Lord Rayleigh and Sir James Jeans derived a distribution law of the form

$$R_\lambda = \frac{c_1}{c_2}\lambda^{-4}T \tag{28}$$

Max Planck, seeking to improve the agreement between distribution equation and the experimental data, arrived at the correct expression for the spectral distribution law that may be expressed în these alternative forms

$$R_\lambda = \frac{c_1\lambda^{-5}}{e^{\frac{c_2}{\lambda T}} - 1} = \frac{2\pi hc^2\lambda^{-5}}{e^{\frac{h\nu}{kt}} - 1} = \frac{2\pi hc^2\lambda^{-5}}{e^{\frac{hc}{\lambda kt}} - 1} \qquad (29)$$

Here c_1 and c_2 are referred to as the first and second radiation constants, h is Planck's constant, k is the Boltzmann constant, c the speed of light, ν the frequency, and λ the wavelength of the radiation. The last three quantities are related by $c = \lambda\nu$.

The Wien and Rayleigh-Jeans distribution laws are based on the ideas of classical physics. Wien assumed that the distribution of radiant energy with respect to frequency followed the same Maxwell distribution law used for molecular speeds. The resulting distribution law, Eq. (27), agrees with experiment in the short-wavelength region of the spectrum but predicts values of R_λ which are too low in the region where λT is large. Rayleigh assumed that radiation in a cavity has degrees of freedom which correspond to the frequencies of standing waves that are possible in the cavity, and that the energy is divided equally among these different degrees of freedom. The resulting distribution law, Eq. (28), agrees with experiment in the long-wavelength region but fails elsewhere.

After a long series of observations, speculations, and mathematical researches had failed to bring harmony between theoretical deductions and the experimental blackbody distribution curves, Planck departed from the ordinary lines of reasoning of classical physics. He introduced an empirical and revolutionary assumption: the idea that energy is emitted from a surface not as a steady stream but in small discrete bundles of magnitude $h\nu$ that he named *quanta*. Another name used is *photon*. It is noteworthy that the quantum of energy $h\nu$ is proportional to frequency. We do not have a simple unit of energy similar to the elementary unit of electricity represented by the unvarying electronic charge.

The distribution law, Eq. (29), derived as a consequence of Planck's innovation agrees with the experimental spectral radiation curves. For a wide range of temperatures (300 to 1700°K) and a wide range of wavelengths (0.5 to 52 μ), Eq. (29) represents the observed data within 1 per cent. Wien's law gives results accurate within 1 per cent for values of λT less than 0.3 cm°K. To attain this same accuracy with the Rayleigh-Jeans law, λT must exceed 77 cm°K.

The older forms of the radiation laws may be shown to be special cases of Planck's law. Thus, for small values of λT the -1 of Eq. (29) is negligible in comparison with $e^{c_2/\lambda T}$ and Eq. (29) reduces to Wien's law. For large values of λT the term $e^{c_2/\lambda T}$ may be replaced by the first two terms of the expansion

$$e^{\frac{c_2}{\lambda T}} = 1 + \frac{c_2}{\lambda T} + \frac{(c_2/\lambda T)^2}{2} + \cdots$$

and Eq. (29) reduces to the Rayleigh-Jeans law.

Wien's law is generally used for practical calculation of temperatures in optical pyrometry since it is usually sufficiently accurate and requires simpler computations than would Planck's law. Calculations based on Planck's law are facilitated by use of tables of the radiation function.[5]

WIEN'S DISPLACEMENT LAW

A blackbody radiation distribution curve has a maximum at wavelength λ_m that can be located by differentiating Eq. (29) with respect to λ and setting the numerator equal to zero. This results in the expression

$$e^{\frac{c_2}{\lambda T}}\left(\frac{c_2}{\lambda T} - 5\right) + 5 = 0 \tag{30}$$

A solution of Eq. (30), found by trial, is $\lambda T/c_2 = 4.96511$. This solution written in the form

$$\lambda_m T = \text{constant} = b = 2897.2 \ \mu°K \tag{31}$$

is often called Wien's displacement law. Actually it represents but one aspect of that law whose full meaning should become evident from the following.

The relation between λ_m and T, Eq. (31), can be used to eliminate λ from Eq. (29), giving

$$R_{\lambda m} = \frac{c_1 T^5}{b^5\left(e^{\frac{c_2}{b}} - 1\right)} = 1.2874 \times 10^{-11} T^5 \tag{32}$$

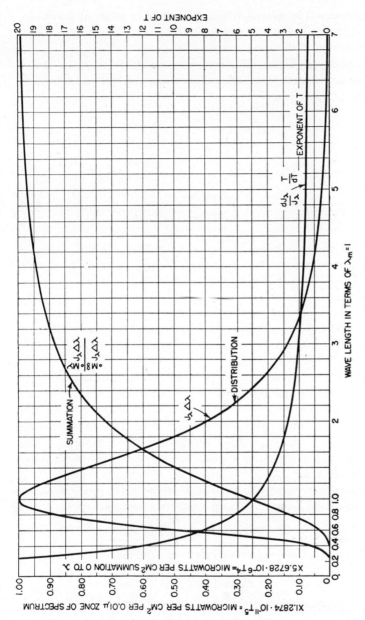

FIG. 6.8.   Radiation characteristics of a blackbody.

This chart may be used to compute the distribution, summation, and rate of change of power at any temperature by using the factors given at the left of the chart. The wavelength scale is found by computing λ_m from $\lambda_m = 2897.2/T$ microns, for the desired temperature. The scale of exponents (on the right) does not change.

105

Here R is expressed in microwatts/cm² per 0.01-μ zone of spectrum. Equation (32) shows that the power at the peak of the curve varies as the fifth power of the temperature.

All blackbody radiation distribution curves have the same form. This can be demonstrated as follows: By using Eq. (31) to substitute for T in Eq. (29), we can write

$$R_{\lambda m} = \frac{c_1 \lambda_m^{-5}}{e^{\frac{c_2}{b}} - 1} \tag{33}$$

Keeping T constant, but selecting some other wavelength $\lambda = n\lambda_m$

$$R_{n\lambda} = \frac{c_1 n^{-5} \lambda^{-5}}{e^{\frac{1}{n}} e^{\frac{c_2}{b}} - 1} \tag{34}$$

It is now apparent that the new factors n^{-5} in the numerator and $e^{1/n}$ in the denominator are independent of the values of λ_m and T selected.   It follows that the intensity at, say, $3\lambda_m$ is always the same fraction of the intensity of λ_m.   *All blackbody radiation distribution curves can therefore be brought into complete coincidence by a suitable adjustment of co-ordinates.*   This is the full significance of Wien's displacement law.

The useful characteristic expressed by Wien's law enables one to start with any plotted blackbody radiation curve and from it obtain the distribution for any desired temperature.   The distribution curve of Fig. 6.8 can be used for this purpose.   The first step is to determine λ_m from Eq. (31) for the desired temperature.   This λ_m is then used as the unit of wavelength as described on the scale at the bottom of the chart.   The power at the peak of the curve is found from Eq. (32), and since the shape of the curve is invariant, the same scale of ordinates applies throughout for R_λ.

The summation curve of Fig. 6.8 gives the total spectral power summed from short wavelengths up to the wavelengths given at the bottom of the graph.   The curve marked $\dfrac{dR_\lambda}{R_\lambda} \dfrac{T}{dT}$ shows how the power changes with small changes in temperature at each wavelength.

SUMMARY

Radiant energy within certain limits of wavelength (3900–7600A) is visible as *light*.

The *radiant intensity*, J, of a source is the flow of radiant energy per unit solid angle in the direction of the axis of that solid angle (erg/sec ω). The analogous term for light is the luminous intensity, I, (lumen/ω, or candle).

The *radiancy*, R, of a source is the flow of radiant energy, in all directions, per unit area (erg/sec cm²).

The *irradiance*, H, of a surface is the rate at which it receives radiant energy per unit area (erg/sec cm²). The analogous light term is illuminance, E, (lumen/m²).

The coefficients α, ρ, and τ are used to indicate respectively the fractional part of incident radiant energy that is *absorbed, reflected,* and *transmitted* by a body.

A *blackbody* is an ideal radiator that, at any specified temperature, emits in each part of the spectrum the maximum energy obtainable per unit time for any radiator as a result of temperature alone.

The *emittance* of an actual radiator is the ratio of its radiancy to that of a blackbody at the same temperature

$$\epsilon = \frac{R}{R_b}$$

Kirchhoff's law states that the emittance of a non-blackbody is equal to its absorptance—good emitters of radiation are also good absorbers

$$\epsilon = \alpha \qquad \text{and} \qquad \epsilon_\lambda = \alpha_\lambda$$

Blackbody sources are approximated experimentally by cavities from which radiation, after many reflections, emerges as blackbody radiation.

A coefficient of absorption k represents the decrease in radiant flux density per unit flux density per unit path distance

$$\frac{J}{J_0} = e^{-kt}$$

The Stefan-Boltzmann law states that the blackbody radiancy is proportional to the fourth power of the absolute temperature of the radiator

$$R_b = \sigma T^4$$

Newton's law of cooling states that the rate at which a warm body loses heat to its cooler surroundings is proportional to the temperature difference

$$\frac{dQ}{dt} = k'(T_1 - T_2) \qquad \text{or} \qquad \frac{dT}{dt} = \frac{k'}{mc}(T_1 - T_2)$$

Planck's law gives the distribution of energy with respect to wavelength for the radiation from a blackbody

$$R_\lambda = \frac{2\pi hc^2 \, \lambda^{-5}}{e^{\frac{hc}{\lambda kT}} - 1}$$

Wien's distribution law is an approximation of Planck's law which, for simplicity, is usually used in optical pyrometry

$$R_\lambda = c_1 \lambda^{-5} e^{-\frac{c_2}{\lambda T}}$$

Wien's displacement law predicts the shift of wavelength of maximum intensity toward shorter wavelengths as the temperature of a blackbody radiator is increased

$$\lambda_m T = 2897.2 \ \mu°K$$

REFERENCES FOR SUPPLEMENTARY READING

1. Am. Inst. Phys., *Temperature—Its Measurement and Control in Science and Industry*, Chap. 12, Reinhold Publishing Corp., 1941.
2. Benford, F., "The Blackbody," *Gen. Elec. Rev.*, **46,** 377, 433 (1943).
3. Forsythe, W. E., *Measurement of Radiant Energy*, McGraw-Hill Book Co., Inc., 1937.
4. Forsythe, W. E., "Temperature Radiation," *J. Optical Soc. Am.*, **16,** 307 (1928).
5. Lowan, A. N., and G. Blanch, "Tables of Planck's Radiation and Photon Functions," *J. Optical Soc. Am.*, **30,** 70 (1940).
6. Marsh, H. E., E. Condon, and L. B. Loeb, "The Theory of the Radiometer," *J. Optical Soc. Am.*, **11,** 257 (1925).
7. Mendenhall, C. E., "A Determination of the Stefan-Boltzmann Constant of Radiation," *Phys. Rev.*, **34** (2), 502 (1929).
8. Nichols, E. F., and G. F. Hull, "The Pressure Due to Radiation," *Phys. Rev.*, **17,** 26, 91 (1903).
9. Richtmyer, F. K., and E. H. Kennard, *Introduction to Modern Physics*, pp. 157–183, McGraw-Hill Book Co., Inc., 1947.
10. Sanderson, J. A., "The Transmission of Infra-Red Light by Fog," *J. Optical Soc. Am.*, **30,** 405 (1940).
11. Worthing, A. G., and D. Halliday, *Heat*, pp. 46–52, 413–479, John Wiley & Sons, Inc., 1948.

QUESTIONS AND PROBLEMS

1. Water absorbs long-wavelength radiation. How is this fact related to the observation that on cloudy nights the earth and air do not become as cool as on clear nights?

2. Conduits for hot-air heating systems are frequently made of bright sheet metal. The addition of a layer of asbestos paper on the conduit may actually increase the loss of heat through the surface. Explain.

3. The manufacturer of a vacuum bottle claims that it will keep liquids hot 24 hours or cold 72 hours. Why is there a difference in the time in the two cases?

4. Describe and interpret an experiment which might be used to demonstrate Kirchhoff's radiation law. What are some important applications of Kirchhoff's law?

5. What experimental procedures are suitable for determining (a) the wavelengths, and (b) the spectral intensity of radiation from a heated body?

6. Given the distribution of energy in the spectrum of radiation from a blackbody, show how the distribution may be found at any other temperature.

7. A diffuse spherical radiator is viewed by its own radiation in a darkened room. In accord with Lambert's law will the observer see a disk of uniform brightness? Is this the case for the sun?

8. How would you define the achromatic surfaces pure white, pure gray, and perfectly black, in terms of the values of spectral emissivity ϵ_λ (or of absorptivity α_λ)?

9. Suggest a procedure for deducing the Stefan-Boltzmann total radiation law from Planck's law.

10. By inspection of the Rayleigh-Jeans law, Eq. (28), state whether it will predict values for R_λ that are too large or too small in the short-wavelength region of a blackbody spectrum.

11. A blackened copper sphere of diameter 10 cm is cooled in an evacuated enclosure whose walls are kept at 0°C. In what time does its temperature change from 228 to 227°C? [Show that heat lost per sec $= \dfrac{4}{3}\pi r^3 \rho c \dfrac{dT}{dt} = 4\pi r^2 \sigma (T^4 - T_0^4)$.]

12. Compare the rates of loss of heat from a body at 1000°C and from the same body at 500°C, assuming that it is placed in an enclosure at 20°C. *Ans.* 7.5.

13. Compare the relative power supplies necessary to maintain a furnace at temperatures of 1000°C and 2000°C, using the Stefan-Boltzmann law.

14. Calculate the ratios of intensities of monochromatic radiation $\mathcal{J}_{1600}/\mathcal{J}_{1000}$ as the temperature of a blackbody is increased from 1000 to 1600°C, considering (a) $\lambda = 0.4\mu$ and (b) $\lambda = 0.6\mu$. Comment on your answer with reference to Fig. 6.7. *Ans.* 8100, 400.

15. Abbot has measured the average value of the energy received from the sun by the earth as 1.94 cal/cm² min. Taking this value of the solar constant, the radius of the sun as 4.3×10^5 miles and the diameter of the earth's orbit as 1.86×10^8 miles, calculate the temperature of the sun, assuming it to be a blackbody.

16. Rays from the sun fall on a convex lens of 15-cm diameter and are brought to focus on a blackened calorimeter containing 25 gm of ice. If all the radiant energy is absorbed in the calorimeter, none in the lens, how long will it be before all the ice is melted? *Ans.* 5.8 min.

17. A monochromatic beam of light loses 0.15 of its energy in passing through 1.0 mm of glass. What is the relative intensity of a beam which has passed through 3.0 mm of the glass?

18. A certain red filter glass has an absorption coefficient of 0.20/mm for wavelength 0.65μ. What thickness is needed to reduce the intensity of a red beam to 0.37 of its original intensity? *Ans.* 5.0 mm.

19. How many reflections are required at 25°C in (a) a platinum cavity, (b) a carbon cavity, to reduce the intensity of an entering light beam to 5 per cent of its initial value?

20. If the total emissivity of tungsten is 0.28 at 2000°C, how many reflections must radiation experience in a cavity source in order that the emergent radiation have 0.95 the radiancy of a blackbody at 2000°C? *Ans.* 9.

21. The wavelength of maximum intensity in the radiation from a blackbody furnace is 7000A. Calculate its approximate centigrade temperature.

22. The operating temperature of a tungsten filament in a lamp bulb (evacuated) is 2450°K and its emissivity is 0.30. Find the surface area of the filament of a 25-watt lamp. *Ans.* 0.40 cm².

23. Compute the number of quanta of radiation from a sodium lamp (5890A) required to make one erg of energy.

24. Calculate the power (watts/square centimeter) reaching the receiver of a

total radiation pyrometer that subtends a solid angle of 0.01 of a blackbody source whose temperature is 1000°K.   *Ans.* 0.15 watt/cm².

25. Find the amount of radiant energy (joules) between wavelengths 9999A and 10,000A in each cubic centimeter of a blackbody enclosure at a uniform temperature of 727°C.

26. A piece of incandescent carbon at 2000°K ($\epsilon_t = 0.8$) is seen reflected from a clean platinum surface ($\epsilon_t = 0.2$) at the same temperature. How does the sum of the normal platinum and the reflected carbon brightness compare with that of a blackbody at 2000°K?   *Ans.* 0.84.

Chapter 7

OPTICAL AND RADIATION PYROMETRY

TOTAL RADIATION PYROMETER |||||||| *OPTICAL PYROMETER* |||||||| *TEMPERATURES OF NON-BLACKBODIES* |||||||| *EXTENSION OF MEASURING RANGE OF INSTRUMENTS* ||||||||

TEMPERATURE ESTIMATES FROM RADIANT ENERGY

The temperatures of very hot bodies are often judged visually by their color and brightness. Roughly, the relationship is: lowest visible red 475°C, dull red 600°C, cherry red 700°C, light red 850°C, orange 900°C, yellow 1000°C, white 1150°C and higher. With practice one can probably estimate temperatures visually to within 50 C°. Thus, temperatures have long been estimated by Wien's displacement relation (Fig. 6.7).

Direct visual estimation of temperature is, naturally, only approximate and is open to all the uncertainties of a purely subjective method. To obtain quantitative measurements of temperature in terms of radiant energy, instruments have been devised which either provide the eye with a standard source for comparison or which contain a sensitive radiation detector which makes visual observation unnecessary.

111

The Stefan-Boltzmann law and Wien's radiation laws suggest three ways in which radiant energy can be used in pyrometry.   We may design a pyrometer to measure as heat the radiant energy of all wavelengths received from a body and to indicate the temperature of the body in terms of the Stefan-Boltzmann law.   Such an instrument is called a *total radiation pyrometer*, or more often merely a radiation pyrometer.   Another type may be made responsive to the radiant energy only in a narrow band of wavelengths, usually in the visible spectrum.   Pyrometers of this type, based on Wien's law, are *spectral radiation pyrometers* and are called *optical pyrometers* if the eye is used for making brightness comparisons, or *photoelectric pyrometers* if a photo cell serves as the detector.   A third general type of instrument is a *color pyrometer* which indicates temperature from the relative intensity of radiation at two different wavelengths, usually in the red and the green.

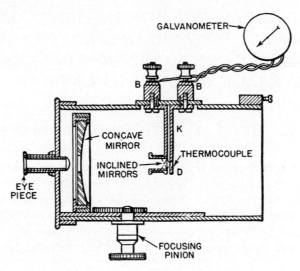

FIG. 7.1.   Féry radiation pyrometer.

TOTAL RADIATION PYROMETERS

In a total radiation pyrometer a concave mirror or a convex lens concentrates radiant energy from the test body upon the measuring element which has a blackened receiving surface.   The measuring element is usually a sensitive thermocouple or a thermopile.   Its emf actuates a galvanometer or potentiometer. Calibration is done empirically using a blackbody and a standard pyrometer, and the scale of the radiation pyrometer is marked to indicate temperature directly.

The Féry radiation pyrometer (Fig. 7.1) has a concave glass mirror front-surfaced with gold, nickel, or aluminum, to concentrate the radiation upon one junction of a small thermocouple. The reference junction of the thermocouple is shielded from radiation and remains at approximately room temperature. The mirror may be moved by rack and pinion to focus the image of the test body on the thermocouple disk. As an aid in securing correct focus, an eyepiece placed behind a central hole in the concave mirror is directed toward two

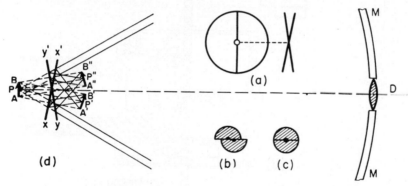

Fig. 7.2. Optical system of a Féry radiation pyrometer: (a) Two semicircular mirrors having 1.5 mm opening at center form a limiting diaphragm immediately in front of thermocouple. Observer views at D the image of furnace formed by concave mirror MM and reflected by inclined mirrors xx' and yy'. If image is not correctly focused on these mirrors, the image appears broken in half as shown in (b). As concave mirror is moved toward right, points P' and P'' of reflected images move toward the point of intersection of mirrors xx' and yy', coinciding there when correct focus is obtained. A single image is then observed (c).

small plane mirrors placed close to the thermocouple and inclined at an angle of 5 to 10° relative to each other. The result is to give an image of the test body when viewed through the eyepiece that appears divided and displaced (Fig. 7.2b) unless the pyrometer is properly focused for the particular distance to source. The eyepiece, also, permits the observer to assure himself that the image of the test body formed by the concave mirror completely overlaps the thermocouple disk, in which case the temperature indications are practically independent of sighting distance.

For industrial use a radiation pyrometer is usually sealed in a case (Fig. 7.3) that protects it from dust, moisture, and stray radiation. Since the radiation enters through a glass lens which is opaque to wavelengths greater than 3μ, the Stefan-Boltzmann law for full radiation is not applicable and the instrument is calibrated empirically over its working range.

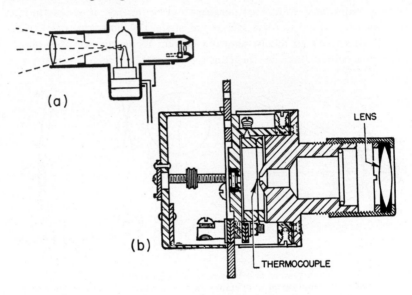

Fig. 7.3. Total radiation pyrometers: (a) for portable use; (b) for fixed installation.

The total radiation pyrometer has become an important industrial pyrometer for service where vibration or corrosion ruins thermocouples, where the test body moves, where protecting tubes make thermocouple response too slow, where the temperatures are above the thermocouple range, or where maintenance of platinum thermocouples is excessive.

CALIBRATION

The calibration of a total radiation pyrometer is made with the aid of an electrically heated furnace cavity which approximates a blackbody. A graphite muffle or a porcelain tube provided with diaphragms can be made to approximate blackbody conditions. The temperature of the furnace is determined by a standard thermocouple or by a standard optical pyrometer (calibrated at the melting point of gold). The calibration of a radiation pyrometer requires a source of relatively large volume maintained at uniform temperature and is more difficult than the calibration of an optical pyrometer.

One might expect the deflection D of a total radiation pyrometer to be proportional to the difference between the fourth power of the temperature T of the blackbody source and the fourth power of the temperature T_0 of the pyrometer case, in accord with the Stefan-Boltzmann law

$$D = c \ (T^4 - T_0^4) \tag{1}$$

It is generally found, however, that the exponent is not 4, but varies from 3.8 to 4.2 for various instruments. In any case, the value of the exponent n may be obtained by plotting the logarithms of the deflections and absolute temperatures. When T is large compared to T_0, T_0^4 becomes negligible compared to T^4, and

$$\log D = n \log T \tag{2}$$

Several factors contribute to produce variations in the value of the exponent n from 4. The emf generated by the thermocouple is not strictly proportional to the difference in temperatures of measuring and reference junctions. Stray reflections from the pyrometer walls falling on the thermocouple disk produce disturbances. The rate of heat loss from the disk is not strictly proportional to its temperature excess. Stray radiation and conduction of heat along the thermocouple wires produce a slight rise in temperature of the reference junction. Owing to these factors, a total radiation pyrometer generally requires an empirical calibration at many temperatures in its working range, whereas calibration at a single temperature usually suffices for an optical pyrometer.

INDEPENDENCE OF DISTANCE

Provided the image of the test body is sufficiently large to overlap the thermocouple disk, it is the irradiance (*flux per unit area*) of the image and not the *total* flux that is measured by the instrument. We can show that the irradiance is *independent* of the distance from the test body.   If, for example, the distance between pyrometer and hot body is doubled, the radiant flux received by the mirror (or lens) is reduced to one-fourth, but the area which the image covers is simultaneously reduced to one-fourth (Fig. 7.4), so that the flux per unit area of

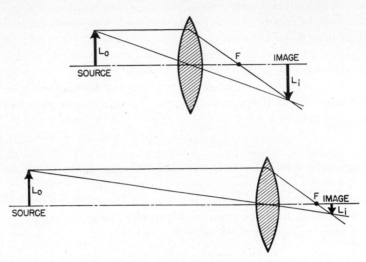

FIG. 7.4.   Irradiance of pyrometer image independent of sighting distance.

image remains constant.   Hence, ideally, the indications of a total radiation pyrometer should be independent of sighting distance.

EXTENSION OF TEMPERATURE SCALE

To measure very high temperatures with a radiation pyrometer one may intercept part of the radiation with a diaphragm placed in front of the pyrometer opening, and then calculate or recalibrate the pyrometer scale.   The instrument then need not be subjected to a detrimental increase in temperature.

Let A_1 and A_2 represent the diaphragm openings for two settings. Let T_1 and T_2 be the temperatures of the test body which produce the *same* galvanometer deflection (say full scale) when the pyrometer is sighted through areas A_1 and A_2, respectively.   Then, by the Stefan-Boltzmann law

$$A_1 T_1^4 = A_2 T_2^4 \tag{3}$$

EXAMPLE: It is desired to extend the maximum reading of a radiation pyrometer from 1000 to 1500°C. What fraction of the pyrometer opening should be closed by a diaphragm?

$$\frac{A_2}{A_1} = \frac{T_1^4}{T_2^4} = \left(\frac{1000 + 273}{1500 + 273}\right)^4 = 0.266$$

$$\text{Fractional part } closed = 1 - \frac{A_2}{A_1} = 1 - 0.266 = 0.734$$

TEMPERATURES OF NON-BLACKBODIES

Radiation pyrometers usually are calibrated for radiation from a blackbody. When sighted on a body that is not an ideal radiator, the radiation pyrometer will indicate a temperature T_a that is lower than the actual temperature T by an amount that depends on the emittance of the test body. The corrected temperature T can be calculated from the Stefan-Boltzmann law provided the total emittance ϵ is known

$$\epsilon \sigma T^4 = \sigma T_a^4 \tag{4a}$$

or
$$T = \left(\frac{1}{\epsilon}\right)^{1/4} T_a \tag{4b}$$

The emittances of many non-blackbodies are small and inaccurately known. Radiation pyrometer readings on such materials are unreliable. Fortunately in many industrial processes it is sufficient to be able to *reproduce* certain temperature conditions without the necessity of measuring the temperatures with high accuracy. For such application a radiation pyrometer is satisfactory provided merely that its calibration remains constant.

EXAMPLE: A total radiation pyrometer indicates a temperature of 1120°K when sighted on a surface of oxidized copper whose emittance is 0.60. Find the corrected temperature for the copper.

$$T = \left(\frac{1}{\epsilon}\right)^{1/4} T_a = \left(\frac{1}{0.60}\right)^{1/4} 1120°K$$

$$T = (1.14)(1120°K) = 1280°K$$

SPECTRAL RADIATION PYROMETERS

The idea of an instrument employing Wien's law to measure temperatures was suggested by Le Chatelier (1892). Most partial radiation pyrometers rely on visual observations. Some employ phototubes. The human eye can judge the *equality* of two illuminations of the same

color with high precision, but not their *ratio*. This characteristic of
the eye is taken into account in the design of many types of precision
scientific instruments, such as photometers, colorimeters, and polarim-
eters, in which the eye is required only to decide when two parts of a
divided field of view are *matched*.

An optical pyrometer may be regarded as an instrument designed
to improve visual estimates of temperature by providing the eye with

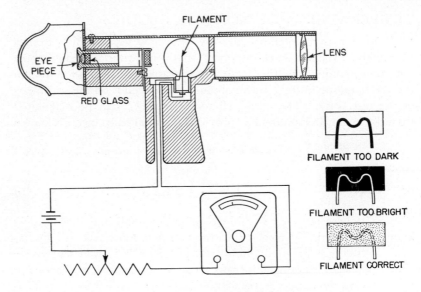

FIG. 7.5.   A Morse-type optical pyrometer.

a comparison source. The comparison source is a lamp filament.
The filament is connected in series with a battery, resistor, and milliammeter (Fig. 7.5). By varying the current through the filament it may
be made to match in brightness the image of the hot body on which the
pyrometer is sighted. The temperature of the test body is then
determined from a reading of the milliammeter and a calibration
curve provided for the lamp used. In another design of optical
pyrometer (Fig. 7.9) the filament current is kept constant and a match
obtained by varying the amount of radiation from the source which is
admitted to the eyepiece.

Temperatures might be measured with an optical pyrometer by
use of the whole visible spectrum. If that were done errors would be

introduced and observers would differ widely in their readings owing to the color difference between the filament and the source being examined. Greater accuracy is obtained if a so-called monochromatic filter is used in the eyepiece. This is usually a glass which transmits a narrow band of wavelengths (0.005 to 0.01μ wide) in the red (0.63 to 0.67μ). Red screens are chosen for the following reasons: (a) At low temperatures red radiation first becomes visible and hence readings may be made at slightly lower temperatures with red glass. (b) Subjectively, the color change with wavelength seems much less in the red than in the green. (c) Better visual monochromatism can be obtained for glasses of this color because the visibility curve fixes the cutoff at the long wavelength end of the red band, and the glass is required to cut off only the short wavelength end of the spectrum.

Truly monochromatic screens are nonexistent. If they were available, the very limited intensity that they could transmit would make them of doubtful value in practical optical pyrometry. In using a pyrometer with a screen which is only approximately monochromatic, it is the integral luminous intensity of the source (at one temperature) transmitted by the screen, and the luminous intensity of the pyrometer filament (at a lower temperature) that are compared. For this reason the *effective wavelength* $\lambda_{T_1 T_2}$ of the screen has been defined as the wavelength for which the ratio Z of the spectral brightness of two blackbodies at temperatures T_1 and T_2 is equal to z, the ratio of the total fluxes which they send through the screen.

CALIBRATION

Basically the calibration of an optical pyrometer depends upon Planck's law, Eq. (28), Chap. 6. Practically, Wien's formula, Eq. (26), Chap. 6, is a sufficiently close approximation and this simpler relation is used almost exclusively in computing brightness and true temperatures.

Spectral brightness B_λ is the luminous intensity in a specified narrow wavelength band at wavelength λ. If $B_{0\lambda}$ represents the spectral brightness of a blackbody at a calibration temperature T_0, then the spectral brightness B_λ of a blackbody at temperature T is seen from Wien's law to be given by

$$\log_e \frac{B_\lambda}{B_{0\lambda}} = -\frac{c_2}{\lambda}\left(\frac{1}{T_0} - \frac{1}{T}\right) \tag{5}$$

An optical pyrometer may be calibrated by comparison with a standard calibrated optical pyrometer (Exp. 17) or with the aid of a blackbody furnace whose temperatures are determined by a platinum thermocouple. These procedures applied to the optical pyrometer of Fig. 7.5 yield a calibration for blackbody temperature t in terms of filament current i that can be represented by a parabolic formula

$$i = a + bt + ct^2 \qquad (6)$$

Alternatively the calibration may be made using a single fixed point, usually the melting point of gold (1063°C) or palladium (1554°C). A reading of the filament current for a brightness match at the standard temperature gives one point on the calibration curve. To obtain another point readings are taken of the filament current for an apparent brightness match with a rotating sector or absorbing glass of known transmission between pyrometer lamp and standard blackbody. This gives a measure, in terms of pyrometer filament current, of a brightness that is some known fraction of that of the standard radiator at the standard temperature. The temperature T of the blackbody corresponding to this brightness, that is to this pyrometer current, can be calculated from the standard temperature T_0 by the following relation, derived from Wien's equation

$$\frac{1}{T_0} - \frac{1}{T} = \frac{\lambda}{c_2} \log_e \tau \qquad (7)$$

where τ is the transmittance of the sector or absorbing glass and λ is the wavelength used.

INDEPENDENCE OF DISTANCE

As in the case of radiation pyrometers, the temperature indications of optical pyrometers are independent of the sighting distance provided there is no appreciable absorption of radiation between the test body and the pyrometer.

EXTENSION OF TEMPERATURE SCALE

An optical pyrometer may be adapted to measure temperatures higher than the maximum operating temperature of its filament by interposing one or more absorbing screens between the objective and the filament. The thickness x of a filter having an absorption coefficient k needed to change the pyrometer range by a specified amount can be calculated by combining the expression for Wien's law, Eq. (26), Chap. 6, with that used in defining an absorption coefficient, Eq. (20), Chap. 6

$$e^{-kx} = \frac{c_1\lambda^{-5}e^{-\frac{c_2}{\lambda T_a}}}{c_1\lambda^{-5}e^{-\frac{c_2}{\lambda T}}} \tag{8}$$

Performing the division indicated and taking the logarithm of each side of the equation, we obtain

$$\frac{1}{T} - \frac{1}{T_a} = -\frac{k\lambda x}{c_2} \tag{9}$$

where T_a is the apparent temperature of a blackbody of temperature T when viewed through a screen of thickness x having an absorption coefficient k.

If a rotating sector of transmission τ is used to extend the range of an optical pyrometer the temperature T of a blackbody can be calculated from its apparent temperature T_a as viewed through the sector using the relation

$$\frac{1}{T} - \frac{1}{T_a} = \frac{\lambda}{c_2}\log_e \tau \tag{10}$$

EXAMPLE: It is desired to extend the maximum reading of an optical pyrometer from 1000 to 1500°C. The pyrometer uses monochromatic light of wavelength 0.65μ. What should be the ratio of open area to total area of a sector placed in front of the optical pyrometer?

$$\log_e \tau = \frac{c_2}{\lambda}\left(\frac{1}{T} - \frac{1}{T_a}\right)$$

$$2.3\log_{10}\tau = \frac{1.438 \text{ cm K}°}{6.5 \times 10^{-5}\text{ cm}}\left(\frac{1}{1773°\text{K}} - \frac{1}{1273°\text{K}}\right)$$

$$\log_{10}\tau = (9.62 \times 10^3 \text{ K}°)(-2.21 \times 10^{-4}/\text{K}°) = -2.125$$

$$\tau = \text{antilog } \overline{3}.875 = 0.0075$$

TEMPERATURES OF NON-BLACKBODIES

An optical pyrometer measures the brightness of a surface for a definite wavelength interval. A temperature can be calculated from this brightness under the assumption that the brightness originates from a blackbody. The spectral *brightness temperature* S_λ of the body is the temperature of a blackbody of equal spectral brightness. Thus, if a non-blackbody has the same brightness as a blackbody at a temperature of 1700°K it is said to have a brightness temperature of 1700°K which is lower than its true temperature. The true temperature T can be calculated from the brightness temperature S_λ and the spectral emissivity ϵ_λ of the source by the following equation

$$\frac{1}{T} - \frac{1}{S_\lambda} = \frac{\lambda}{c_2} \log_e \epsilon_\lambda \qquad (11)$$

The quantities actually compared in optical pyrometry are the integral luminosities as observed through the filter glass. Hence, the value to be used for λ in Eq. (11) is strictly an *effective wavelength*. For any definite temperature interval the ratio of the radiancies for this

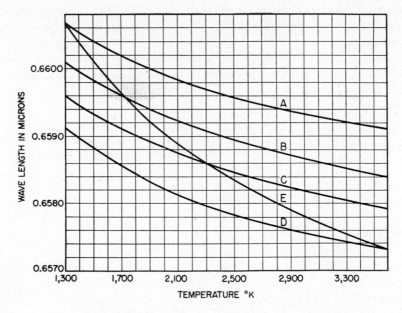

FIG. 7.6.   Effective wavelengths for Corning red glass.

wavelength, given by Wien's law, shall equal the ratio of the integral luminosities as observed through the glass. The effective wavelength can be determined directly from ratios of radiancies measured with a spectrophotometer and the ratio of integral luminosities measured with a Lummer-Brodhun photometer having the red glass over the eyepiece.

The procedure for obtaining values of the effective wavelength is laborious and is resorted to only in the case of standard instruments for use at temperatures above 1500°C. Effective wavelengths for Corning red glass are given in Fig. 7.6.

DISAPPEARING-FILAMENT PYROMETERS

In a Morse-type optical pyrometer, Fig. 7.5, an objective lens focuses a real image of the furnace opening or other source in the plane

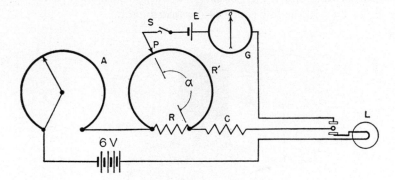

Fig. 7.7. Potentiometer circuit for a portable optical pyrometer.

of a standard lamp filament. Both image and filament are magnified for the observer by an ocular lens. The current is varied until the filament matches the background illumination. The calibration of the instrument gives the temperature of the test body in terms of the filament current. The uncertainty of measurements made with such an instrument is of the order of 10 C°. Its accuracy is limited usually by the milliammeter rather than by the sensitivity of the eye in judging a photometric match.

In precision laboratory optical pyrometers, a potentiometer is used for measuring the lamp current. A potentiometer circuit has been adapted for use in a portable optical pyrometer in the form diagramed in Fig. 7.7. The current through the pyrometer lamp L is adjusted with the slide-wire rheostat A when the switch S is closed. The current from the battery flows through the shunted potentiometer slide-wire R and the resistor C. The potentiometer slide-wire can be considered as being a variable shunt, the resistance of which is adjusted so that the product of the lamp current I and the shunt resistance equals the emf e of the standard cell E.

The lamp is operated with currents ranging from 20 to 60 ma. The galvanometer is sufficiently sensitive to detect a 0.1 per cent unbalance of the potentiometer, which corresponds to approximately 1 C°. A further increase in accuracy of temperature readings cannot be expected by making the current measurements more accurate, since the photometric match cannot be made consistently to better than 1 per cent, which corresponds to a temperature uncertainty of the order of 1 C° in the low range of the instrument.

Fig. 7.8.   Pyrometer lamp.

The rheostat and potentiometer slide-wire contacts are coupled mechanically with a friction clutch so that when the rheostat contact is moved to adjust the current the potentiometer contact is carried with it in the direction required to maintain potentiometer balance, but when the potentiometer contact is operated by its knob the rheostat contact remains at rest. This device facilitates manipulation of the instrument and protects the standard cell from unnecessary currents.

Improvements in lamp design as well as in current-measuring circuits have contributed to the increased accuracy of modern optical pyrometers. The pyrometer lamp (Fig. 7.8) should have a very clear glass bulb and, for the most accurate work, should have plane glass windows on both sides. These windows should not be perpendicular to the axis of the telescope, but should be mounted at an angle of about 15° from perpendicularity so as to avoid reflecting images of the filament into the field of view. The vacuum in the bulb should be the best obtainable. A tungsten filament if not used above the melting point of palladium (1828°K) will last almost indefinitely, and any failure will probably be due to accident rather than to any deterioration in the filament.

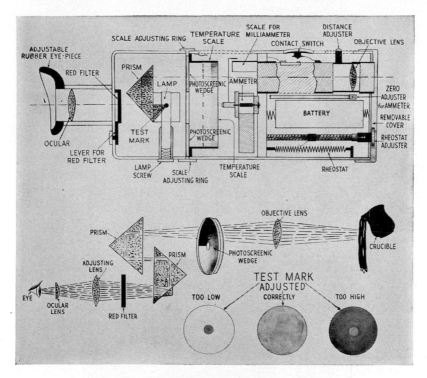

FIG. 7.9. A Pyro optical pyrometer.

Figure 7.9 illustrates a compact type of gray wedge optical pyrometer. The filament current is adjusted with the aid of the rheostat and milliammeter to the value for which the lamp was calibrated. Then, with the pyrometer sighted on a hot body, the circular wedge is rotated until the brightness of the incident radiation is reduced to match the brightness of the comparison lamp. The temperature is read directly from the scale affixed to the wedge. The appearance of the field of view is indicated in the lowest part of the diagram.

In a laboratory-type gray wedge pyrometer designed by Ribaud the constancy of the filament temperature is indicated by measuring the filament resistance on a Wheatstone bridge.   The radiation from the source is reduced to match that of the filament by a progressive gray filter like the one described above.   The accuracy attained by such an instrument is limited by the ability of the eye to judge the equality of the two illuminations.   This uncertainty is only about 1° at 1000°C and 2° at 2000°C.

PHOTOELECTRIC PYROMETERS

In a photoelectric pyrometer the radiation from a hot body is directed on a phototube and causes it to pass a current that bears a definite relation to the temperature of the test body.   This current is amplified by an especially stable vacuum tube amplifier and the amplified current is used to actuate an indicator, recorder, or controlling instrument.   The principal advantages of such a pyrometer are its rapid response and the fact that it can be used to provide continuous temperature records.   A vacuum type phototube with a caesium-oxygen-silver cathode is employed in the photoelectric pyrometer. While such a tube is far less sensitive than a gas-filled tube, it is also much more stable.

FIG. 7.10.   The first optical pyrometer.

SUMMARY

TABLE 7.1 COMPARISON OF OPTICAL PYROMETERS AND TOTAL RADIATION
PYROMETERS

	Optical Pyrometer	Total Radiation Pyrometer
Principle	Temperature determined from monochromatic luminosity of source.	Temperature determined from total radiation.
Construction	Viewing telescope contains lamp whose brightness is matched visually with source. Calibration in terms of filament current. See Figs. 7.5, 7.9.	Mirror or lens concentrates radiant energy on thermocouple, actuating galvanometer. See Figs. 7.1, 7.3.
Radiation law	Wien formula: $$R_\lambda = c_1 \lambda^{-5} e^{\frac{-c_2}{\lambda T}}$$	Stefan-Boltzmann law: $$R = \sigma T^4$$
Extension of scale	Glass filter: $$\frac{1}{T} - \frac{1}{T_a} = -\frac{\lambda}{c_2} kt$$	Diaphragm or rotating sector: $$\frac{A_1}{A_2} = \frac{T_2^4}{T_1^4}$$
Non-blackbody temperatures	$$\frac{1}{T} - \frac{1}{T_a} = \frac{\lambda}{c_2} \log_e \epsilon_\lambda$$	$$T_a^4 = \epsilon_t T^4$$

REFERENCES FOR SUPPLEMENTARY READING

1. Barber, C. R., "Factors Affecting the Reproducibility of Brightness of Tungsten Strip Lamps for Pyrometer Standardization," *J. Sci. Instruments*, **23**, 238 (1946).
2. Benford, F., "Temperature Corrections in Optical Pyrometry," *J. Optical Soc. Am.*, **29**, 162 (1939).
3. Cunnold, F. A., "The Optical System of the Disappearing Filament Pyrometer," *Proc. Roy. Soc. (London)*, **152A**, 64 (1935).
4. Forsythe, W. E., and E. Q. Adams, "A Color-Temperature Scale," *Gen. Elec. Rev.*, **47**, 26; 59 (1944).
5. Forsythe, W. E., "Intercomparison of the High Temperature Scale," *Phys. Rev.*, **38**, 1247 (1931).
6. Forsythe, W. E., "Optical Pyrometers," *J. Optical Soc. Am.*, **10**, 19 (1925).
7. Forsythe, W. E., "Optical Pyrometers," *J. Applied Phys.*, **11**, 408 (1940).
8. Griffiths, E., *Methods of Measuring Temperature*, Chaps. 5–7, Charles Griffin & Co., Ltd., 1947.

9. Harrison, T. R., "Industrial Use of Radiation Pyrometers under Non-Blackbody Conditions," *J. Optical Soc. Am.*, **35**, 708 (1945).

10. Judd, D. B., "Changes in Color Temperature of Tungsten-filament Lamps at Constant Voltage," *J. Research Nat. Bur. Standards*, **17**, 679 (1936).

11. Kind, W. R., "The Photoelectric Pyrometer," *Gen. Elec. Rev.*, **39**, 526 (1936).

12. Machler, R. C., "Potentiometer Circuit for a Portable Optical Pyrometer," *Rev. Sci. Instruments*, **10**, 386 (1939).

13. Wensel, H. T., D. B. Judd, and W. F. Roeser, "Establishment of a Scale of Color Temperature," *J. Research Nat. Bur. Standards*, **12**, 527 (1934).

14. Worthing, A. G., "Temperature Radiation Emissivities and Emittances," *J. Applied Phys.*, **11**, 421 (1940).

QUESTIONS AND PROBLEMS

1. Give several alternative definitions of a blackbody. What is the utility of this concept?

2. Show that the diameter L_i of image formed by the concave mirror of a Féry radiation pyrometer is related to the diameter L_0 of the object by the equation

$$L_0 = L_i \left(\frac{p}{f} - 1 \right)$$

where p is the distance from the object to the mirror, and f the focal length.

3. Why is a sector diaphragm rather than a glass filter generally used to extend the temperature range of a total radiation pyrometer?

4. Smoke, moisture, and carbon dioxide absorb radiant energy in the infra red. Which type of instrument will have its temperature indications affected more by such absorption, an optical pyrometer or a total radiation pyrometer? Explain.

5. Are uncertainties in the emissivities of test bodies liable to introduce larger errors in temperature measurements made by an optical pyrometer or by a total radiation pyrometer? Why?

6. A rise in the temperature of the body of a total radiation pyrometer introduces an error in the temperature indicated by its thermocouple. Discuss the probable suitability of the following schemes for compensating: (a) use of a movable shutter carried on a bimetal strip within the pyrometer body, arranged to cut off more of the heat rays reaching the thermocouple as the pyrometer body becomes hotter, (b) use of thermoelectric connecting wires from the pyrometer body to a point having constant temperature, (c) use of a shunt across the terminals of the thermocouple, the shunt consisting of a metal (iron, nickel) having a high temperature coefficient of resistance.

7. Several laboratories wish to compare their optical pyrometers to insure consistent temperature scales. Suggest a practical method for doing so which does not require transporting the pyrometers.

8. Show how an optical pyrometer, somewhat similar to that of Fig. 7.9, might be made with a rotating Nicol prism to vary the beam intensity. Show that if the intensity transmitted is proportional to $\tan^2 \phi$, where ϕ is the angle between polarizing and analyzing Nicol prisms, the calibration of a polarizing pyrometer will have the form

$$\log_e \tan \phi = a + \frac{b}{T}$$

9. An optical pyrometer filament is made of tungsten wire 3 mils in diameter and 3 cm long. The filament is heated to 1200°K and the current then decreased to the value that will bring the filament to 1000°K. It takes about 4 min for the middle of the filament to get within 1° of its final temperature. With a similar filament three times as long it gets within 1° in about 15 sec. Explain. What bearing has this on the design of optical pyrometers?

10. For what types of temperature measurements would you consider the use of photoelectric cell pyrometers desirable? What advantages and what limitations would you anticipate?

11. A radiation pyrometer sighted on clean, melting copper reads 1970°F. Find the percentage error in its calibration.

12. A radiation pyrometer indicator gives full-scale deflection for 1400°F. What fraction of the pyrometer aperture should be diaphragmed to make the same deflection correspond to 2100°F? *Ans.* 0.72.

13. A radiation pyrometer sighted on the surface of molten metal indicates the temperature 1100°C while a standard thermocouple gives the temperature as 1210°C. What is the emissivity of the surface?

14. A dusty radiation pyrometer mirror has a coefficient of reflection of 95 per cent of the value for which the instrument was calibrated. If the pyrometer indicates 1600°C what is the true temperature? *Ans.* 1625°C.

15. A radiation pyrometer is sighted through a "gray" window of absorption coefficient k and thickness x on the surface of a molten metal which has a total emissivity ϵ. Derive the relation between the true temperature of the metal T_t and the temperature indicated on the pyrometer T_a.

16. What thickness of glass of absorption coefficient 0.1/mm is needed to change the maximum reading of a Morse optical pyrometer from 1500 to 2000°C? Where should the filter be placed? *Ans.* 2.74 cm.

17. A certain optical pyrometer has an objective lens of focal length 10 in. What provision should be made for change of focus if the sighting distance varies from 10 to 25 ft?

18. An optical pyrometer sighted on a furnace through a glass window indicates a temperature of 1200°C. If an additional window similar to the first is placed in the light path the temperature indicated is 1100°C. Find the true temperature. *Ans.* 1317°C.

19. What is the effective absorption coefficient of the glass windows in Problem 18 if each had a thickness of 1.5 mm?

20. In determining temperatures with an optical pyrometer, the following approximate formula, based upon Wien's law

$$\log_e \frac{\mathcal{J}_t}{\mathcal{J}_{Au}} = \frac{1.438}{\lambda} \left(\frac{1}{1336} - \frac{1}{t_w + 273} \right)$$

will usually yield values which are not significantly different from those yielded by Eq. (29), Chap. 6. Using $\lambda = 65 \times 10^{-6}$ cm, compute values of t_w corresponding to (a) 1063.0, (b) 2500.0, and (c) 5000.0°C (Int 1948). (d) What percentage error results from using Wien's law instead of Planck's law to determine a temperature of about 2500°C? *Ans.* (a) 1063.0°C, (b) 2500.6°C, (c) 5016.8°C, (d) 0.016 per cent.

21. An optical pyrometer receiving radiation from the inside of a hollow metal wedge indicates the temperature 1400°C. When sighted on the outer surface it indicates the temperature 1270°C. What is the emissivity of the metal?

Chapter 8

॥॥॥॥॥॥॥॥॥॥॥॥॥॥॥॥॥

RESISTANCE THERMOMETRY

CONSTRUCTION OF RESISTANCE THERMOMETERS ॥॥॥ *CALIBRATION* ॥॥॥ *RESISTANCE MEASUREMENTS* ॥॥॥ *APPLICATIONS* ॥॥॥

RESISTANCE AND TEMPERATURE

The electrical resistance of most metals changes with temperature. The change is rather large, being 39 per cent for platinum between 0°C and 100°C. Resistances can be compared with high precision. These facts suggest that it should be possible to make temperature measurements accurately in terms of the electrical resistance of a conductor provided the appropriate relation between resistance and temperature can be found.

Siemens[11] outlined a method of temperature measurement by means of a platinum resistance thermometer in a lecture before the Royal Society of London in 1871. In the early Siemens thermometer the wire was wound on a clay cylinder and enclosed in a wrought iron tube. This instrument was not satisfactory and fell into disuse owing to the fact that the resistance suffered large changes after the thermometer had been heated to high temperatures. Later experiments showed that the changes in the resistance of the platinum were due to its combining with traces of reduced silicon from the pipe clay at high temperatures. This work emphasized the need for protecting the platinum coil from chemical contamination and pointed to the desirability of a neutral or oxidizing atmosphere around the wire.

The precision and reliability of modern resistance thermometry began with the work of Callendar.[3, 4] He described the essential elements required, namely, a resistor properly mounted and protected, a means for measuring its resistance, and a relation between resistance and temperature.

Platinum is an especially suitable material for resistance thermometry. It is one of the most reproducible of materials in its refining and manufacture, it is easily workable, and is not too readily contaminated. Most important, the resistance-temperature relation for platinum is simple and holds over a wide range of temperatures. Platinum resistance thermometers are used over the range from -260 to $1100°C$, with uncertainties of the order cf 0.04 to 0.3 $C°$ at low and high temperatures.

Copper resistance thermometers are suitable for the measurement of moderate temperatures, usually below $100°C$. Copper has the advantage of a resistance-temperature relation which is nearly linear, but has the disadvantage of low resistivity. Nickel is an inexpensive substitute for platinum for measurements below $300°C$. Below about $-260°K$ a platinum thermometer fails, chiefly because the platinum loses its last vestige of resistance, a phenomenon known as supraconductivity. Resistance thermometers of phosphor bronze or lead have been used to temperatures as low as $-272°C$.

RESISTANCE THERMOMETER CONSTRUCTION

A resistance thermometer (Fig. 8.1) generally consists of the resistor, a mica framework for its support, a protecting casing, connecting wires extending from the ends of the resistor to the top of the tube, and flexible leads joining them to the resistance measuring apparatus. For precise resistance thermometry[6,8] the resistor is almost always made of platinum wire. In a common type the wire is 0.1 mm in diameter adjusted in length to have a resistance of about 25.5 ohms at $0°C$, so that the resistance changes by about 0.1 ohm/$C°$. The requisite purity of platinum wire is assured by specifying that the resistance ratio R_{100}/R_0 must be greater than 1.391.

The platinum wire is doubled on itself (to avoid inductive effects) and then wound in a double spiral on a frame of thin, serrated mica. The ideal mounting is one that leaves the wire as free as possible from mechanical constraint, so that thermal expansion produces negligible stress on the wire. The platinum must not be in contact with materials which may contaminate it. Furthermore, the mounting should be such that the thermometer does not have an excessive time lag, and

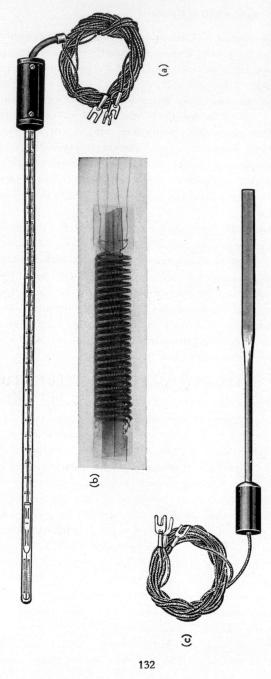

FIG. 8.1. Platinum resistance thermometers: (a) pyrex-tube type; (b) temperature-sensitive coil; (c) calorimetric type.

that the heating effect of the measuring current is not excessive.

In an especially compact form of construction, the wire is first wound in a fine helix and the helix then wound like a wire on a mica cross (Fig. 8.1b) to form a coil about 2 cm long. In the calorimetric type of thermometer (Fig. 8.1c) the wire is wound on a flat mica support and encased in a flat sheath designed to attain thermal equilibrium with its surroundings rapidly.

The platinum wire, on its supporting frame, is annealed by heating it electrically to relieve strains and to insure the reproducibility of later resistance measurements. The annealing temperature (often about 700°C) should be above the maximum to which the thermometer will be subjected in measuring temperatures.

Protecting casings for resistance thermometers are made of pyrex glass, fused quartz, nickel, or porcelain, sometimes with an additional outer jacket of iron or chromel. Figure 8.1 shows two laboratory-type resistance thermometers, one in a pyrex protecting tube (about 40 cm long), the other in a flat sheath of copper-nickel alloy. The thermometer case is usually filled with dry air at a pressure of $\frac{1}{3}$ to $\frac{1}{2}$ atm at room temperature.

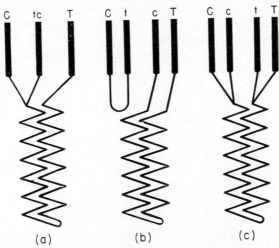

FIG. 8.2. Three types of connections used in resistance thermometers: (a) Siemens three-lead type; (b) Callendar's type with pair of compensating leads; and (c) four-terminal type with pair of current leads *CT* and pair of potential leads *ct*.

RESISTANCE MEASUREMENTS

In order to attain an accuracy of 0.001 C° in temperature measurements with a platinum thermometer one must be able to determine its

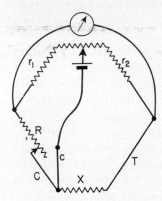

FIG. 8.3. Siemens three-
lead method of measuring
resistance X with a Wheatstone bridge.

resistance with a precision of two to
four parts in a million. Such measurements usually are made with a special
form of Wheatstone bridge or with a
potentiometer.

The sensitive element of the thermometer often is remote from the measuring instrument. The connecting wires
are subject to varying temperature along
their lengths and hence vary in resistance. Three types of connections have
been devised for resistance thermometers in order to cancel the effect of
resistances other than that due to the
coil only. These types of lead-wire
connections are illustrated in Fig. 8.2
with the notation suggested by Mueller.

The Siemens three-lead compensation method is illustrated in
Fig. 8.3. From the principle of the balanced Wheatstone bridge

$$\frac{R + C}{r_1} = \frac{X + T}{r_2} \tag{1}$$

The lead wires of the thermometer are made to have equal resistances,
so $C = T$. The ratio arms are set for equal resistance, so $r_1 = r_2$.
It follows that $R = X$. The measured resistance is independent of
lead-wire resistance.

Callendar used a thermometer (Fig. 8.2b) with a pair of dummy
leads Ct that were connected in the measuring arm R of the bridge.
The leads cT from the thermometer coil were connected in the adjacent
arm. With the ratio arms equal, $r_1 = r_2$, the lead wire resistance was
automatically subtracted.

The resistance S of a four-terminal coil (Fig. 8.2c) can be measured
very simply with a Wheatstone bridge by making two observations, as
illustrated by Fig. 8.4. The ratio arms r_1 and r_2 are equal. The

resistances R_a and R_b are those required to balance the bridge in Figs. 8.4a and 8.4b, respectively.

From Fig. 8.4a

$$R_a + C = X + T$$

From Fig. 8.4b

$$R_b + T = X + C$$

Adding we have

$$X = \frac{R_a + R_b}{2} \tag{2}$$

With terminals C, c, t, and T short-circuited, the ratio arms r_1 and r_2 may be adjusted to equality. In practice, this initial adjust-

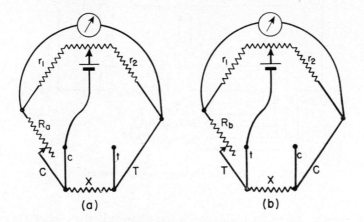

(a)   (b)

FIG. 8.4. Method of measuring resistance of four-terminal resistor X with a Wheatstone bridge.

ment can be made to within one or two parts in ten million. The change from the connections of Fig. 8.4a to those of Fig. 8.4b is made by means of a commutator, which is in principle equivalent to a three-pole, double-throw switch.

In the potentiometer method, Fig. 8.5, a standard resistor R and a resistance thermometer X are connected in series with a battery B. Measurements of the potential drops E_R and E_X across the two resistors,

in which the same current is maintained, then give directly the ratio
of the two resistances, or

$$X = \frac{E_X}{E_R} R \qquad (3)$$

A potentiometer has an advantage when the resistance to be
measured varies over a wide range.   This is the case when a platinum
thermometer having 25-ohm resistance at 0°C is used at liquid hydrogen

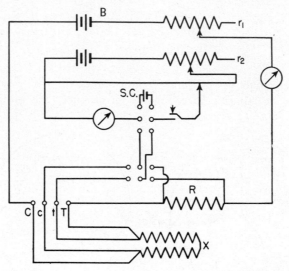

FIG. 8.5.   Potentiometer method of measuring
resistance X.

temperatures where its resistance is less than 0.1 ohm.   For the low
resistances the desired precision may be obtained by using a standard
resistor of suitable small resistance and adjusting the measuring current.
Thus with a potentiometer, the percentage precision of measurement
may be kept nearly the same over a wide range of resistance.   Use of a
bridge keeps the precision usually to a certain fraction of an ohm for all
measured resistances.   A further advantage of the potentiometer is its
versatility.   It has many uses other than that of measuring resistance.

Although the potentiometer method is capable of as high a sensitivity as the bridge methods, it is in general less convenient to use.
The difficulty lies in the elimination of stray emf's.   Since dR/dt is

about 0.004 ohm/C° in the neighborhood of 0°C, in order to determine a temperature to within 0.01 C° the resistance must be measured with an error of less than one part in a hundred thousand. For a 10-ohm thermometer using a measuring current of 0.00004 amp this corresponds to a precision of $0.4\mu v$ in the potentiometer measurements. For this one needs a low-voltage type of potentiometer with a circuit designed to eliminate the effects of parasitic thermal emf's.

RESISTANCE-TEMPERATURE RELATIONS

If the resistance of a platinum thermometer varied directly as the temperature, this relation could be represented by a straight line in the graph of Fig. 8.6, or by an equation of the form

$$R_t = R_0 \left(1 + a_0 t_{pt}\right) \tag{4}$$

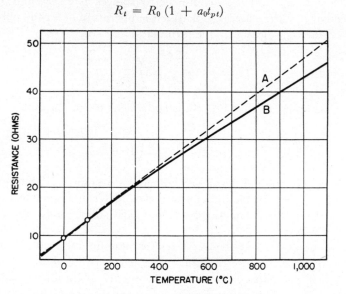

FIG. 8.6.   Resistance-temperature relations:
For A, $R_t = R_0 \left(1 + a_0 t\right)$
For B, $R_t = R_0 \left(1 + at + bt^2\right)$

where a_0 is the mean temperature coefficient of resistance between 0°C and t.   Actually the relation is not linear, and it is found necessary to use a second degree equation to express the resistance R_t at a given temperature in terms of the resistance R_0 at 0°C

$$R_t = R_0 \left(1 + at + bt^2\right) \tag{5}$$

The constants a_0, a, and b depend on the particular resistor. This parabolic equation is represented by curve B in Fig. 8.6. Callendar justified by experiment the use of a parabolic calibration equation for a platinum resistance thermometer in the range from 0 to 600°C. He also suggested a nomenclature which has come into general use and a method of solving Eq. (5) by successive approximations.

The temperature t_{pt} determined from Eq. (4) is called the *platinum temperature* and is nearly equal to the true temperature t. The platinum temperature is defined by

$$t_{pt} = \frac{R_t - R_0}{R_{100} - R_0}\, 100°C \tag{6}$$

in which R_t, R_0, and R_{100} denote the resistances at $t°$, $0°$, and $100°C$, respectively. The difference between temperature t and the platinum temperature t_{pt} is given by the formula

$$t - t_{pt} = \delta\left[\left(\frac{t}{100}\right)^2 - \frac{t}{100}\right] \tag{7}$$

It will be observed that Eq. (7) is equivalent to the formula

$$t = \frac{R_t - R_0}{R_{100} - R_0}\, 100 + \delta\left(\frac{t}{100} - 1\right)\frac{t}{100} \tag{8}$$

which is the original form of Callendar's equation. The constant δ is characteristic of the individual thermometer and is determined by calibration of the thermometer at some fixed point, usually the boiling point of sulfur.

Equation (8) may be regarded as the fundamental, empirical equation for platinum resistance thermometry. Using Callendar's method of calculation, one first computes the platinum temperature from Eq. (6). This value is inserted in the δ-term of Eq. (8) which is then solved to obtain a better value, say t', for the true temperature. The approximation may be repeated: one inserts t' in the δ-term of Eq. (8) and solves for a still closer value t'' for the true temperature. Tables are available to facilitate routine calculations.[2,7]

EXAMPLE: A platinum-resistance thermometer is found to have the following resistances: $R_0 = 10.000$ ohms at 0°C, $R_{100} = 13.861$ ohms at 100°C, $R_{444} = 26.270$ ohms at 444.6°C, and $R_t = 21.000$ ohms at temperature t. Find the value of temperature t.

For the sulfur boiling point

$$t_{pt} = \frac{26.270°C - 10.000°C}{13.861°C - 10.000°C} (100°C) = 421.4°C$$

From Eq. (7)

$$\delta = \frac{t - t_{pt}}{\dfrac{t^2}{100^2} - \dfrac{t}{100}} = \frac{444.6 - 421.4}{\dfrac{444.6^2}{100^2} - 4.446} = 1.503$$

The platinum temperature to be determined is

$$t_{pt} = \frac{21.000 - 10.000}{13.861 - 10.000} = 284.9°C$$

From Eq. (8) a better approximation is

$$t' = 284.9 + 1.503 \left(\frac{284.9^2}{100^2} - 2.849 \right) = 292.8°C$$

Using 292.8°C for t in the δ-term of Eq. (8) a second approximation is

$$t'' = 284.9 + 1.503 \left(\frac{292.8^2}{100^2} - 2.928 \right) = 293.8°C$$

In describing a thermometer, the quantity $R_{100} - R_0$ is called the fundamental interval. The mean value of the temperature coefficient of resistance between 0 and 100°C, $a_0 = (R_{100} - R_0)/100R_0$, is called the fundamental coefficient.

The value of δ for platinum wires may be expected to be between 1.49 and 1.50. The higher the purity the greater is a_0 (about 0.00392/C°).

EXAMPLE: Determine δ in terms of the constants a and b of Eq. (5).

From Eq. (6)

$$t - t_{pt} = t - \frac{R_t - R_0}{R_{100} - R_0} 100$$

On substituting for R_t and R_{100} their values from Eq. (5) we have

$$t - t_{pt} = t - \frac{R_0 + atR_0 + bt^2R_0 - R_0}{R_0 + 100aR_0 + 100^2bR_0 - R_0} 100$$

which reduces to

$$t - t_{pt} = t - \frac{at + bt^2}{a + 100b}$$

or

$$t - t_{pt} = - \frac{100^2b}{a + 100b} \left[\left(\frac{t}{100} \right)^2 - \frac{t}{100} \right]$$

Comparison with Eq. (7) shows that

$$\delta = -\frac{100^2 b}{a + 100b}$$

The Callendar formula, Eq. (8), for platinum resistance thermometers holds fairly well down to $-50°C$ and it may be extrapolated to at least $1000°C$ to give results in excellent agreement with the thermodynamic temperature scale. However, the Callendar equation is not applicable to resistors of metals other than platinum.

CALIBRATION PROCEDURE

The calibration of a resistance thermometer for use above $0°C$ requires the determination of the three constants in Eq. (5). This is accomplished by measuring the resistance R_t at the ice, steam, and sulfur points, respectively. An ice bath and a hypsometer of the type described in Chap. 5 will serve for the first two temperatures. Measurements at the sulfur point are more troublesome.

A form of sulfur-boiling apparatus[10] suited for general laboratory use is illustrated in Fig. 8.7a. A pyrex tube holds the sulfur. An electric heater for boiling the sulfur is made of insulated nichrome wire wrapped around an iron cylinder that surrounds the lower part of the tube. Asbestos paper and rock wool insulate the upper part of the tube. The thermometer is inserted into the boiling-point tube sufficiently far to minimize the effect of thermal conduction. A light metallic shield surrounds the thermometer to prevent loss of heat by radiation.

The more elaborate form of sulfur-boiling apparatus[1] shown in Fig. 8.7b is used in attaining higher precision of measurement at the sulfur point. The side arm near the top of the tube leads to a reservoir of inert gas and a manometer to control and measure the pressure at which boiling occurs. Thus measurements can be made at the standard pressure of 760 mm of mercury regardless of the barometric pressure. A second heating coil surrounds the upper part of the tube. The current in this heater is adjusted so that the sulfur condenses just above the top of the heating jacket. The radiation shield is in the form of two concentric cylinders of aluminum, blackened inside, and provided with a horizontal dish at the bottom to protect the thermometer from splashing. Apparatus of similar design is used to reproduce the boiling points of water and mercury with high accuracy for calibrating thermometers.

APPLICATIONS

Resistance thermometers have many applications in the range of moderate temperatures, particularly where a high inherent accuracy or an extremely short range is needed. A resistance thermometer is free from reference-junction annoyances common to thermocouples.

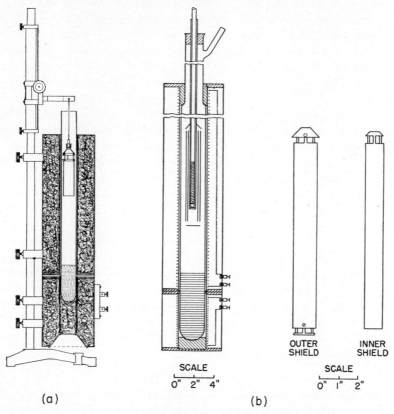

Fig. 8.7. Two forms of sulfur boiling-point apparatus.

In the measurement of extreme temperatures the applicability of resistance thermometers for industrial measurements is limited by their fragility and by the numerous precautions necessary for accurate measurements.

In comparison with resistance thermometers, thermocouples are, in general, simpler—easier to make, easier to inspect, and easier to maintain. Usually cheaper to buy, they are generally preferred whenever they meet the requirements of a given application for range, sensitivity, and accuracy. The use of thermocouples is sometimes dictated by space limitations.

For some applications the Wheatstone bridge used with the resistance thermometer is not adjusted to give a null reading on the galvanometer. Instead the galvanometer deflection is calibrated to indicate directly the temperature of the sensitive coil. This sort of differential galvanometer method is employed in remote-indicating temperature instruments for aircraft.

A special form of resistance thermometer of amazing sensitivity is the bolometer.[9]   It consists essentially of two strips of thin foil, usually blackened platinum, which form two arms of a Wheatstone bridge. The bolometer is used as a detector of radiation.   One strip is exposed to the source of radiation while the other is protected from it.   Absorption of energy by one of the strips results in a rise in its temperature and a corresponding increase in its electrical resistance, which changes the bridge balance.   Changes in temperature as small as 0.000001 C° can be detected, permitting relative measurements of the distribution of power in the spectrum of a laboratory light source or of a distant star.   Bolometers have been used for direction finding by infrared rays.

Electric power plants depend on temperature measuring equipment for protection against overheating and for determining maximum safe loading of generators, frequency changers, synchronous condensers, and motors.   The resistance of the windings of a dynamo serves as an index of their temperature.   Because this resistance is too low for accurate measurement with a Wheatstone bridge, a Thomson (Kelvin) double bridge[5] is employed.

SUMMARY

Temperature can be measured in terms of the electrical resistance of a metallic conductor, usually platinum, nickel, or copper.   Platinum resistance thermometers are used over the range −250 to 1100°C and provide the most accurate method of measurement in the range of medium temperature.

The reproducibility of the scale of a resistance thermometer depends on the purity and homogeneity of the resistance element and its protection from strain and contamination.

Boiling point apparatus used in the calibration of a resistance thermometer must provide for adequate depth of immersion and radiation shielding.

An accurate manometer is an essential part of the calibrating apparatus.

Electrical measurements are best made with a Wheatstone bridge or potentiometer, so constructed as to minimize the effect of contact resistance and emf and to eliminate the effect of the resistance of the thermometer lead wires.

REFERENCES FOR SUPPLEMENTARY READING

1. Beattie, J. A., M. Benedict, and B. E. Blaisdell, "Absolute Temperature Scale," Part II, *Proc. Am. Acad. Arts Sci.*, **71**, 327 (1937).
2. Callendar, G. S., and F. E. Hoare, *Correction Tables for Use with Platinum Resistance Thermometers*, London: E. Arnold & Co., 1933.
3. Callendar, H. L., "On the Practical Measurement of Temperature," *Phil. Trans. (London)*, **178**, 160 (1887).
4. Callendar, H. L., "On the Construction of Platinum Thermometers," *Phil. Mag.*, **32**, 104 (1891).
5. Gilbert, N. E., *Electricity and Magnetism*, p. 127, Macmillan and Co., Ltd., 1943.
6. Griffiths, Ezer, *Methods of Measuring Temperature*, Chap. III, London: Charles Griffin & Co., Ltd., 1947.
7. Hoare, F. E., "Note on the Platinum Thermometer Temperature Scale," *Phil. Mag.*, **7**, 384 (1929).
8. Mueller, E. F., *Precision Resistance Thermometry*, "Temperature, . . ." p. 162, Reinhold Publishing Corp., 1941.
9. Langley, S. P., "The Actinic Balance," *Am. J. Sci.*, Series 3, **21**, 187 (1881).
10. Niven, C. D., "Calibration of Platinum Thermometers at the Boiling Point of Sulphur," *Can. J. Research*, **14**, 1, Sec. A (1936).
11. Siemens, K. W., "On the Increase of Electrical Resistance in Conductors with Rise of Temperature," *Proc. Roy. Soc. (London)*, **19**, 351 (1871).

QUESTIONS AND PROBLEMS

1. Assume that you have a Siemens-type thermometer (Fig. 8.2a) mounted in an opaque tube with lead wires unmarked. How could you identify the lead wires in order to connect thermometer to bridge correctly?

2. What are the relative merits of the different types of compensating leads shown in Fig. 8.2?

3. Why is it undesirable to use ordinary stranded lamp cord for the extension leads of a resistance thermometer?

4. The measuring current used in resistance thermometers is usually so small that the power dissipated in the thermometer coil is less than 1 milliwatt. What factors govern the choice of a suitable value of current? What demands does this make on the characteristics of the galvanometer?

5. Show that a standard cell is not necessary, or even desirable, in determining the resistance of a resistance thermometer by the potentiometer method.

6. Show that the precision of measurement with a potentiometer may be kept nearly the same over a large range of resistance (by appropriate choices of R, Fig. 8.5), whereas with a Wheatstone bridge the precision is generally kept to a certain fraction of an ohm for all resistances.

7. How may a resistance thermometer be adapted as a sensitive device for measuring radiant energy?

8. Diagram a circuit in which the heating coil of a small platinum-wound furnace is used as a platinum resistance thermometer to measure its temperature.

9. Consider two platinum thermometers at the same platinum temperature. Let

$$X = t - pt = d(t - 100)t,$$
$$X' = t' - pt = d'(t - 100)t',$$

and $t' = t + x,$ and $d' = d + y$

Show that for $x \ll 2t - 100$

$$x = \frac{yX}{d[1 - d'(2t - 100)]}$$

If correction tables are available for a particular thermometer show how they may be applied to any other thermometer using this equation.   (Reference 2.)

10. State, with reasons, the type of temperature-measuring device you consider most suitable for use at temperatures of (a) $-250°C$, (b) $-50°C$, (c) $50°C$, (d) $700°C$, and (e) $2000°C$.

11. Show from the characteristics of platinum that, in order to attain an accuracy of ± 0.001 C° in temperature measurement, a precision of resistance measurement of two to four parts in a million is required.

12. A platinum thermometer and a nickel thermometer each have a resistance of 10.00 ohms at 0°C.   Compute the resistance of each (a) at 100°C, and (b) at 300°C.   (Use tables in Appendix.)   Ans. 13.92, 16.63, 21.42, 36.11 ohms.

13. A platinum resistance thermometer has the following resistances: 11.00 ohms at 0°C, 15.247 ohms at 100°C, and 28.887 ohms at 444.60°C.   Find the numerical value of δ in the Callendar correction formula.   Ans. 1.533.

14. At what temperature would the resistance of this thermometer (Problem 13) become zero assuming the same equation held at low temperature?   What is found experimentally?

15. The resistance of a sample of platinum wire is measured at three temperatures as follows: 16.18 ohms at 20°C, 24.26 ohms at 100°C, and 42.06 ohms at 400°C.   (a) Compute the constants for a formula, Eq. (5), giving its resistance at any temperature.   (b) At what temperature is the resistance of the wire 19.50 ohms?

16. In the Wheatstone bridge of Fig. 8.3, $r_1 = r_2 = 1000$ ohms.   At 0°C, $R = x = 10.00$ ohms.   The potential drop across the bridge is 0.50 v.   Find (a) the smallest graduation of resistance R, and (b) the current sensitivity of the 1000-ohm galvanometer needed to detect a change in temperature of 0.1 C°.

Ans. 0.004 ohm, 4×10^{-6} amp/div.

Chapter 9

||||||||||||||||||||||||||

TEMPERATURE RECORDING AND CONTROL

RECORDING POTENTIOMETERS |||||| *CHARAC-TERISTICS OF AUTOMATIC CONTROL* |||||| *TYPES OF ACTION IN CONTROL EQUIP-MENT* |||||| *THERMOSTATS* ||||||

RECORDING THERMOMETERS

Permanent temperature records are of primary importance in every industrial process and laboratory research whose results are dependent upon the maintenance of certain optimum temperatures. The pyrometers that can be made to record automatically are of the following classes: (a) expansion thermometers, using a gas, liquid, or solid in the sensitive element; (b) resistance thermometers; (c) thermo-electric pyrometers; (d) total-radiation pyrometers and (e) partial-radiation pyrometers balanced photoelectrically.

Of these types, the thermoelectric pyrometer has the greatest applicability, especially for the higher temperatures at which the first two are not suitable. The constant-volume gas thermometer for industrial use is satisfactory up to about 400°C, and the mercury ther-mometer to about 550°C. The resistance thermometer is capable of very high accuracy up to 1100°C. At such high temperatures, how-ever, thermocouples are more serviceable, since deterioration of the wire from repeated heating does not so seriously alter the emf developed by a couple as it does the resistance of a resistance thermometer. Base-metal thermocouples serve satisfactorily up to 1100°C and Pt–PtRh couples up to 1500°C, though above 1400°C it becomes very difficult to protect the couple from contamination. Radiation pyrometers are useful at the highest attainable temperatures. However, processes in which temperatures greater than 1600°C are used are not, in general, susceptible of very precise temperature control.

Temperature records are usually kept on disk, drum, or strip charts whose temperature-time scales are proportioned to fit the range and accuracy of a particular service. The precision of modern industrial recorders has been improved until a considerable part of the residual error is associated with the effect of humidity changes on the paper charts.

PRESSURE THERMOMETERS

Liquid-, vapor-, and gas-filled thermometer bulbs are used to actuate recording pens through some form of Bourdon tube. When the bulb is remote from the recorder, as is desirable in many installa-

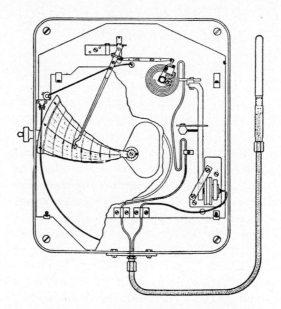

Fig. 9.1.   Compensated mercury recording
thermometer.

tions, it is necessary to compensate for the effect of temperature changes on the pressure-transmitting tube. In the recording mercury thermometer illustrated in Fig. 9.1, the mercury-filled capillary is paralleled by a casing containing nitrogen. The gas-filled space acts as a long bulb which inflates and deflates a sylphon (capsular spring) inside the recorder case as the temperature fluctuates along the tubing. The sylphon operates through a lever movement to shift the center of the Bourdon spring in the proper sense to compensate for the effect of the varying temperature in the connecting tubing.

In another method of compensation a fine wire is placed in the capillary bore of the pressure-transmitting tube. By the proper choice of expansion coefficients and dimensions, the expansion of the wire can be made to cancel the effect of the expansion of the capillary tube keeping constant the volume occupied by the liquid.

RECORDING GALVANOMETER

A galvanometer may be so modified as to become a recording instrument for use with resistance thermometers or thermocouples. A galvanometer suspension is used that permits the galvanometer needle to be depressed by a bar that periodically brings it in contact with a graph sheet. The graph paper is moved at constant speed and the temperature-time curve obtained is a series of closely-spaced dots made by an ink pen, by a stylus on waxed paper, or by an electric spark which perforates the paper. An obvious disadvantage of a recording galvanometer is that the weight of the recording mechanism is detrimental to the sensitivity and balance of the galvanometer.

RECORDING POTENTIOMETER

The advantages of the null-indicating principle of a potentiometer are so great in a wide variety of measurements that numerous ingenious methods have been devised to make a potentiometer self-balancing, recording, and even automatic in checking itself against a standard cell.

In all recording potentiometers the galvanometer merely indicates the position of balance. It is required to do no work that would reduce its sensitivity. An electric motor takes the place of an operator in moving the resistance contacts to secure a balance. A commercial recording potentiometer is an interesting example of a delicate, expensive laboratory instrument which has become a reliable industrial instrument of moderate cost through quantity production.

The balance-type recording mechanism which can apply the potentiometer method for use with thermocouples can be used equally well to apply the Wheatstone or Kelvin bridge methods for resistance thermometer measurements.

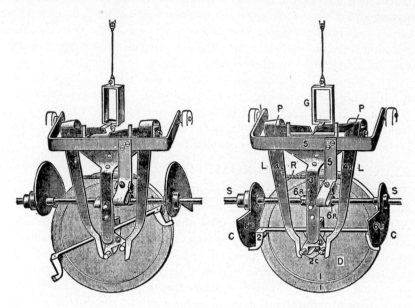

FIG. 9.2.   Potentiometer balancing mechanism.

The operation of a self-balancing potentiometer may be well illustrated by a consideration of one of the older forms of balancing mechanisms, Fig. 9.2.   The slide-wire is a long helix mounted on the periphery of the central disk.   In balancing, the wire is moved past a stationary contact.   Balance is achieved by the following cycle of operations.   Suppose the galvanometer G is deflected toward the left. Shaft S is rotated continually by a motor not shown.   With each revolution the small cam $6R$ raises bar 5 which catches the pointer under one of the right-angle levers, L.   This lever, pivoted at P, is thus made to swing the arm 2 by pressing against one of the eccentrically-located lugs $2c$.   The rocker arm 5 is then immediately lowered to allow the galvanometer to swing freely.   Cam $6R$ is so fixed on shaft S that it recedes from spring R allowing R to press 2 against the disk

D just before cams *C* straighten arm 2. In so doing, they rotate the disk and the slide-wire is brought nearer the position for balance. If balance has not been attained, the galvanometer remains deflected, and the same cycle of operations is carried out with the next revolution of the shaft. When balance is attained, the upward movement of 5 simply raises the pointer into the V-shaped space between levers *L*,

Fig. 9.3.   Micromax balancing mechanism.

and no rotation of the disk follows. The position of the slide-wire controls the position of a pen carriage on a horizontal rod over the graph sheet. At intervals the pen drops to make a mark on the sheet. The scale of the potentiometer may be graduated in millivolts or directly in temperature for a given type of thermocouple.[6]

An improved form of balancing mechanism is pictured in Fig. 9.3. In the original mechanism accuracy was largely limited by mechanical clearances, and these had to be adjusted occasionally owing to wear. In the newer design accuracy and responsiveness are practically unaffected by wear. Deflections of the galvanometer needle as small as 0.001 in. actuate the balancing mechanism. The balancing operations are explained by the illustrations of Fig. 9.3. The galvanometer has a free period in which to deflect (1). Then, about once every 2 sec, a cushioned clamp grips the pointer and setting levers close on it quickly. If the levers find the pointer undeflected (2) the balancing mechanism and slide-wire do not move. If the temperature has changed, the setting levers find the pointer deflected (3). A clutch arm is positioned to match the extent of pointer deflection, and is clamped there against the slide-wire disk. Cams restore the arm promptly to the normal position, thus simultaneously turning the disk and the slide wire (4).

Fig. 9.4.   Micromax recorder, chart swung out.

The appearance of a typical recorder is illustrated by Fig. 9.4 which shows the chart holder swung out, exposing the slide-wire disk.

Such recorders are made in single-point, two-point, and multiple-point types. A single-point, curve-drawing instrument indicates continuously and traces an uninterrupted record. It concentrates on one couple and is never disconnected when an important change takes place—especially desirable in a recorder which operates signals. A two-point, curve-drawing instrument switches automatically from one to the other of two couples at short regular intervals. Its pointer indicates the two temperatures alternately, and its pen records them side by side for easy comparison. It can be equipped to operate signals. A multiple-point, curve-printing instrument measures successively the temperatures of as many as sixteen couples. It is especially useful where processes are of long duration, where temperatures tend to change gradually, or where temperatures differ but are always in the same approximate relationship. Its pointer indicates

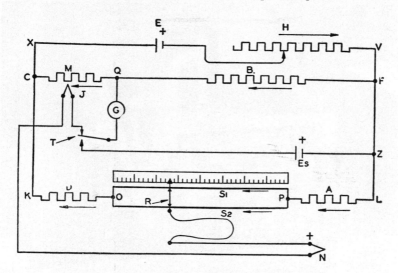

Fig. 9.5.   Recording potentiometer circuit.

the several temperatures alternately and its printing device records them either in one color or in contrasting colors. In addition, it can be equipped to operate a remote indicator and pilot lights to show at any instant which couple is connected.

A circuit diagram for a recording potentiometer used with a thermocouple is shown in Fig. 9.5. The balancing mechanism (Fig. 9.6) adjusts the position of contact R on the two slide-wires, S_1 and S_2. When the potential difference between Q and R has been made zero the galvanometer reads zero, and no further motion of R takes place. A recording pen and an indicating arrow mounted on the same carriage as R show the thermocouple emf (temperature). Since the emf of the working battery E changes slightly from time to time, provisions are made whereby the potential difference between X and V can be held constant by adjusting the resistor H. This is done by depressing switch T, thus temporarily replacing the thermocouple circuit by the circuit between Z and T of like polarity, containing a standard cell E_s of constant emf. By adjusting H until the galvanometer deflection is zero the emf between X and V is restored to its intended value. This

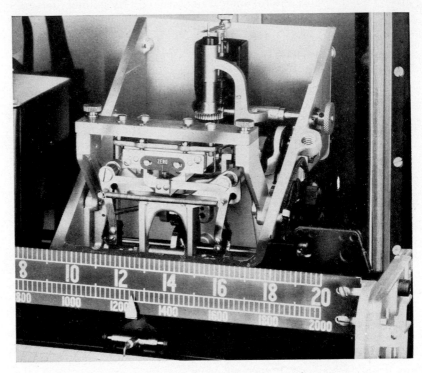

FIG. 9.6.   Bristol potentiometer recorder.

operation of standardizing the current through the potentiometer slide-wire is done manually on some instruments, automatically on others.

Another type of potentiometer balancing mechanism is shown in Fig. 9.7. At intervals of a few seconds, the galvanometer pointer B is lightly clamped. A step on the selector table C rests against the pointer and positions a secondary pointer D. The step lever E periodically moves downward into contact with the secondary pointer and rotates the gear *G*, secured to the shaft *H*, an amount depending upon the position of the secondary pointer. This readjusts the slide-wire contact *J*, simultaneously moving the pen *P*.

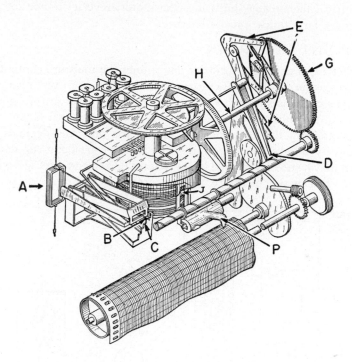

FIG. 9.7. Brown potentiometer balancing mechanism.

HIGH SPEED RECORDING

To measure the temperature of metals being rolled, so quickly that even the gradients along their lengths are recorded, a quick-acting radiation pyrometer is used with a rapid recorder. Rapid balancing combined with rapidity of chart movement (of the order of 2 in./min) result in clear graphs which permit analysis of even rapid temperature fluctuations.

One such recorder, the Speedomax, has a measuring circuit practically identical with that of the recorder shown in Fig. 9.4. Instead of balancing by mechanical means, however, the Speedomax has a motor which balances the instrument rapidly whenever a temperature change unbalances the circuit.   To assure fast recording, this motor provides higher speeds as temperature changes become larger; big changes record nearly as fast as small ones.   To prevent overshooting, an electrical tachometer, built into the motor, reverses motor torque as required for a quick, precise balance.

DEWPOINT RECORDER

One type of dewpoint recorder determines the moisture content of a gas by measuring the temperature at which moisture from a sample of the gas condenses on the surface of a mirror.   A beam of light is focused on the mirror by a lens (Fig. 9.8).   The reflected beam falls on a photocell.   The internal resistance of the photocell depends on the intensity of light directed on it.   The mirror is part of a cup which is alternately heated and cooled by an electric heater and a refrigerating system.   During part of a cycle, the temperature of the mirror decreases

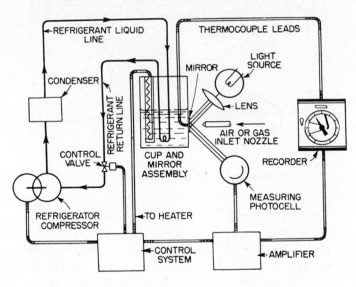

Fig. 9.8.   A dewpoint recorder

until fog forms on it due to condensation of moisture in the gas under test.   At this dewpoint the amount of light reflected to the photocell is decreased, the resistance of the photocell increases, and the decrease in photocell current causes a record to be made of the temperature of the mirror as measured by a thermocouple which is attached to the mirror. Although the temperature of the mirror is continually changing, the record shows only successive dewpoint temperatures since the balancing motor and the potentiometer are kept disconnected except for the fraction of a second during each cycle when the dewpoint temperature exists.

TEMPERATURE CONTROL

"Have you ever tried to eliminate the fluctuations of temperature in your home? If so, you must have gone through the mental processes required to analyze automatic control problems. You deal with time lags: (a) the time required to build up a draft and a fire, (b) the time required to build up the temperature of the equipment so that heat can be transferred to the air, (c) the time required for the heat to be carried throughout the house, and (d) the time required for your thermometer to show this new temperature value. You may not have recognized the various factors to the point where you could separate each one and determine its effect and the way to compensate for it, but you have dealt with the problems which good controllers analyze and solve. . . . The best control system is one that is so well regulated by metered control and so quick to smooth out slight deviations, that it appears to be doing nothing."[13]

Temperature regulation in its crudest form is accomplished by the use of indicating instruments and manual control. Substitution of recording instruments for indicating instruments permits closer manual control by focusing the operator's attention on the importance of time and the rate of change of temperature (both dT/dt and d^2T/dt^2) in correcting for departures of the temperature from the desired value.

In analyzing regulation problems, it is customary to assume a linear differential equation (of the second or higher order) of the type that describes oscillating systems

$$\frac{c_2 d^2\phi}{dt^2} + \frac{c_1 d\phi}{dt} + c_0 = 0 \qquad (1)$$

where ϕ is the fractional deviation of the temperature from the desired value. For a given case, this equation must be reduced to a specific form and its coefficients evaluated. The effectiveness of the control can then be specified in terms of the time constants.

All control problems are fundamentally somewhat similar. Often it requires only an exchange of sensitive elements to adapt a controller for either temperature or pressure regulation. Temperature control is a relatively young branch of that automatic-control technology which seeks improvement of the product and reduction in cost, and which often brings, too, a more fundamental knowledge of the process being controlled. The practical achievements of automatic temperature control have preceded and outstripped mathematical theory. In the present status of control technology, efforts are being directed toward (a) development of a generally accepted terminology,[14] (b) classification of the processes to be controlled and the methods of control, (c) determination of time constants which, when inserted in the theoretical equations, will yield at least approximate solutions in the application of theory to practical problems, and (d) the use of time constants to define a figure of merit which describes the effectiveness of a given method of control in a given process.

A uniform terminology and an exact method for the applications of temperature control would facilitate the interchange of pertinent, quantitative data between process equipment manufacturer, instrument manufacturer, control consultant, and user.

PROCESS TO BE CONTROLLED

A *process* comprises the collective functions performed in and by the equipment in which a variable is to be controlled. An *automatic controller* (or automatic regulator) is a mechanism which measures the value of a variable quantity or condition and operates to correct or limit deviation of this measured value from a selected reference.

Figure 9.9 represents a fluid heat exchange process with automatic temperature control. The *controlled variable* (temperature) of the *controlled medium* (fluid leaving the process) is measured by the automatic controller which acts in a predetermined way to vary the value of the *manipulated variable* (flow) of the *control agent* (fluid entering the process). The action of the automatic controller restores, or tends to restore, the value of the controlled variable to the desired value.

The *capacity* of a process is the maximum energy or material that can be stored. For a thermal process, capacity may be expressed in Btu.

The *capacitance* of a process is the change in energy or material per unit change in some reference variable. For a thermal process, capacitance may be stated in Btu/degree.

Resistance is opposition to flow, measured as change of potential per unit change in flow. For a thermal process resistance is expressible in degrees per Btu per second.

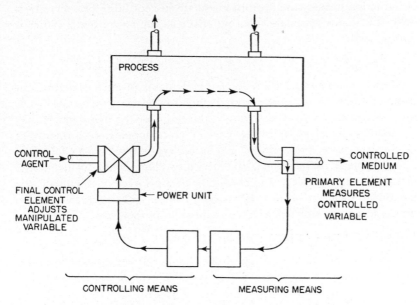

F<small>IG</small>. 9.9. Elements of process to be controlled and of controller.

Dead time is the delay period between two related actions. The dead time, capacitance, and resistance, together determine the *lag* or over-all delay inherent in the dynamic characteristics of a given controlled system. Distance-velocity lag is illustrated by Fig. 9.10. Delay occurs in detecting a change in the temperature of the mixture if the thermocouple is placed at *b* because the material must be transported a distance *ab* to the thermocouple. A change in the setting of value *A* or *B* is not made until the new mixture covers the distance from *a* to *b*.

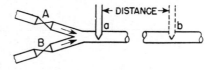

F<small>IG</small>. 9.10. Distance—velocity lag.

Self-regulation is a sustained reaction inherent in the process which assists or opposes the establishment of equilibrium. A hydraulic example of self-regulation is a water tank with inflow at the top and outflow through a fixed orifice at the bottom.   If the inflow is increased a fixed amount, the water level will rise at a decreasing rate as a result of increased outflow due to the increasing liquid head.   In one type of induction furnace the drop in magnetic susceptibility of a ferromagnetic sheath decreases the heating effect as the Curie temperature is approached.

ELEMENTS OF AUTOMATIC CONTROLLERS

The *measuring means* consists of the elements of an automatic controller that ascertain and communicate to the control means either the value of the controlled variable, the error, or the deviation.

The *controlling means* is the part of an automatic controller that produces a corrective action.   The *power unit* applies power for operating the *final control element* that directly changes the value of the manipulated variable.   In Fig. 9.9, the primary element of the measuring means may be a thermometer bulb.   The corrective action occurs when a motor sets a valve to pass the proper flow.

CHARACTERISTICS OF AUTOMATIC CONTROL

Cycling, or oscillation, is a periodic change of the controlled variable from one value to another.   Three types of cycling are illustrated in

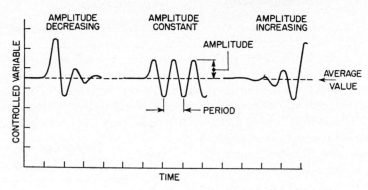

FIG. 9.11.   Cycling.

Fig. 9.11.   Only cycling with constant or decreasing amplitudes is suitable for automatic control.

The *set point* is the position to which the control-point-setting mechanism is set.

The *control point* is the value of the controlled variable which at any instant is maintained by the automatic controller.

Error is the difference between the instantaneous value and the desired value of the controlled variable.

Deviation is the difference between the instantaneous value of the controlled variable and the value corresponding with the set point.

Offset is a sustained deviation and is the difference existing between the control point and the value of the controlled variable corresponding with the set point.

CONTROLLER ACTIONS

The simplest control device has a *two-position action* (on-off) at a single point. The control element is moved from one of two fixed positions to the other at a single value of the controlled variable. In another two-position action there is a *differential gap*. The final control element is moved from one of two fixed positions to the other when the controlled variable reaches a predetermined value from one

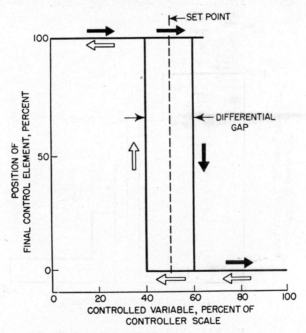

FIG. 9.12.   Two-position differential-gap action.

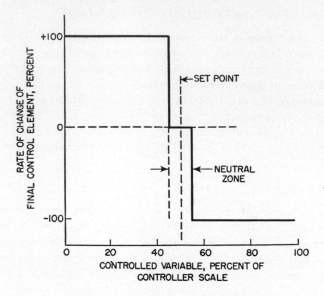

FIG. 9.13.   Single-speed floating action.

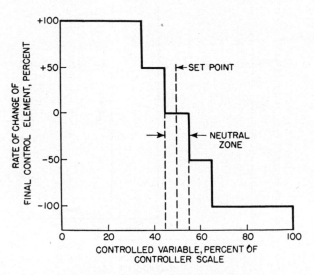

FIG. 9.14.   Multispeed floating action.

160

direction and, subsequently, is moved to the other position only after the variable has passed in the opposite direction through a range of values to a second predetermined value, as illustrated in Fig. 9.12.

In *single-speed floating action* the control element is moved at a single rate between its extreme positions (Fig. 9.13). No corrective action

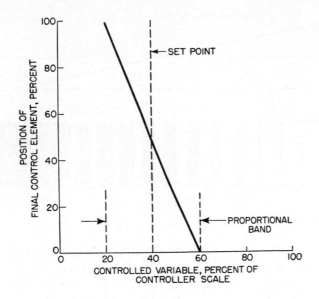

FIG. 9.15.   Proportional-position action.

occurs in a predetermined range of values called the *neutral zone*. In *multispeed floating action* the final control element is moved at two or more rates, each corresponding to a definite range of values of the controlled variable (Fig. 9.14).

Proportional-position action is that in which there is a continuous linear relation between the value of the controlled variable and the position of a final control element, within a range of values of the controlled variable called the *proportional band* (Fig. 9.15).

Average-position action is that in which there is a predetermined relation between the value of the controlled variable and the time-average position of a final control element which is moved periodically from one of two fixed positions to the other (Fig. 9.16). As early as 1897 Gouy designed a thermoregulator using this action. An iron

wire was used to make contact with the mercury column in a thermometer. The wire was given a vertical oscillating motion of a
20-sec period. Thus the contact was closed turning the heater "on"
from 0 to 20 sec per cycle, depending upon the position of the mercury
column, as indicated by the lower part of Fig. 9.16.

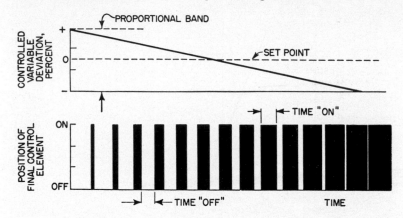

FIG. 9.16.   Average-position action, proportional type.

In *proportional-speed floating action* there is a continuous linear relation
between the value of the controlled variable and the rate of motion
called the *floating rate* of a final control element.   When proportional-
speed floating action is combined with proportional-position action,
the former is termed *reset action*.

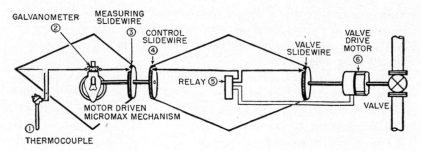

FIG. 9.17.   A proportional controller.

A proportional controller is suggested in Fig. 9.17.   In it there is
a fixed relationship between the positions of control and valve slide-

wires, so that for any temperature there is a fixed valve position. In the controllers of Figs. 9.18 and 9.19 this relationship is varied by reset action. In Fig. 9.18 (a) an operator watches the recorder chart and when necessary turns rheostats m and n to establish a new relationship between control and valve slide-wires. In Fig. 9.18, there is a

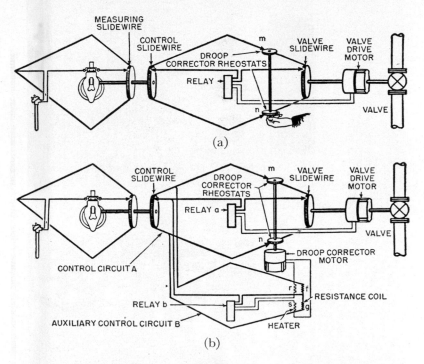

(a)

(b)

FIG. 9.18. A proportional controller with reset action: (a) manual; (b) automatic.

motor to turn the rheostats and an auxiliary control circuit which directs the motor. The action of the auxiliary circuit persists until the temperature is at the control point.

The pneumatic controller shown in Fig. 9.19 is a system that provides proportional action, reset action, and rate or second-derivative action control. The control operates on the flapper and nozzle principle.

As the measuring slidewire rotates, a nozzle moves closer or farther from a movable baffle, thus changing the back pressure inside the air

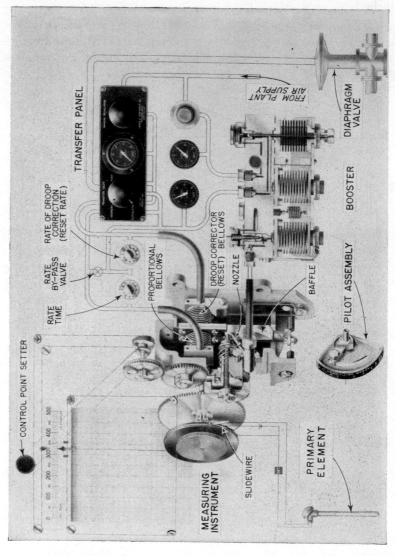

Fig. 9.19. A controller employing pneumatic balance for reset action and rate control.

passage connected to the nozzle.   This air pressure is then used, through
a booster, to actuate a diaphragm motor valve.   A proportional
bellows applies air pressure to the movable baffle in a direction to
offset the movement of the nozzle, and thus keeps the nozzle pressure
characteristic linear.   The process is subject to *proportional control*.

Automatic reset is provided by applying a force to the baffle arm
opposing the proportional force, by means of a second bellows supplied

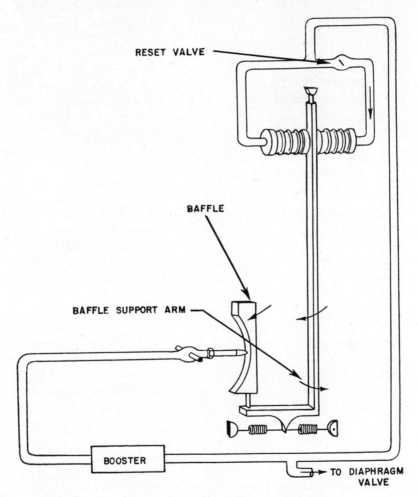

FIG. 9.20.   Droop corrector (reset) mechanism.

with air through a valve. The opening of the droop corrector or reset valve (Fig. 9.20) determines the amount of reset action.

Rate control or second-derivative control action is accomplished by means of a rate valve in series with the proportional bellows (Fig. 9.21). With the rate valve partly open, an increase in output air pressure cannot fully act upon the proportional bellows. Consequently the follow-up action provided by the bellows is reduced. The output pressure change is greater than it would be with proportional action only, by an amount proportional to the speed of the recorder pen motion. The rate valve is set initially according to the time lag in the process being regulated. The diaphragm valve is then moved not merely the amount necessary to provide proportional action, but in addition an amount sufficient to help compensate for the time lag. Thus the diaphragm valve tends to be brought to the position it would have reached had there been no lag in the process. As soon as the recorder pen stops moving (whether at the control point or not), rate action drops out. The diaphragm valve is brought back to the setting produced by proportional and droop correcting (reset) actions.

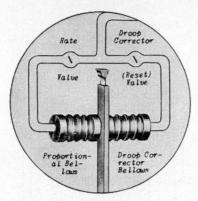

Fig. 9.21.   Mechanism for rate control.

THERMOSTATS

The temperature-sensitive element used in a thermostat is often a bimetallic coil or a liquid-filled bulb arranged to open or close a heater circuit when the temperature passes a predetermined value. A bimetallic regulator is set by adjusting the tension in the coil. A liquid-in-glass regulator is set by adjusting the level of the liquid or the position of a contact-making wire. High sensitivity and small lag are obtained by using a large ratio of surface to volume.

An a-c bridge and amplifier for continuous control of furnaces and thermostats is illustrated in Fig. 9.22. The power output of the control circuit is doubled for a change of only 0.03 per cent in the resistance of the thermometer. The circuit regulates a 500-watt heater and maintains the temperature of an oil bath constant within 0.03 C°.

Figure 9.23 is a diagram of the a-c control circuit for a small thermostat, used in the measurement of heat capacities of vapors, which maintains temperatures constant to 0.0025 C° in the range 25 to 210°C. The temperature sensing element is a Thermistor in a

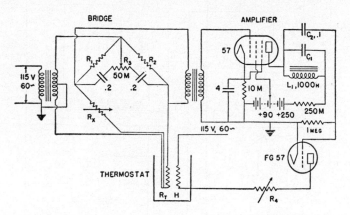

Fig. 9.22. Resistance thermometer and a-c bridge control circuit.

Wheatstone bridge. The proportional control circuit employs saturable reactor output. The thermostat comprises two brass cylinders connected side by side in which Silicone fluid is circulated by a stirrer.

The Thermistor, R_3 of Fig. 9.23, is a glass-coated rod-type resistor which is placed in the bath fluid. The resistance changes from 145,000 ohms at 0°C to 305 ohms at 200°C. Unbalance of the Wheatstone bridge, R_1, R_2, R_3, is amplified by a three-stage amplifier. The Wheatstone bridge output is of one phase when the Thermistor is warmer than the equilibrium temperature and of opposite phase when it is cooler. The detector is made phase sensitive by feeding the screen grid of the 6 AC 7 with 60-cycle alternating current from a phase shift circuit which permits compensation for phase shift through the amplifier. The plate current of the detector passes through the control coil of the saturable reactor and thus controls the current in the nichrome heater elements, R_{20}, of the thermostat.

The advantage of the Thermistor lies in reduction of degree of amplification required, and in the reduced size and thermal inertia

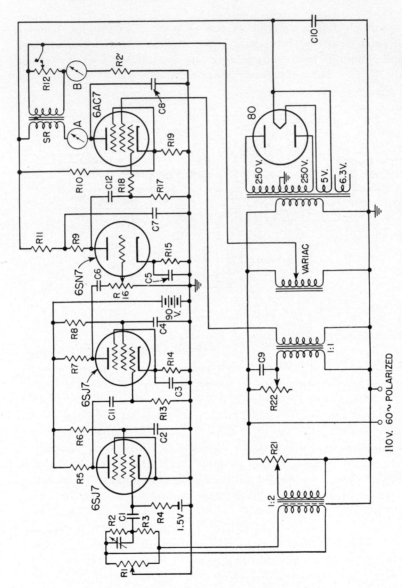

FIG. 9.23. Temperature control circuit employing a Thermistor (R_3) and a saturable reactor (SR).

of the sensing unit. The avoidance of thyratrons in this circuit reduces the effects of transients and harmonics. The thermostat heater may be actuated by low voltage currents and stability is increased.

SUMMARY

Permanent temperature records are obtained by providing mechanical or electrical recording devices for thermometers of the expansion, resistance, thermoelectric, or radiation type.

The recording potentiometer offers the advantages of a balance method of measuring temperature in terms of an emf, and is widely used for laboratory and industrial records.

Reliable records are obtained only when the sensitive element is used under conditions for which it was calibrated. Automatic temperature-control equipment may be classed according to the following types of action:

1. Two-position
   (a) Single-point
   (b) Differential-gap
2. Floating
   (a) Single-speed
   (b) Two-speed
   (c) Proportional-speed
3. Proportional-position
4. Proportional-plus-floating (reset)
   (a) With other compensation

REFERENCES FOR SUPPLEMENTARY READING

1. Adcock, F., "Apparatus for Raising or Lowering the Temperature of a Laboratory Furnace," *J. Sci. Instruments*, **12**, 285 (1935).
2. Am. Inst. of Physics, *Temperature—Its Measurement and Control in Science and Industry*, Chap. 7, Reinhold Publishing Corp., 1941.
3. Ansley, A. J., *Temperature Control*, Chapman & Hall, Ltd., 1942.
4. Barnes, R. B. and A. Silverman, "Brownian Motion as a Natural Limit to All Measuring Processes," *Rev. Modern Phys.*, **6**, 162 (1934).
5. Batcher, R. R. and W. E. Moulic, *The Electronic Control Handbook*, New York: Caldwell-Clements, Inc., 1946.
6. Behar, M. F., *Fundamentals of Instrumentation; Temperature and Humidity Measurement and Control*, Pittsburgh: Instruments Publishing Co., 1932.
7. Benedict, M., "Use of an Alternating Current Bridge in Laboratory Temperature Control," *Rev. Sci. Instruments*, **8**, 252 (1937).
8. Burwell, R. L., A. H. Peterson, and G. B. Rathman, "A Temperature Control Device Employing Thermistors and a Saturable Reactor," *Rev. Sci. Instruments*, **19**, 608 (1948).
9. Callendar, A., D. R. Hartree, and A. Porter, "Time Lag in a Control System," *Phil. Trans. Roy. Soc.*, **A235**, 415 (1936).

10. Eckman, D. P., *Principles of Industrial Process Control*, John Wiley & Sons, Inc., 1945.
11. Feller, E. W., "Measuring and Controlling Temperature and Pressure," *Power*, **90**, 65 (1946).
12. *Fundamentals of Pressure and Temperature Instruments*, Albany, New York: Delmar Publishers, Inc., 1947.
13. Grebe, J. J., "Elements of Automatic Control," *Ind. Eng. Chem.*, **29**, 1225 (1937).
14. Horn, J. G., *Graphical Representation and Analysis of Automatic Control Terminology*, The Brown Instrument Co., 1947.
15. *Instruments and Process Control*, Albany, New York: Delmar Publishers, Inc., 1947.
16. Rhodes, T. J., *Industrial Instruments for Measurement and Control*, McGraw-Hill Book Co., Inc., 1941.
17. Roebuck, J. R., "Mechanical Thermostats," *J. Optical Soc. Am. & Rev. Sci. Instruments*, **10**, 679 (1925).
18. Smith, E. C., *Automatic Control Engineering*, McGraw-Hill Book Co., Inc., 1944.
19. Timoshenko, S., "Theory of Bi-metal Thermostats," *J. Optical Soc. Am. & Rev. Sci. Instruments*, **11**, 233 (1925).
20. Yee, J. Y., and R. O. E. Davis, "An Adjustable Sensitive Thermoregulator," *Ind. Eng. Chem., Anal. Ed.*, **8**, 477 (1936).

Chapter 10

IIIIIIIIIIIIIIIIIIIIII

CALORIMETRY

TYPES OF CALORIMETERS IIIIIII *MEASURE-MENTS OF SPECIFIC HEATS AND HEATING VALUES* IIIIIII *PROCEDURES FOR MINIMIZING ERRORS* IIIIIII

MEASUREMENT OF HEAT

Heat measurements are frequently required in science and in industry since most physical and chemical processes involve the generation of heat, its transfer from one body to another, or its conversion into other forms of energy. The theory and practice of making measurements of quantities of heat is called *calorimetry*.

Since heat is a form of energy, we would naturally expect heat quantities to be expressed in ordinary energy units—foot-pounds, ergs, and joules. They often are. But heat was measured before anyone understood its real nature, and the most convenient methods of calorimetry are still those which use the most obvious effect of heat, namely that (with certain exceptions) it raises the temperature of bodies to which it is applied. Further, the increase in temperature is practically proportional to the quantity of heat supplied. We thus have a simple way of defining heat units by specifying what body is to have the heat applied to it and what increase in temperature is to correspond to a unit quantity of heat.

The *calorie* is defined as the amount of heat required to raise the

171

temperature of 1 gm of pure water from 14.5 to 15.5°C when the pressure is 1 atm. The *kilogram calorie* is one thousand gram calories. It is the unit used in dietetics.

The *British thermal unit* (Btu) is defined as the amount of heat required to raise the temperature of 1 lb of water 1 Fahrenheit degree. One Btu is equivalent to approximately 252 cal.

The *specific heat c* of a substance, for specified conditions during heating, is defined as the heat per unit mass per degree change in temperature

$$c = \frac{Q}{M\Delta T} \tag{1}$$

Common units of specific heat are calories per gram centigrade degree, Btu per pound Fahrenheit degree, and joules per gram Kelvin degree. If the unit of mass chosen is the gram-atom or the mole, the corresponding specific heat is known as the *atomic heat* or the *molecular heat*.

The *thermal capacitance* or the *heat capacity* of a body is defined as the product of its mass and its specific heat. The units are calories per centigrade degree or Btu per Fahrenheit degree. Thermal capacitance is a characteristic of a particular body and not of a substance, as is specific heat.

The *water equivalent* of a body is defined as the product of the mass of the body and the ratio of its specific heat to that of water. Its units are those of mass.

The experimental technique followed in making heat measurements depends upon such factors as the source of heat, the quantity of heat, and the degree of precision desired. The common methods of calorimetry depend upon (a) the change of temperature of a liquid, usually water, (b) the change of temperature of a solid (aneroid calorimetry), (c) the melting of ice, (d) the condensation of steam, (e) comparison with a constant known electric source of heat, or (f) cooling by radiation.

WATER CALORIMETER

The experimental determination of the specific heat of a metal in a water calorimeter (Fig. 10.1) by the method of mixtures is familiar to every student of physics. The method consists essentially of adding a known mass of metal at a known high temperature to a known mass of water at a known low temperature and determining the equilibrium temperature that results. The heat absorbed by the water and the containing vessel can be computed and this is equaled to the expression for the heat given up by the hot metal. From this equation the unknown specific heat can be computed.

EXAMPLE: Eighty grams of iron shot at 100.0°C are dropped into 200 gm of water at 20.0°C contained in a 50-gm iron vessel. The resulting temperature is 23.6°C. Find the specific heat of iron.

FIG. 10.1. Double-walled water calorimeter.

In this mixture heat is lost by the shot and heat is gained by the water and its container.

Heat lost by shot

$$= m_x c_x \Delta t_x$$
$$= (80 \text{ gm}) c_x (100.0°C - 23.6°C)$$

Heat gained by water

$$= m_w c_w \Delta t_w$$
$$= (200 \text{ gm})(1.00 \text{ cal/gm C°})(23.6°C - 20.0°C)$$

Heat gained by vessel

$$= m_c c_c \Delta t_c$$
$$= (50 \text{ gm}) c_c (23.6°C - 20.0°C)$$

Heat lost by shot = heat gained by water + heat gained by vessel
$$(80 \text{ gm}) c_x (100.0°C - 23.6°C) =$$
$$(200 \text{ gm})(1.00 \text{ cal/gm C°})(23.6°C - 20.0°C) + (50 \text{ gm}) c_c (23.6°C - 20.0°C)$$
$$c_x = c_c \text{ (both for iron)}$$

Hence
$$c_x = \frac{720 \text{ cal}}{593 \text{ gm C°}} = 0.121 \text{ cal/(gm C°)}$$

Precise calorimetry by this method requires minimizing and correcting for the effects of thermal communication between the water and its surroundings during the equalization period and the absorption of heat by parts of the apparatus other than the water itself (the container, the stirrer, the thermometer, etc.). In the precision calorimeter shown in Fig. 10.2, a jacket of continuously stirred water, with heater, surrounds the metal chamber containing the calorimetric fluid, thus providing an environment of uniform temperature. A convection and radiation shield S serves to decrease heat losses by convection and radiation. A tight cover practically eliminates evaporation effects. Temperature measurements are made with sensitive platinum resistance thermometers.

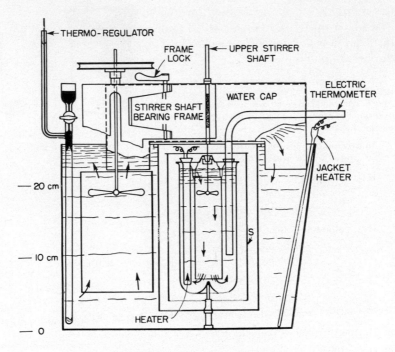

FIG. 10.2.   Precision calorimeter.

CORRECTIONS AND CALCULATIONS

Calorimetric data must generally be corrected for the escape or entrance of heat due to the fact that the test chamber cannot be kept at the same temperature as its surroundings. This transfer is most simply accounted for by assuming that it follows Newton's law of thermal leakage: The rate of transfer of heat $(dQ/dt)_L$ to the calorimetric fluid, by leakage, is proportional to the difference in temperature between fluid and jacket $(T - T_j)$

$$\left(\frac{dQ}{dt}\right)_L = -k(T - T_j) \tag{2}$$

The heat lost from the calorimetric fluid by leakage during the equalization period can be evaluated, in principle, from the relation

$$Q = k \int (T - T_j) dt \tag{3}$$

in which k represents the heat lost per unit time per unit temperature
difference and is called the *thermal-leakage modulus*.

In addition to thermal leakage, it is necessary, in precise measurements, to make allowance for heat generated or converted into other
forms of energy within the calorimeter. Friction of the stirring
mechanism, evaporation of liquid, and adsorption of gases chiefly
require attention.

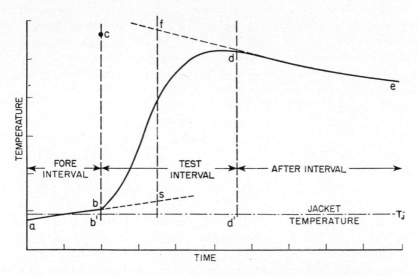

FIG. 10.3.   A temperature-time plot for a calorimeter.

Combining heat terms, we may write the equation which gives the
quantity of heat Q measured by a water calorimeter

$$Q = c_w(m_w + m'_w)(T_f - T_i) + k \int (T - T_j) dt - Q' \tag{4}$$

where c_w is the specific heat of calorimeter water, m_w the mass of
calorimeter water, m'_w the water equivalent of calorimeter and accessories, $(T - T_j)$ the variable temperature difference between calorimeter and jacket integrated through the equalization period, and Q'

the heat, contributed by internal processes, other than the quantity Q to be measured.

In practice it is convenient to write the equation for the water calorimeter in the form

$$Q = c_w(m_w + m_w') \Delta T \qquad (5)$$

in which ΔT represents the effective rise in temperature which would have occurred in the absence of thermal leakage and the heating due to stirring. The corrected temperature rise ΔT is obtained from a temperature-time plot, Fig. 10.3. During the *fore interval* the small temperature variation shown by ab is due to the effects of stirring and thermal leakage. During the *test interval*, the heat to be measured, say from the combustion of a fuel sample, is transferred to the calorimeter water and the rapid rise of the water temperature, bd, is largely determined by that heat transfer. During the *after interval* the temperature variation shown by de is again determined by the effects of thermal leakage and stirrer action. The corrected temperature rise ΔT is equal to the observed temperature rise, $T_d - T_b$, plus a thermal-leakage correction, plus a stirring correction

$$\Delta T = T_c - T_b = (T_d - T_b) +$$
$$\frac{k}{mc} \int_{t_b}^{t_d} (T - T_j)dt - \left(\frac{dT}{dt}\right)_s (T_d - T_b) \qquad (6)$$

The first term of Eq. (6), the uncorrected temperature rise $(T_d - T_b)$, is read from the graph. To evaluate the third term, $(dT/dt)_s$, which is the rate at which the temperature rises due to stirring, one measures the slope of the line ab. During the fore interval the thermal leakage is negligible, since the water temperature is nearly the same as the jacket temperature. The integral in the second term is obtained by determining in suitable physical units the quantity represented by area $bdd'b'b$. The factor k/mc is the thermal-leakage modulus divided by the thermal capacitance of calorimeter and its contents. It is evaluated from the slopes of lines ab and de. During the after interval the rate at which the temperature decreases, dT/dt, is due to both thermal leakage and stirring. The net variation due to leakage alone is then $(dT/dt)_s - dT/dt$. If one divides this by $T - T_j$ the average difference in temperature between water and jacket during interval de, one obtains the average rate of temperature change per unit temperature difference

$$\frac{k}{mc} = \frac{(dT/dt)_s - dT/dt}{T - T_j} \tag{7}$$

The product of k/mc (1/min) and the area $\int (T - T_j)dt$ (C° min) gives the net temperature change due to thermal leakage during the test period. The corrected temperature rise as determined from Eq. (6) may then be used in the calorimeter relation, Eq. (5).

BOMB CALORIMETER

The quantity of heat released when unit mass of a fuel is completely burned is called the *heat of combustion* of the substance. In one form of fuel calorimeter the sample is burned in a metal bomb containing oxygen at some 25 atm pressure (Exp. 22). The sample is ignited electrically by a fuse wire. The heat evolved is transferred to the bomb and to the water in which it is immersed, in the calorimeter. The rise in temperature may be only several degrees and usually is measured by a mercury thermometer reading to hundredths of a degree, by a Beckmann thermometer, or by a resistance thermometer of small thermal capacity.

ANEROID CALORIMETERS

In an aneroid calorimeter, the substance whose change in temperature measures the heat is a solid, such as copper, silver, or platinum. The use of a solid calorimetric substance eliminates troubles associated with stirring and evaporation and permits measurements at very high or very low temperatures.

Calorimetry in furnaces is undertaken to obtain information about metals at high temperatures. The experimental difficulties in achieving an accuracy of even 1 per cent are considerable, for (a) useful materials of construction become less available at high temperatures, (b) it is harder to provide uniformity of temperature in the surroundings of the calorimeter, and (c) the rate of heat loss from the calorimeter increases rapidly with temperature.

Figure 10.4 represents a high-temperature vacuum calorimeter of the copper-block type. The five essential parts are: A, the copper block with a central hole into which the specimen is dropped; B, a guard system surrounding the block in order to control the heat loss from it; C, the furnace in which the specimen is heated to its initial temperature. Thermocouples are used to measure the initial temperature of the specimen in the upper furnace and the temperatures of the block A and its mantle. The whole apparatus operates inside the evacuated vessel D, and the external furnace E maintains the block and its immediate surroundings at the desired operating temperature.

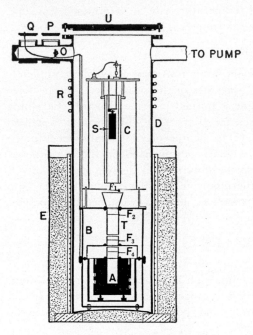

FIG. 10.4.   High-temperature vacuum calorimeter and furnace.

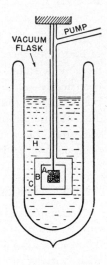

FIG. 10.5. Low-temperature adiabatic vacuum calorimeter.

The specimen S is heated in the upper furnace C. It is then dropped into the copper block to which it gives up heat until the two are in thermal equilibrium. The product of the thermal capacity of the copper block and its rise in temperature on the introduction of the specimen, together with a correction for the heat lost by the block during the attainment of equilibrium, is equal to the difference between the heat content of the specimen at its initial and final temperatures.

Measurements of specific heats at low temperatures are of particular theoretical interest. Figure 10.5 represents an adiabatic vacuum calorimeter of the type designed by Nernst and modified by Simon and Lang. The substance to be investigated is placed in a thin-walled copper vessel A. Inside of A are also a heating coil and a resistance thermometer. Surrounding A is a thermostat B equipped with a separate heating coil. Junctions of a differential thermocouple are placed in contact with A and B. By adjusting the heating currents to make the thermocouple indicate zero it is possible to keep $T_A = T_B$, and hence avoid heat loss.

The power supplied to the heating coil of A is EI. The temperature T is measured as a function of the time t. The value of dt/dT for any T can be evaluated from a graph of t vs. T. The heat capacity C_p for any temperature is given by

$$C_p = \left(\frac{\delta Q}{\delta T}\right)_p = \frac{EI}{J}\frac{dt}{dT} \qquad (8)$$

ICE CALORIMETER

In an ice calorimeter the heat to be measured is introduced into a mass of ice and the amount of ice melted is observed.[5] In Bunsen's

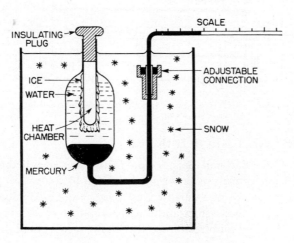

FIG. 10.6.   Bunsen ice calorimeter.

instrument, Fig. 10.6, the amount of melting is determined by volume. The heat liberated in the heat chamber melts some of the layer of ice.

This results in a definite contraction, indicated by motion of the mercury thread in the capillary tube.

The capillary scale may be calibrated by introducing known quantities of heat, conveniently by an electric heating coil, and noting the result.

STEAM CALORIMETER

The steam calorimeter developed by Joly[7] consists of an equal-arm balance each of whose pans has a second pan suspended below it by a wire extending downward into a steam chamber. If the lower pans are empty, equal amounts of steam condense on each. A test body is placed on a lower pan and weights are added to the opposite pan above to restore balance. When steam is admitted to the chamber the test body collects an amount of condensate corresponding to the heat required to raise the temperature of the body to that of the steam, and more weights must be added to restore balance. The thermal capacity of the test body may then be calculated from the mass of condensate and the known heat of vaporization of water.

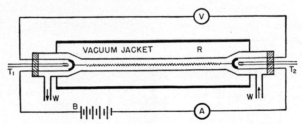

FIG. 10.7.   Callendar and Barnes continuous-flow
calorimeter.

ELECTRICAL CALORIMETER

In the Callendar and Barnes apparatus,[2] shown schematically in Fig. 10.7, an electric current is maintained in a resistance wire R placed along the axis of a narrow glass tube through which a constant stream of water flows. Inlet and outlet temperatures of the water are measured with platinum resistance thermometers. The flow of liquid and the electric current I are adjusted to give a rise in temperature ΔT of only a few degrees. From measurements of the power supplied, EI, and the mass of water m collected in a time t, the equation

$$EIt = Jmc\,\Delta T + Q' \tag{9}$$

can be used to calculate the specific heat c of the liquid, or the mechanical equivalent of heat, J. The term Q' represents the heat lost by radiation, etc. If the experiment is repeated with a different flow and a different current, but with the same ΔT, Q' will be the same in the two cases and can be eliminated from the corresponding equations.

This type of apparatus has been used to show that the specific heat of water is not constant but varies with the temperature, passing through a minimum value at about 38°C.

CONSTANT-FLOW GAS CALORIMETER

The heating value of a gaseous fuel can be measured by comparison with a standard source of heat in an apparatus of the type illustrated schematically in Fig. 10.8. When the thermometers 1 and 2 indicate

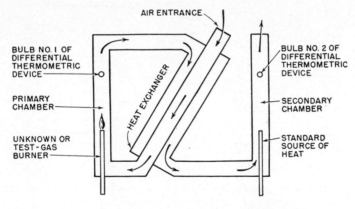

Fig. 10.8. A constant-flow thermal-balance calorimeter.

the same temperature, the test gas is producing heat at the same rate as the standard source. The latter may be an electric heater or a burner consuming gas of known heating value.

Such a thermal balance calorimeter obviates the necessity for measuring a temperature rise in the working substance. Being a null method, its accuracy is independent of the calibration of the temperature-measuring device. It compensates for heat losses, change in barometric pressure, room temperature, or specific heat of the working substance. The method is readily adaptable to recording and controlling the heating value of gases, and hence has considerable industrial importance.

RADIATION CALORIMETER

In one form of radiation calorimeter a small polished silver bulb is suspended in an evacuated enclosure with blackened walls that are kept at 0°C by an ice bath.   If the difference in temperature between

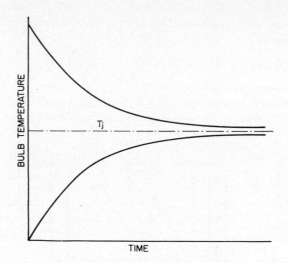

FIG. 10.9   Temperature-time plot for radiation calorimeter with bulb contents thermally inactive.

bulb and jacket is small, the bulb temperature T will approach the jacket temperature T_j in accord with Newton's law of thermal leakage

$$-\frac{dT}{dt} = \frac{k}{mc}(T - T_j) \tag{10}$$

in a manner indicated by the curves of Fig. 10.9.   If heat is evolved in the bulb at a steady rate, as by a radioactive material or a slow chemical reaction, the cooling or heating curve will approach an equilibrium temperature T_a higher than that of the jacket temperature, Fig. 10.10.   One way of determining the rate of heat production dQ/dt is to use the tangent dT/dt to the heating curve at the instant (point 0) when the temperature of the surface of the bulb is the same as that of the jacket, and solve the relation

$$dQ/dt = mc(dT/dt) \tag{11}$$

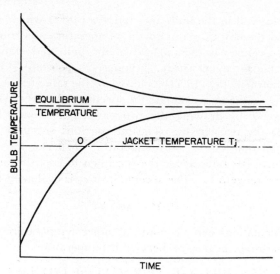

FIG. 10.10.   Temperature-time plot for radiation calorimeter with bulb contents thermally active.

Newton's law of thermal leakage does not apply when the temperature difference is made larger.   Still, the rate at which the bulb
radiates energy to the jacket is a function of the bulb temperature T.
One may determine and plot the value of this function for different
temperatures (Fig. 10.11a).   One way of doing this is to enclose a

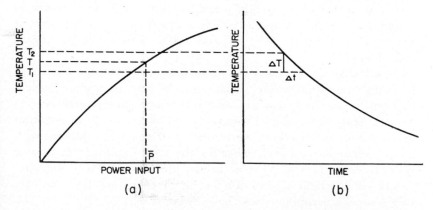

FIG. 10.11.   Curves for determination of specific heat by a radiation calorimeter.

small heating coil in the bulb and note the rate at which energy must
be supplied thereby to maintain the temperature at various constant
levels. A specimen is then placed in the bulb and allowed to cool
from the higher temperature, keeping T_j constant. The cooling
curve is shown in Fig. 10.11b, plotted to the same temperature scale
as curve (*a*). One may evaluate the specific heat c_p of the specimen at
temperature T by drawing the two parallel horizontal lines shown
intersecting the two curves. The intersections on curve (*a*) give an
average radiation rate $\bar{P}_t$ at temperature T. The intersections on
curve (*b*) give the time Δt for the specimen to cool through the same
temperature range ΔT. The specific heat c_p is evaluated from

$$\bar{P}_t \, \Delta t = m c_p \, \Delta T \tag{12}$$

Similar calculations can be made at other temperature intervals to
give the variation in specific heat with temperature.

RESISTANCE BRIDGE FOR CALORIMETRY

When the temperature measurements needed in calorimetry are
made with a resistance thermometer, a bridge designed for high precision is required. Designed primarily for calorimetry, the Mueller
bridge is a modification of the conventional Wheatstone network which
provides higher accuracy over a comparatively narrow range. Mueller
bridges increase the accuracy with which heats of combustion of
coals, gases, oils, and other fuels are determined by measuring temperature changes in calorimetry with an accuracy comparable to or
higher than that of the weight measurements. A Mueller bridge in
combination with a suitable resistance thermometer is capable of
greater accuracy between −190 and 500°C than any other means
available.

Slight changes in value occur in the resistors of a bridge when they
are subject to temperature variations. As used in routine testing,
unthermostated and without ambient temperature corrections, a
Mueller bridge is capable of measuring resistance changes of the order
of 0 to 0.6 ohm with a limit of error of ±0.0001 ohm. Equipped with
a constant temperature chamber for the most important measuring
resistors, the type G-2 Mueller bridge provides resistance measurements within a limit of error of a few hundred-thousandths of an ohm
or a few parts per million, whichever is larger.

The Mueller circuit (Fig. 10.12) is essentially that of a conventional

Wheatstone bridge. Decades A, B, D, E, F, and G comprise the measuring resistors; Q and Q_1 are ratio arms; L, the thermometer coil, is the resistance to be measured.

The construction of the measuring arm is distinctive in that the

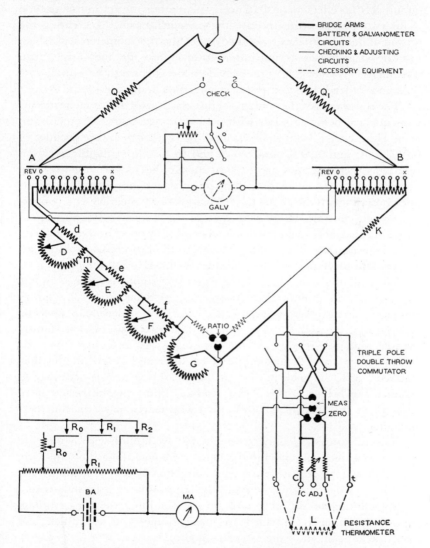

FIG. 10.12. Circuit of the type G-2 Mueller bridge.

1 and 0.1 ohm decades (A and B) are permanently connected in series with the galvanometer. These decades, at the ends of the ratio arms, have the effect of transferring resistance between the lower arms of the bridge and the galvanometer circuit. Resistance in the galvanometer circuit has no effect upon balance. Increasing the setting of decade A inserts resistance directly into the measuring arm. Increasing the setting of decade B takes resistance out of the thermometer arm which has the same effect as putting resistance into the measuring arm. Terminals "1 Check 2" are provided for checking the equality of resistance of leads between resistors and studs in decades A and B.

The resistances of the contacts of decades A and B are of negligible consequence, being in series with comparatively high resistance ratio arms Q and Q_1. Contact resistances in the three lowest decades of 0.01, 0.001, and 0.0001 ohm (D, E, and F) have a negligible effect on results as these decades are so constructed that a permanently connected resistor of low value is shunted by a comparatively high resistance in series with the contact. A low-resistance mercury-cup copper-bar switch controls the 10-ohm decade G. Leads to its resistors are equal in resistance, as are the leads from all resistors of decades A and B to their respective switch studs. Leads to the ratio resistors and leads to the ratio reversing points of decades A and B are also equal.

With all dials on zero, there exists a residual resistance in the measuring arm due to the construction of decades D, E, and F. Balanced against this residual is the resistance of decade B plus the resistance of the coil K. The sum of these two resistances is slightly greater than the residual of the measuring arm, so that when the thermometer arm is short-circuited by inserting a plug in the hole marked "zero," a small portion of the measuring arm is necessary to balance the bridge. This "zero reading" must be subtracted from subsequent measurements to obtain the true resistance of the thermometer.

The ratio arms Q and Q_1 are joined by a slide-wire S and are interchangeable. By moving the battery contact along the slide-wire, the ratio can be adjusted to an equality that is only limited by the sensitivity of the galvanometer and the adjustability of the slide-wire.

In addition to the plug position for obtaining the zero reading, another position is provided to make connections for quick and accurate adjustment of the ratio to equality.

To measure the resistance between the branch points of a four-terminal thermometer, that is, the resistance between the potential terminals of a thermometer provided with current and potential terminals, two readings are required. When the commutator is in the normal position, the battery supply lead is the one marked *c*. One balances the bridge with the lead *C* in the measuring arm, and both *L* and *T* in the measured arm. When the commutator is in the reversed position, the lead marked *t* becomes the battery supply lead, and the bridge is balanced with the lead *T* in the measuring arm, and both *L* and *C* in the measured arm. The average of the two balances, except for the correction for bridge zero, represents the resistance of *L*.

Important internal leads to the commutator are equal in resistance. The terminal *C Adj* is provided to be used in place of terminal *C* when the bridge leads to the thermometer element are not practically equal in resistance. A variable resistor in series with *C Adj* is then adjusted to equalize the resistance so that the two bridge readings, with the commutator normal and reversed, are nearly equal.

One to five dry cells in series, with resistors connected across them, provide the current. Three keys R_2, R_1, and R_0 tap off different potentials providing low, medium, and high sensitivity respectively. Currents provided by keys R_1 and R_0 are variable. When measuring, the current in the thermometer can be adjusted to the same value as that at which it was calibrated. Thermometer current is indicated on a milliammeter.

The switch and variable resistor in the galvanometer circuit provide adjustable series or parallel resistance for damping.

SUMMARY

Determination of the heating value of fuels and the specific heats of solids, liquids, and gases is based on calorimetry. Calorimetry is the measurement of heat quantities in terms of temperature changes, changes of state, or the transformation of electrical or mechanical energy into heat. Principal sources of error are the thermometer readings and heat losses. The latter are minimized by corrections from blank experiments, or in the method of mixtures by insuring adiabatic conditions. The temperature measuring instruments customarily used in calorimetry are, in order of accuracy: resistance thermometers, thermocouples, and mercury-in-glass thermometers.

REFERENCES FOR SUPPLEMENTARY READING

1. Aitchison, G. J., "Measurement by Induction Heating of the Temperature Variations of the Specific Heats of Ferromagnetic Materials," *J. Sci. Instruments*, **24**, 200 (1947).

2. Callendar, H. L., and H. T. Barnes, "Note on the Variation of the Specific Heat of Water Between 0°C and 100°C," *Phys. Rev.*, **10**, 202 (1900).
3. Carpenter, L. G., and A. R. Bryant, "A High-Temperature Vacuum Calorimeter of the Copper Block Type," *J. Sci. Instruments*, **16**, 183 (1939).
4. Gas Calorimeter Tables, *Nat. Bur. Standards*, Circular 417 (1938).
5. Ginnings, D. C., and R. J. Corruccini, "Improved Ice Calorimeter Developed," *J. Chem. Eng., News Edit.*, **25**, 1757 (1947).
6. Hyde, C. G., and F. E. Mills, *Gas Calorimetry*, London: E. Benn, 1932.
7. Joly, J., "On the Steam Calorimeter," *Proc. Roy. Soc.* (*London*), **A47**, 218 (1889–90).
8. Keffler, L. J. P., . . . "Adiabatic Bomb Calorimetry of High Precision," *J. Phys. Chem.*, **34**, 1006 (1930).
9. Keith, R. W., "A New Gas Calorimeter," *Mech. Eng.*, **58**, 225 (1936).
10. Osborne, N. S., H. F. Stimson, and D. C. Ginnings, "Heat Capacity and Heat of Vaporization of Water in the Range from 0°C to 100°C," *J. Research Nat. Bur. Standards*, **23**, 197 (1939).
    "Thermal Properties of Saturated Water and Steam," *J. Research Nat. Bur. Standards*, **23**, 261 (1939).
11. Powell, R. W., "History of the British Thermal Unit," *Nature*, **149**, 525 (1942).
12. Swietoslawski, W., *Microcalorimetry*, Reinhold Publishing Corp., 1946.
13. Washburn, E. W., "Calorimetric Method for Determining the Intrinsic Energy of a Gas as a Function of Pressure," *Bur. Standards J. Research*, **9**, 521 (1932).
14. White, W. P., *The Modern Calorimeter*, Chemical Catalog Co., 1928.

QUESTIONS AND PROBLEMS

1. What distinctions are made among the terms calorie, specific heat, thermal capacity, and water equivalent?

2. How is it possible for a gas to possess a great number of specific heats?

3. Would a Joly steam calorimeter be a suitable apparatus for determining the specific heat at constant volume c_v of a gas? Explain.

4. Explain the usefulness of the concept of "water equivalent" as used in calorimetry. Would it be equally convenient to know the water equivalent of the metal parts of a calorimeter that employed Silicone fluid instead of water as the thermometric liquid?

5. Construct a chart showing the conversion of 1 erg, 1 joule, 1 cal, 1 ft-lb, and 1 Btu of energy into each of the other four units.

6. Given a standard sample of benzoic acid whose heat of combustion is known (6320 cal/gm), how could this material be used to determine the water equivalent of an oxygen bomb calorimeter?

7. Discuss Newton's law of cooling from the standpoint of its derivation, range of validity, and practical usefulness.

8. The quantity k/mc in Eq. (7) has the units of reciprocal seconds or minutes. Give a physical interpretation of this quantity.

9. Show that the equilibrium temperature T_a for a calorimeter is given by

$$T_a = T_j + \frac{mc}{k} \left(\frac{dT}{dt} \right)_s$$

10. Show that the equation for the after interval of a calorimeter is

$$T - T_a = (T_0 - T_a)e^{-\frac{k}{mc}t}$$

where T_0 is the initial value of T, and T_a is the equilibrium temperature.

11. When 2.00 lb of brass at 212°F are placed in 5.00 lb of water at 35.0°F, the resulting temperature is 41.2°F. Find the specific heat of brass.

12. Assuming a constant specific heat, what weight of liquid at 45°C and what weight of the same liquid at 15°C must be mixed to obtain 1000 gm at 36°C?
Ans. 700 gm, 300 gm.

13. Sixty grams of liquid A, having specific heat of 0.45 cal/(gm C°), at 30°C are mixed with M grams of liquid B, having specific heat 0.25 cal/(gm C°), at 10°C. The final temperature of the mixture is 20°C. Find M.

14. A 500-gm calorimeter vessel is made of aluminum; its specific heat is 0.212 cal/(gm C°). What is the water equivalent of the vessel?   *Ans.* 106 gm.

15. A calorimeter contains 2000 gm of water and has a total water equivalent of 2500 gm. A certain combustion reaction carried out in the calorimeter results in a temperature rise of 7.24 F°. What temperature rise would the same amount of heat produce if the calorimeter contained 2000 gm of ethylene glycol, specific heat 0.528 cal/(gm C°), instead of water?

16. A 450-gm cylinder of copper is used as the sensitive element of an aneroid calorimeter (Fig. 10.4). The heat imparted raises the temperature of the copper from 185 to 204°C, while the jacket heater is adjusted to follow the temperature of the copper throughout the change. Taking the specific heat of copper as 0.102 cal/(gm C°) in this range, calculate the heat imparted.   *Ans.* 872 cal.

17. To find the water equivalent of a calorimeter vessel and its accessories, sheet copper weighing 98.2 gm and having a temperature of 98.0°C is dropped into the vessel, which contains 245.3 gm of water at 19.5°C. The temperature rises to 22.3°C. Compute the water equivalent of the vessel, assuming no heat losses and taking the specific heat of copper as 0.092 cal/(gm C°).

18. When 5.6 gm of alcohol at 26.4°C are placed in a Bunsen ice calorimeter the change in scale reading indicates that 1.11 gm of ice are thereby melted. Calculate the specific heat of alcohol.   *Ans.* 0.60 cal/(gm C°).

19. Water enters a continuous flow calorimeter 5 C° below room temperature and emerges 5 C° above room temperature. What must have been the power input, in watts, if the water flowed at 300 gm/min?

Chapter 11

|||||||||||||||||||||||||

PHASE DIAGRAMS,
THERMAL ANALYSIS

THE PHASE RULE |||||| *COOLING CURVES* ||||||
DETERMINATION OF TEMPERATURE-
COMPOSITION DIAGRAMS ||||||

GIBBS' PHASE RULE

The progress of physical science is marked by a multitude of isolated experiments and the rarer synthesis of their results into laws or theories that unify whole fields of the science. One of the monuments of nineteenth century scientific activity was the treatise by Josiah Willard Gibbs, "On the Equilibrium of Heterogeneous Substances." In it he formulated the phase rule which deals with systems in equilibrium. It is usually expressed by the formula

$$F = C + 2 - P \tag{1}$$

showing the relations existing between the degree of freedom F of the system, the number of components C, and the number of phases P.

To understand the phase rule and its application it is necessary and sufficient to have an accurate understanding of the meaning of the terms employed in its statement. A *system* is that part of the physical world being considered. It may be separated from its surroundings by definite boundaries, or the boundaries may be imaginary.

A system is said to be in *equilibrium* when the net rate of any possible

190

chemical changes within it is zero and there is an absence of molecular transformations (changes of state or allotropic changes). A system in equilibrium cannot alter with time without gain or loss of energy. In thermodynamic terms, its free energy is a minimum or its entropy a maximum. The phase rule is often applied also to systems whose free energy is not a minimum, but whose properties do not change appreciably during the time of observation.

The *phases*[1] of a system refer to its homogeneous parts separated from one another by definite physical boundaries. Mechanically separable parts of a system are called phases if one of them, or some of its constituents, can become part of another in a reversible way. Water, ice, and vapor, for example, are phases possible in the water system. It is apparent that phases are necessarily elements, gaseous mixtures, chemical compounds, or solutions.

We speak of a *change of state* whenever there has occurred a change of pressure, or of temperature, or of some other state-defining variable, no matter how small that change may be. A *change of phase*, however, refers to a more fundamental change, as from a liquid to a vapor, or a change from one crystalline form to another.

The *components* of a system are the chemical substances required to make the phases in any quantity in which they may be present. The choice of the independent components of a system is somewhat arbitrary. The number of independent components of a system is the smallest number of independently variable constituents from which the phases can be made in any relative quantities. That is, the number of independent components equals the total number of components minus the number of equations existing among the components. The *number of components* of a system is understood to mean the number of independent components.

By the *degree of freedom*, or variance, of a system is meant the number of variables which may be arbitrarily changed without disturbing the equilibrium of the system. The variables commonly considered in defining the state of a system are composition, temperature, and pressure.

As a simple example, apply the phase rule to the system of ice and water in equilibrium. It is a one component system. From Eq. (1), the degree of freedom is $1 + 2 - 2 = 1$. If it is decided to hold the system at a given temperature, the pressure is determined, and vice versa. The phase rule applied to a system of ice, water, and vapor gives a variance of zero. The presence of three phases in a system of one component fixes both the temperature and the pressure. Only at the triple point and under the vapor pressure of ice can all three phases exist in equilibrium.

Consider further the equilibrium system represented by

$$CaCO_3 \rightleftarrows CaO + CO_2 \tag{2}$$

There are, in all, three components related by one equation. Hence the number of independent components is two. These may be chosen as any of the following pairs: CaO and CO_2; CaO and $CaCO_3$; or CO_2 and $CaCO_3$. The degree of freedom is: $2 - 3 + 2 = 1$. Hence for a given temperature, the CO_2 has a definite pressure, independent of the quantities of the substances. If the reaction is carried out in an atmosphere of N_2, then the total number of components is four and the degrees of freedom two. Then for a definite temperature, the pressure of CO_2 can have any value. Whether the partial pressure of CO_2 is independent of the total pressure is a question for experiment; it is not determined by the phase rule.

DEDUCTION OF THE PHASE RULE

The deduction of the phase rule consists in finding the total number of variables which may determine the properties of a system and in subtracting from this the number of independent equations connecting those variables.[9] Thus the number of variables whose values must be specified to determine completely the properties of the system is found.

A distinction is made between extensive and intensive properties, and the phase rule is based upon this distinction.[9] *Extensive* properties depend on mass. Volume, weight, energy, and thermal capacity are examples of extensive properties. *Intensive* properties are independent of mass. Temperature, pressure, concentration, density, molal volume, and dielectric constant are examples of intensive properties.

In a *homogeneous* system consisting of two identical parts, the intensive properties have the same value for the parts and for the total system. The value of an extensive property of the total system, however, is twice its value for either part.

In a *heterogeneous* system we speak of an intensive property only if it is defined for each phase and has the same value for each. Any sum of extensive properties of the phases is an extensive property of the system. All properties can be expressed by means of intensive and extensive properties.

We can express all properties of a single phase by means of intensive properties and one extensive property, for example its weight. We can therefore completely describe a system of P phases by a number of intensive properties and P extensive properties.

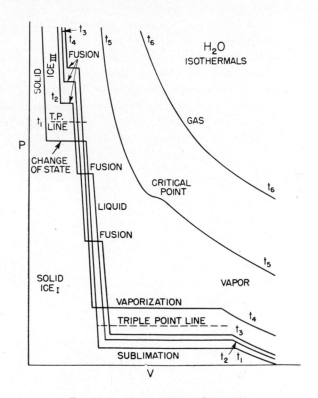

FIG. 11.1. A p-v diagram for water.

The number of independent variables which determine the equilibrium state of a system can be deduced from a construction of the system. Consider an example. We may take 100 gm of water, 5 gm of sulfuric acid, and 1 gm of benzene, all at 15°C, pour them into a 2-l flask, and insulate the flask. We have specified the amounts of the three independent components, their energy, and the volume.

These five variables are independent; if any one is changed the result will be a different system.

The phase rule is derivable from the basic assumption that this description completely defines the system in its final equilibrium state. This means that the properties of the equilibrium system will be the same regardless of the order of mixing the components, the shape of the flask, its elevation above sea level, etc. Thus we assume that the system is described by $C + 2$ variables, where C is the number of independent components.

The system can also be described by P extensive variables and a number of intensive variables. Hence there must be $F = C + 2 - P$ *independent* intensive properties. There cannot be more, because P of the $C + 2$ independent variables are extensive variables. Hence the number of degrees of freedom F is the number of intensive variables that can be arbitrarily changed while P phases are present.

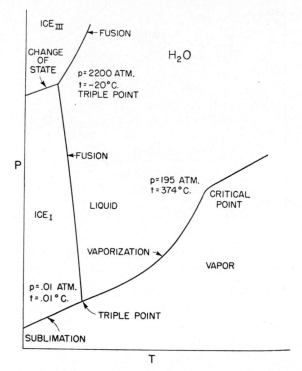

FIG. 11.2.   A p-T diagram for water.

The phase rule is essentially a qualitative relation. To be of practical utility, the phase rule must be extended by experimental data to give quantitative information about a system. Such information is conveniently represented graphically in what are called equilibrium diagrams, phase diagrams, or phase rule diagrams.

GRAPHICAL REPRESENTATION OF PHASES

For convenience in representing phases and phase phenomena in two-dimensional graphs, the familiar *p-v* and *p-T* diagrams, shown

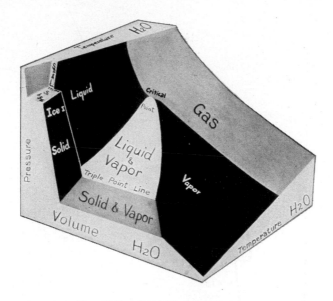

FIG. 11.3. A *p-v-T* surface for water.

for water in Figs. 11.1 and 11.2, are much used. For a more complete representation we may combine this information by constructing a three-dimensional *p-v-T* surface. This has been done for water in Fig. 11.3. Viewed parallel to the *T*-axis, Fig. 11.3 appears as a *p-v* diagram (Fig. 11.1); viewed parallel to the *v*-axis, it appears as a *p-T* diagram (Fig. 11.2). A constant pressure curve is shown in the *T-v* diagram of Fig. 11.4. In none of these figures are the variables plotted to scale, but rather a large range of values is represented qualitatively.

PHASE DIAGRAMS FOR BINARY ALLOYS

For metallic systems the effect of pressure is not important, and a two-dimensional temperature-composition diagram suffices to describe the conditions of equilibrium in the system. The vapor phase is omitted since the vapor pressure of metals is usually negligible.

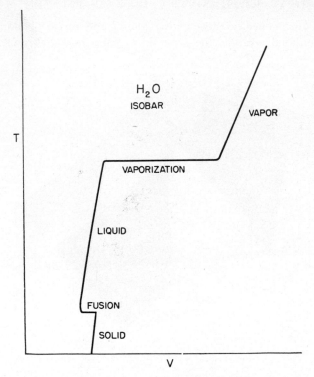

FIG. 11.4.   A T-v diagram for water.

Figure 11.5 is a temperature-composition diagram for the Cd-Bi system. At the side, Fig. 11.6, are examples of cooling curves for different compositions of the Cd-Bi alloy. Consider an alloy of 25 per cent Cd which has been heated well above its melting point and allowed to cool. The cooling may be represented by the temperature-time curve B of Fig. 11.6, or by the dotted line fg in Fig. 11.5. At 180°, Bi will begin to solidify from the melt, changing the rate of cooling. The remaining liquid will become richer in Cd, the point representing its composition following along curve *hze*. Point *e*, called the *eutectic* point, represents the lowest melting composition of the alloy. When the eutectic composition is reached and the temperature still further lowered, a liquid phase is no longer possible and the remaining liquid

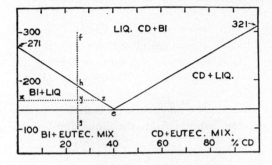

FIG. 11.5. Cd-Bi equilibrium diagram.

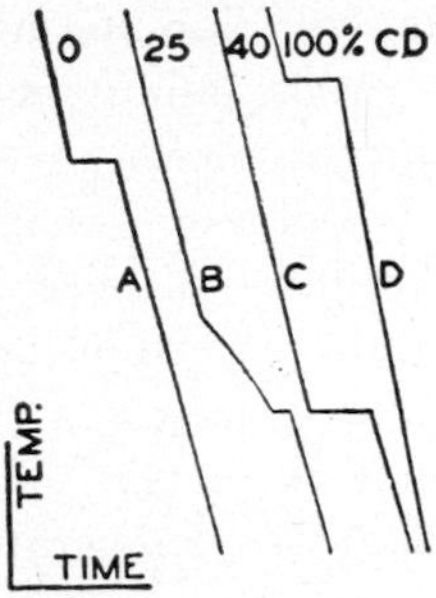

FIG. 11.6. Cd-Bi cool-
ing curves.

freezes at a definite temperature (140°C) and composition (40 per cent Cd). This is an exothermic change resulting in a pause in the cooling curve *B*, Fig. 11.6.

The Sn-Pb equilibrium diagram is shown in Fig. 11.7. The areas at the side of Fig. 11.7 represent the existence of solid solutions in

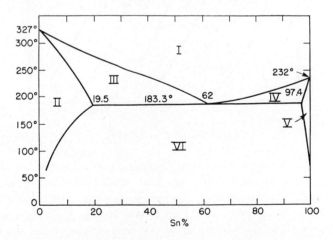

FIG. 11.7. Sn-Pb equilibrium diagram.

the lead-rich and tin-rich alloys, respectively. A *solid solution* is a homogeneous crystalline phase containing both components, but in indefinite proportions (not in atomic or molecular ratios as in a compound). Some substances form solid solutions in all proportions, just as some liquids mix in all proportions. Other substances have only limited solubility in each other.

It is important to distinguish between a solid solution and a eutectic mixture. A solid solution is a single crystal containing two kinds of atoms or molecules. It is one phase. A eutectic mixture is a mixture of pure crystals of each component. These often solidify in alternate thin layers or plates, and are separable. Hence there is no such thing as a "eutectic phase." The *eutectic mixture* is that intimate mixture of two solid phases that solidify from the liquid of lowest solidifying temperature.

COOLING CURVES

Temperature-time curves, usually taken during cooling, provide an important method for studying phase changes in metals and alloys and for measuring specific and latent heats. Any change in state or

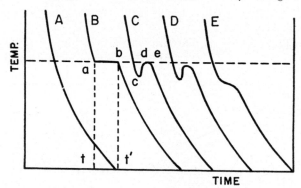

Fig. 11.8.   Cooling curves.

constitution is accompanied by an energy change which is revealed by heat evolution during cooling or heat absorption during heating. When a body cools without such change occurring, its cooling curve has the logarithmic form of *A*, Fig. 11.8. If the specimen is molten metal, regular cooling is arrested by the heat evolved when the metal solidifies. If no undercooling occurs, the cooling curve has the form of *B*. However, the beginning of solidification is always accompanied by some undercooling. Nuclei do not become sufficiently stable to serve as starting points for crystallization until the melt is cooled to a temperature lower than the highest temperature at which solidification can occur. Actual cooling curves for pure metals resemble curve *C*.

The exact form of curve obtained after freezing begins depends on the relation between the rate of removal of heat from the cooling metal and the rate of evolution of heat of crystallization. The time $t_1 - t_2$ required to abstract a given amount of heat depends on the rate of cooling.

The rate of evolution of heat (rate of solidification) does not always keep pace with the rate of abstraction of heat. Solidification begins below T_1, as at point *c* in curve *C*. If there is no limit on the rate of solidification, other than that *T* cannot exceed T_1, then the heat evolved will raise *T* to T_1 and keep it there during the solidifying process (giving *cde*, curve *C*). If, however, there exists some limitation on the rate of solidification, conditions are different. It actually appears that for each temperature below the freezing point a definite maximum rate of solidification exists. This is comparatively small at the freezing point, increases to a maximum, then decreases as the temperature is lowered. Hence for rapid cooling the temperature after undercooling may not reach T_1, giving a curve of the form *D*.

In the ideal case, the temperature of the metal will remain constant during melting and freezing, with the result that the portions of the curves *AB* and *A'B'* (Fig. 11.9), respectively, will be flat and parallel to the time axis. The ideal curve is further characterized by a discontinuous change of slope, rather than by a gradual change, as shown.

In the actual case, however, only a part of the cooling curve will be flat, and this part of the heating curve will usually have greater obliquity than the freezing curve. Because of this, freezing point determinations are considered more reliable. For practical purposes, they may be considered equal to melting points.

The reason for obliquity and its existence to a greater degree in the heating curves is due partly to conditions relating to equipment and technique employed in obtaining data. When a crucible of metal is uniformly heated in a furnace, a temperature gradient exists between the walls of the furnace and the crucible. The metal in immediate contact with the crucible is the first to melt, and during the process of melting, the heat necessary for fusion is supplied by the walls of the crucible and the remaining solid metal. The melted outside layer of metal then tends to remain at fairly constant temperature. The temperature-measuring instrument, located in the center of the charge, measures the temperature of the solid metal and, since heat is being abstracted from this portion of the charge, the rate at which the inside temperature increases is greatly diminished with the result of a rounding off of the curve.

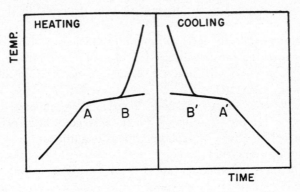

Fig. 11.9.   Heating and cooling curves for a pure metal.

As the metal progressively melts inward, the temperature of the center metal rises slowly.   When the metal surrounding the thermocouple melts, the temperature remains fairly constant for a short interval of time and indicates the true melting point, as represented by point *B* in Fig. 11.9.   While the center of the charge is melting, the temperature of the outside layer of molten metal rises rapidly, owing to the heat supplied from the furnace walls.   A large temperature gradient is thus established between the outside and the center of the charge.   This temperature gradient promotes rapid melting of the metal and, if the remaining solid metal is unevenly distributed about the thermocouple, causes the temperature readings to increase, resulting in another rounding off of the curve.   The degree of obliquity at the beginning and at the end of melting depends to a great extent on the sensitivity of the temperature-measuring instrument and, of course, on the coordinate scales used in plotting.   In addition, the obliquity is governed by such factors as the size and wall thickness of the crucible, the amount of metal constituting the charge, and the rate at which the charge is heated. It may be diminished by slow heating and a small amount of charge.

Upon cooling of the molten metal, a temperature gradient exists between the crucible and the walls of the furnace. The metal in immediate contact with the walls of the crucible is the first to solidify, forming an isothermal layer, which decreases the temperature difference between the center and the outside of the charge. This, in effect, decreases the rate at which the temperature falls at the center of the charge, thereby causing a rounding off of the first part of the cooling curve. During the freezing of the center of the charge, the solid outside layer of metal drops in temperature, thus increasing the temperature gradient between the center and outside portions of the charge. The freezing of the last traces of liquid metal is thereby accelerated, with the result that the last part of the curve is rounded off.

It is evident, therefore, that the first part of the approximately flat portion of the cooling curve and the latter part of the flat portion of the heating curve indicate the true freezing and melting points, respectively. Whenever considerable obliquity is present, the true temperature of freezing may be obtained by extrapolating the straight portion of the cooling curve and noting at what temperature the constructed straight line deviates from the original curve. In like manner, the true melting temperature may be obtained from the heating curve. This method of extrapolation is shown at points B and B', respectively, in Fig. 11.9. In general, cooling curves are more sharply defined than heating curves of the same metal, and are, therefore, more frequently used to obtain transformation data.

There are four principal ways of recording cooling curve data in thermal analysis.

Direct cooling curves, while easy to obtain and to interpret, have several disadvantages. They become progressively less steep, and hence less sensitive to heat changes, as the temperature of the specimen falls. It is difficult to detect transformations that involve small heat changes. In practice the time required for the stabilization of conditions following a major heat effect in the specimen makes it difficult to detect any small heat effects that may occur only a few degrees lower.

Inverse rate curves are obtained by plotting as ordinates the temperature, and as abscissas the time required for the temperature to fall through successive equal intervals (of the order of 2 to 5°). Merica has suggested a method of obtaining the time intervals with two stop watches. One is stopped and the other started at the end of each time interval. During each time interval, it is thus possible to record the length of the preceding interval.

Differential curves are obtained with the metal sample cooling beside another body known to undergo no phase changes in the temperature range investigated. The temperature of the metal under test is plotted against the difference in temperature between it and the inert sample. If no changes involving latent heat effects occur, the curve is a vertical line. But if such changes occur, cooling is delayed and the curve departs from the vertical.

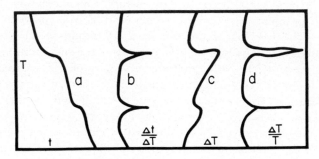

Fig. 11.10. Cooling curves: (a) direct; (b) inverse rate;
(c) differential; (d) derived differential.

Derived differential curves have temperature plotted against the slope at each point of the curve showing the difference in temperature for the two samples.

These four methods of recording cooling data are illustrated in Fig. 11.10, which shows their relative sensitivity in locating transition points.

EXPERIMENTAL METHOD

The furnace for obtaining thermal data should be capable of heating the charge uniformly to the highest temperature required and should be so insulated that the specimen may be allowed to cool at a moderate, uniform rate. A satisfactory rate of cooling is about 2 C°/min from 10 C° above the melting point, and the flat portion of the curve should extend a distance equivalent to about 10 min on the time axis. Furnaces that are neither properly designed nor sufficiently insulated will result in a non-uniform rate of cooling. This will affect the shape of the curve and may introduce irregularities that will mask important transformation points.

In the preparation of the charge, if the metal is to be heated for the first time, it should be broken into small pieces, placed in a crucible of the proper size and composition, and heated approximately 10 C° beyond the melting point. The surface of the molten metal, except when it is nickel, should be covered with a layer of graphite to prevent oxidation of the metal. Small amounts of oxide in a test metal such as in copper, may appreciably alter the shape of the cooling curve and indicate the occurrence of transformations at temperatures lower than normal for the pure metal.

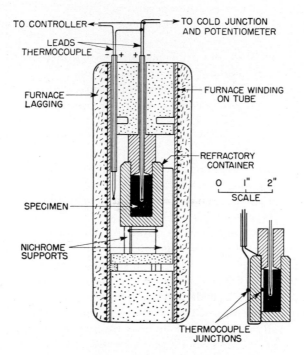

FIG. 11.11.   Furnace for thermal analysis.

The selection of a crucible that is to hold the charge is of considerable importance.   For most metals, crucibles composed of Acheson graphite are found satisfactory.   At high temperatures the gases formed from its oxidation provide a reducing atmosphere which, in addition to the powdered graphite, protects the surface of the molten metal. Metals—such as iron and nickel—that react with graphite at high temperatures should be melted in crucibles composed of magnesia or alumina, or mixtures of the two.

Accurate results are obtained only when the metal melt and the thermocouple wires are protected from contamination. The molten metal may be protected as described above, and the thermocouple by means of a suitable protecting tube. For low-temperature work, up to approximately 500°C, pyrex tubing, sealed at one end, serves very well. The use of porcelain or quartz protecting tubes is recommended for higher temperatures and with all metals except aluminum, which readily attacks silica at high temperatures. Above 1100°C protection tubes having a composition approximating that of sillimanite are available.

Figure 11.11 illustrates a furnace for thermal analysis whose temperature may be maintained a constant amount above or below the specimen temperature. This apparatus not only provides conventional cooling curves, but also permits quantitative measurements of specific heats and latent heats.[10] Another advantage is that it makes possible the detection of any small heat effect at a temperature only a few degrees below that at which a major effect has occurred. (With the conventional differential-thermocouple analysis method, sufficient stabilization after a large heat effect for the detection of a small one may not occur until the furnace has reached a temperature as much as 30 to 50 C° from that at which the large effect occurred.)

The specimen is placed in an insulating refractory container across which a constant temperature gradient is automatically maintained by the use of a differential thermocouple and a controller. Two ways of connecting the differential couple are shown in Fig. 11.11. Heat flow to the sample depends only on the constants of the container, which may be determined by the use of a sample of known specific heat. The time taken to cool or heat through a given temperature interval (after correction from a blank experiment) is directly proportional to the heat capacity of the sample, and the duration of the arrest is directly proportional to the latent heat. The method of control eliminates accelerated cooling following prolonged arrests and provides a simple way of obtaining a constant cooling rate at all temperatures.

These advantages may be increased by substituting for the refractory container of Fig. 11.11 two concentric nichrome cylinders inside of which is placed a very thin-walled crucible, say, of graphite. Alumel wires welded to the nichrome cylinders form multi-junction thermocouples for controlling the temperature difference between the cylinders.

Methods of thermal analysis have been applied to specimens as small as 0.1 gm. The samples are sealed in silica tubes, and difference curves obtained with a thermopile used in a high-temperature, thermostated furnace.[4]

MAGNETIC, ELECTRIC, AND MECHANICAL CHANGES

The methods of thermal analysis so far described are primarily for use in determining transformations of state that are accompanied by marked thermal changes. Their sensitiveness depends to a great extent upon the rate of heating and cooling, and, because of this, they fail in detecting transformations in solid solubilities with constituents having slow reaction rates. Furthermore, the quantitative comparison of reaction rates is delicate and when the speed varies between wide limits, it is practically impossible to study the phenomenon by ordinary thermal methods.

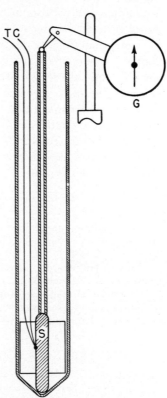

Fortunately other methods are available. Transformations which occur in many metals and alloys, most notably in steel, can be detected by quenching a series of specimens from temperatures progressively nearer the transformation temperature and noting the progress of the change, as made apparent in the microstructure. This method is of special value in determining solid-solubility lines or studying conditions where it is difficult to obtain true equilibrium. One serious difficulty, however, is encountered in this method. Certain structural

FIG. 11.12. Differential dilatometer.

changes may take place during the time required to remove the specimen from the high temperature zone of the furnace to the quenching medium.

Transformations occur in steel that are accompanied by changes in magnetic susceptibility. These changes can be determined by a circuit which responds to a variation in magnetic flux in the specimen. The transformations thus determined are then correlated with temperature (Exp. 28).

In most metals the transformations occurring in the solid state are accompanied by an expansion or contraction. An example is the contraction that occurs in iron at about 910°C as its crystal structure changes from body-centered to face-centered with rise in temperature. A dilatometer is used to magnify the small dimensional changes so that they can be read or recorded.

The principle of a dilatometer is illustrated by Fig. 11.12. The sample S is supported in a quartz tube Q and a quartz rod transmits any change in the length of the sample to a sensitive dial indicator G. The measurements give the differential expansion of the quartz and the sample. From a knowledge of the expansion coefficient of quartz, the expansion of the specimen can be determined. The particular apparatus illustrated was designed to permit measurements of expansion coefficients from −180 to 600°C rather than to provide information on high-temperature transformations.

SUMMARY

Gibbs' phase rule states that for a C-component system the number of intensive variables that can be arbitrarily changed while P phases are present is $F = C + 2 - P$.

Plots of temperature against time permit detection of phase changes and measurement of specific heats, heat of fusion, and heat of vaporization.

Equilibrium diagrams, constructed from cooling curve data, describe equilibrium states of a system. For many metallic and ceramic systems two-dimensional temperature-composition diagrams are useful.

REFERENCES FOR SUPPLEMENTARY READING

1. Antonoff, G., "What Is a Phase?," *J. Chem. Education*, **21**, 195 (1944).
2. Am. Soc. Testing Materials, "Recommended Practice for Thermal Analysis of Steel," *ASTM Standards*, pp. 806–9 (1936).
3. Brescia, F., "The Critical Temperature," *J. Chem. Education*, **24**, 123 (1947).

4. Brown, W. E. L., "Micro-Apparatus for Temperature-Time Curves, and a High-Temperature Thermostat," *J. Sci. Instruments*, **16**, 195 (1939).
5. Carpenter, H., and J. M. Robertson, *Metals*, Oxford University Press, 1939, (2 vol.).
6. Kehl, G. L., *The Principles of Metallographic Laboratory Practice*, p. 359, McGraw-Hill Book Co., Inc., 1939.
7. Millard, E. B., *Physical Chemistry for Colleges*, pp. 328–353, McGraw-Hill Book Co., Inc., 1936.
8. National Research Council, *International Critical Tables.* . . , Vol. II, pp. 400–455, McGraw-Hill Book Co., Inc., 1927.
9. Redlich, O., "On the Phase Rule," *J. Chem. Education*, **22**, 265 (1945).
10. Smith, C. S., "A Simple Method of Thermal Analysis Permitting Quantitative Measurements of Specific and Latent Heats," *Am. Inst. Mining Met. Eng., Tech. Pub.*, No. **1100**, 9 (1939).

QUESTIONS AND PROBLEMS

1. What assumptions are made in the statement of Gibbs' phase rule which in principle limit its applications? When can these limitations be relaxed in practice?

2. Sketch an apparatus which might be used to determine the vaporization curve for water, Fig. 11.2.

3. The vapor pressure of arsenic may not be small compared with atmospheric pressure at elevated temperatures. Would this fact influence the way one might draw phase diagrams for alloys containing arsenic?

4. A Cd-Bi alloy is in a state represented by point *e* in Fig. 11.5. What is the maximum number of phases that may be present? the minimum number?

5. A Cd-Bi solution is cooled below its freezing temperature. What phase or phases are formed?

6. Identify the phases represented by each of the areas in the Pb-Sn diagram (Fig. 11.7).

7. Draw qualitative examples of the cooling curves (temperature *vs* time) that would be obtained by cooling Pb-Sn alloys of the following compositions: (a) pure Pb, (b) pure Sn, (c) 62 per cent Sn, (d) 85 per cent Sn. Refer to Fig. 11.7.

8. A Pb-Sn alloy of 10 per cent Sn is cooled from 350 to 0°C. Indicate all transitions that occur and the temperatures at which they occur.

9. How might the equilibrium diagram of a ternary alloy be represented by contour lines drawn in an equilateral triangle?

10. The melting points of pure metals often are used to calibrate thermocouples and other temperature measuring devices. What precautions should be observed in this method of calibration to insure reproducible results?

11. Gold (m.p. 1063°C) and thallium (m.p. 300°C) form no compounds or solid solutions. The eutectic composition is 28 per cent Au, and the eutectic temperature 120°C. Draw a phase diagram, indicating phases present in each field. Draw cooling curves showing the behavior of melts containing 0, 10, 28, and 75 per cent Au.

12. Bismuth (m.p. 271°C) and tellurium (m.p. 450°C) form a compound Bi_2Te_3 (m.p. 580°C) containing 48 per cent Te by weight.   No solid solutions form.   The two eutectic temperatures are 370°C and 253°C for 15 and 98.8 per cent Bi respectively.   Draw an equilibrium diagram and letter its fields.   What would happen at 400°C if Te were added gradually to Bi, assuming equilibrium to be maintained at all times?

Chapter 12

IIIIIIIIIIIIIIIIIIIIIIIIIIIII

THERMODYNAMICS

FIRST AND SECOND LAWS OF THERMODY-
NAMICS IIIIIIIII *SPECIFIC HEATS* IIIIIIIII *HUMIDITY*
IIIIIIIII *THERMODYNAMIC EFFICIENCY* IIIIIIIII
ABSOLUTE TEMPERATURE SCALES IIIIIIIII

SCOPE OF THERMODYNAMICS

When the temperature of a body is raised, many different kinds of change may take place. Gases expand, liquids and solids usually expand, the electrical resistance of a conductor increases or decreases, thermocouples develop an emf, and many other physical and chemical phenomena occur. *Thermodynamics* is primarily the study of the energy relations and the sense in which change occurs in such processes that involve a flow of heat and the performance of work. Starting from the very general first and second laws of thermodynamics, we can derive practical relations about a particular system that are independent of detailed assumptions about atomic structure or the exact mechanism by which energy is exchanged. Despite its simplicity and generality, thermodynamics has the limitation of giving quantitative information only for systems in equilibrium, and of predicting certain relations between measurable properties but not numerical values.

Statistical mechanics deals with the motion of each particle of the substance and how these motions lead to the observable, large-scale properties. For example, how do the motions and collisions of gas

209

molecules produce a pressure at a wall?   Statistical mechanics is more detailed and somewhat more complicated than thermodynamics. Like thermodynamics, it is limited to the treatment of systems in equilibrium.

Kinetic theory treats of the rates of atomic and molecular processes by fairly direct means, without much benefit of general principles. It is superior to statistical mechanics and to thermodynamics in just two respects: it makes use of only well-known elementary methods and it can handle problems (such as reaction rates) relating to systems not in equilibrium.

Our concern with thermodynamics will be limited here to these practical questions.   What are the logical steps in defining an absolute temperature scale?   How can measurements made with a gas thermometer be reduced to the thermodynamic temperature scale?   What methods are effective in attaining temperatures approaching absolute zero?   How can we determine these temperatures?

FIRST LAW OF THERMODYNAMICS

When heat is added to a substance, the internal energy increases. If at the same time, the substance is allowed to perform external work, by expanding, for example, the total heat Q required will be the heat necessary to change the internal energy by an amount ΔU plus the heat equivalent to the external work W performed

$$Q = \Delta U + W \qquad\qquad (1)$$

The first law of thermodynamics states that when heat is transformed into any other form of energy, or when other forms of energy are transformed into heat, the total amount of energy (heat plus other forms) in the system is constant.   The experiments of Count Rumford[14] (1798), James Prescott Joule[9] (1849), and others led to this law.   The accepted value of the *mechanical equivalent of heat* is 4.185 joules/cal. By extension to apply to interchanges of all forms of energy it has become the law of the conservation of energy.

The principle of the conservation of energy has been seriously questioned only in atomic phenomena.[12]   With the discovery of the disintegration of radioactive elements, calorimetric experiments were performed to show that energy is conserved even in radioactivity. More recently it has been found expedient to invent a new particle, the elusive neutrino, to balance the energy equation in certain nuclear processes.

Nineteenth-century physics recognized three separate *conservation laws* expressing the constancy of the *mass*, the *momentum*, and the *energy* of an isolated system. Einstein introduced a far-reaching generalization: the equivalence of mass and energy. "Every quantity of energy U of any form whatever represents a mass m, which is equal to this same energy divided by c^2, where c is the speed of light, and every quantity of energy in motion represents momentum."

$$U = mc^2 \tag{2}$$

Bohr extended Planck's quantum hypothesis for blackbody radiation to apply to the radiant energy emitted by an atom when its internal energy diminishes by an amount U

$$U = h\nu \tag{3}$$

where ν is the frequency and h is Planck's constant.

THERMODYNAMIC PROCESSES

A process that takes place at constant temperature is called an *isothermal* process. For an ideal gas expanding isothermally the general gas law becomes

$$pV = MRT = \text{constant} \tag{4}$$

A process that takes place without transfer of heat to or from the substance is called *adiabatic*. The pressure and volume of a gas undergoing an adiabatic change are related by the equation

$$pV^\gamma = \text{constant} \tag{5}$$

where γ is the ratio of the specific heats c_p/c_v, whose value lies between 1.0 and 1.67 and depends on the gas used.

Any process that can be made to go in the reverse sense by an infinitesimal change in the conditions is called a *reversible* process. No actual change is fully reversible, but many processes when carried out slowly near equilibrium are nearly reversible. Any process that is not reversible is *irreversible*.

IDEAL GAS

Similarities in the behavior of gases make it convenient to postulate an *ideal gas* which, by definition, obeys Boyle's law

$$p_1V_1 = p_2V_2 \tag{6}$$

and Charles's law

$$V_t = V_0(1 + \beta_0 t) \tag{7}$$

where t is the centigrade temperature and β_0 is the coefficient of expansion (0.003660/C°).

Consider a process in which the gas is expanded at constant pressure from its original state

$$p_0 = 1 \text{ atm} \quad \text{and} \quad t_0 = 0°C$$

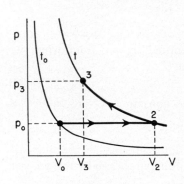

to another (point 2, Fig. 12.1), and then compressed isothermally to point 3. From Charles's law

$$V_2 = V_0(1 + \beta_0 t) \tag{8}$$

and from Boyle's law

$$p_3 V_3 = p_0 V_2 \tag{9}$$

By substituting the expression for V_2 from Eq. (9) in Eq. (8), we obtain

$$p_3 V_3 = p_0 V_0 (1 + \beta_0 t) \tag{10}$$

which we may write as

FIG. 12.1. Isobaric change followed by an isothermal change.

$$p_3 V_3 = p_0 V_0 \beta_0 \left(t + \frac{1}{\beta_0} \right) \tag{11}$$

If we now set $V_0 = 22,400$ cm³/mole, $p_0 = 1$ atm $= 1.013 \times 10^6$ dynes/cm², and $\beta_0 = 0.00366/C°$, the term $p_0 V_0 \beta_0$ can be evaluated.

$$p_0 V_0 \beta_0 = n \times 8.31 \times 10^7 \text{ ergs/mole C°} \tag{12}$$

where n is the number of gram-moles. This constant is the same for all gases and is called the *universal gas constant R*

$$R = 8.31 \text{ joules/mole C°} = 0.08207 \text{ liter-atm/mole C°} \tag{13}$$

In the term $\left(t + \frac{1}{\beta_0} \right)$ in Eq. (11), $1/\beta_0$ is in centigrade degrees and represents a temperature. Using the expression $(t + 1/\beta_0)$ is equivalent to expressing temperatures on a new scale whose zero is lower than the centigrade zero by $1/\beta_0$ degrees, but in which the unit temperature interval is the same as on the centigrade scale. Temperatures expressed on this scale are called *ideal-gas temperatures*, and will be represented by T. Since $1/\beta_0 = 1/.00366 = 273.2$

$$T = t + 273.2 \qquad (14)$$

We may now write Eq. (11) as

$$pV = nRT \qquad (15)$$

which is known as the *equation of state* of an ideal gas.

To investigate changes in the internal energy of a gas, we may cause the gas to undergo a process and measure the heat transferred and the work done. The energy change ΔU is then computed from the first law, Eq. (1). The internal energy of a *real* gas is found experimentally to depend upon temperature and pressure. At low pressures, however, ΔU is small, and we infer that at vanishingly small pressures the internal energy is independent of the pressure. We therefore add to the definition of an *ideal* gas that *its internal energy is a function of temperature alone.*

SPECIFIC HEATS OF AN IDEAL GAS

The heat required to cause unit rise in temperature in unit mass of gas depends on the conditions of the process. A gas has many different specific heats. Only two, however, are of practical use, namely c_v the specific heat at constant volume, and c_p the specific heat at constant pressure.

It is convenient to choose as a unit of mass the number of grams equal to the molecular weight, that is, a mole. The corresponding heat capacities C_v and C_p are called molar heat capacities.

If we have n moles of an ideal gas and we raise its temperature from T_1 to T_2 at constant volume, then the heat transferred is $nC_v(T_2 - T_1)$ and the work done is zero. The first law, Eq. (1) states

$$nC_v(T_2 - T_1) = U_2 - U_1 + 0 \qquad (16)$$

If the same gas were heated at constant pressure p from temperature T_1 to T_2, then the heat transferred would be $nC_p(T_2 - T_1)$ and an amount of work $p(V_2 - V_1)$ would be done by the expanding gas. Using the first law, we have

$$nC_p(T_2 - T_1) = U_2' - U_1' + p(V_2 - V_1) \qquad (17)$$

Using the fact that for an ideal gas $U_1 = U_1'$ and $V_2 = V_2'$, and combining the gas law, Eq. (15), with Eqs. (16) and (17), we arrive at an important relation between the molar heat capacities

$$C_p - C_v = R \tag{18}$$

CHANGE OF STATE

When an ideal gas is compressed isothermally, it remains a gas, and the volume decreases continually with increasing pressure according to Boyle's law (Fig. 12.1). When a real gas is compressed isothermally its behavior may be that indicated by Fig. 12.2. The pressure rises at first along *ab*. When point *b* is reached, the volume

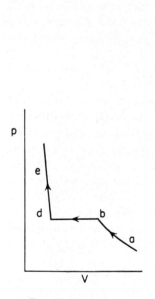

Fig. 12.2. Isothermal compression of a real gas.

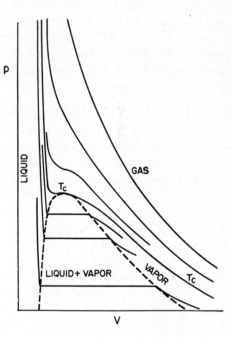

Fig. 12.3. Isotherms of a real gas.

continues to decrease without further increase of pressure, accompanied by *liquefaction* or *condensation* of the gas. At point *d* all of the substance has been converted to the liquid phase and, since liquids are nearly incompressible, a very large pressure increase is necessary to reduce the volume further, along *de*.

When the experiment illustrated by Fig. 12.2 is repeated at successively higher temperatures, it is found that greater and greater pressures must be used before condensation begins. In Fig. 12.3, it will be seen that points b and d eventually coincide at the temperature lettered T_c. This temperature, called the *critical temperature*, is the highest temperature at which a gas can be liquefied. The *critical pressure* p_c is the lowest pressure that will produce liquefaction at the critical temperature.

We may read off a series of vapor pressures and their corresponding temperatures from the straight portions of the curves of Fig. 12.3. If we plot these as in Fig. 12.4, we obtain the *vapor pressure curve* of the substance. There exist similar curves representing the pressure and temperature at which solid and liquid can be in equilibrium and at which solid and vapor can be in equilibrium (Fig. 12.5). These curves intersect at the *triple point* at which all three phases can exist simultaneously.

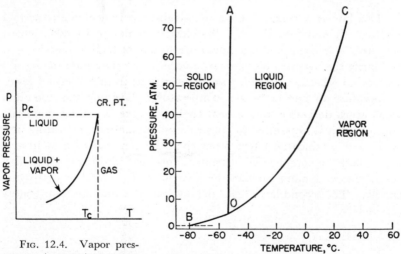

FIG. 12.4. Vapor pressure *vs.* temperature curves for a real gas.

FIG. 12.5. Triple point diagram for CO_2.

HUMIDITY

Air is a mixture of gases and water vapor. The mass of water vapor per unit volume is called the *absolute humidity*. The pressure exerted by the gas is the sum of the partial pressures of the components.

If the partial pressure of water vapor equals the vapor pressure of water (Fig. 12.4) at that particular temperature, the vapor is said to be *saturated*. If the partial pressure is less than the vapor pressure, the vapor is *unsaturated*. The *relative humidity* is defined as the ratio of actual partial pressure of water vapor to the saturated vapor pressure at that temperature, and is usually expressed as a percentage. The temperature at which the water vapor in a sample of air becomes saturated is called the *dew point*.

EXAMPLE: In a weather report the temperature is given as 20°C and the dew point 10°C. What is the relative humidity?
From Table 24 (Appendix) we find the vapor pressures

$P_1 = 17.6$ mm of mercury = saturated vapor pressure at 20°C

$P_2 = 9.2$ mm of mercury = partial pressure of water vapor

$$\text{Relative humidity} = \frac{P_2}{P_1} = \frac{9.2 \text{ mm of mercury}}{17.6 \text{ mm of mercury}} = 0.52 = 52 \text{ per cent}$$

SECOND LAW OF THERMODYNAMICS

This law is a generalization of certain experiences with thermal engines. It expresses the fact that heat will not of its own accord flow from a body of lower temperature to one of higher temperature. To clarify the meaning of "of its own accord" we may state the second law as: no self-acting engine can transfer heat from a body of lower temperature to one of higher temperature. Turning our attention to the work derivable from a heat engine, we see that the second law asserts that it is impossible to construct an engine that, operating in a cycle, will produce no effect other than the removal of heat from a source and the complete conversion of this heat into work. The first law of thermodynamics denies the possibility of creating or destroying energy. The second law denies the possibility of utilizing heat energy completely.

EFFICIENCY

In relating the heat transferred to the work performed by a heat engine, we consider for simplicity a *reversible* engine operating in *closed cycles*. That is, the material that expands against a piston is periodically brought back to its initial state so that in any one cycle there is no change in the internal energy of this material, called the *working substance*.

If heat Q_1 is supplied to the engine (Fig. 12.6) and a portion Q_2 of this heat is discharged in the exhaust, then the portion of the heat which the engine converts into mechanical work W is

$$W = Q_1 - Q_2 \qquad (19)$$

The *efficiency* E of the engine is the ratio of work output W to heat input Q_2 or

$$E = \frac{Q_1 - Q_2}{Q_1} \qquad (20)$$

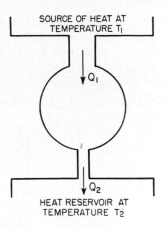

SOURCE OF HEAT AT TEMPERATURE T_1

HEAT RESERVOIR AT TEMPERATURE T_2

Fɪɢ. 12.6. Flow diagram of a heat engine.

THE CARNOT CYCLE

Sadi Carnot (1796–1832) approached the problem of the efficiency of a heat engine from a fundamental stand-point. His theoretical contribution provided the basis for practical improvements in steam engines and supplied the logical basis for the definition of an absolute temperature scale.

Carnot studied the fundamental features of heat engines in terms of an idealized engine which operated in a sequence of reversible iso-thermal and adiabatic steps now known as a *Carnot cycle*. Consider a cylinder fitted with a piston and filled with any substance that expands with rising temperature and decreasing pressure. The initial state is represented by point A in Fig. 12.7. In the first step the gas is allowed to expand at constant temperature T_1 taking in heat Q_1, this change being represented by the isothermal curve AB. Next, the container is insulated and expansion allowed to continue. This expansion is adiabatic, along BC, and the temperature drops from T_1 to T_2. The cylinder is then placed on a heat reservoir at tempera-ture T_2, and the gas is compressed isothermally, along CD, the heat of compression Q_2 being transferred to the low temperature reservoir. Finally, the cylinder is again insulated and the compression continued adiabatically, along DA, the gas now being heated to its original temperature T_1.

We may attribute the following significance to areas on the Carnot cycle diagram:

The area $ABMKA$ represents the energy Q_1 taken from the heat source and converted into work W in moving the piston.

The area $BCNMB$ represents the energy taken from the working substance in cooling it from T_1 to T_2.

The area $CNLDC$ represents the energy taken from the external machinery and given as heat Q_2 to the low temperature reservoir.

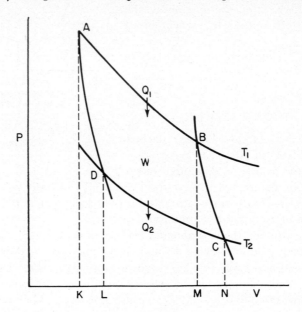

Fig. 12.7.   Carnot cycle.

The area $ADLKA$ represents the energy taken from the external machinery and given to the working substance, heating it from T_2 to T_1.

The area $BCNMB$ equals the area $ADLKA$, since the same amount of heat is required to raise the temperature of the working substance as is given off in lowering its temperature a like amount.   Hence area $ABMKA$ − area $CNLDC$ = area $ABCDA$ = the net useful work done by the heat engine during one cycle.   This work is the difference between Q_1 and Q_2.

$$\text{Efficiency} = \frac{\text{work output}}{\text{heat input}} = \frac{\text{area } ABCDA}{\text{area } ABMKA} = \frac{Q_1 - Q_2}{Q_1} \qquad (21)$$

No engine can have an efficiency greater than that of a reversible (Carnot) engine operating between the same two temperatures. Consider that in Fig. 12.8 a practical (irreversible) engine is driving an ideal (reversible) engine backward. The heat Q_1 which the reversible engine delivers per cycle to the high temperature reservoir equals the heat it would take from this reservoir if it were operating in the forward sense. The efficiencies of the two engines are

Reversible $E = \dfrac{W}{Q_1}$

Irreversible $E' = \dfrac{W'}{Q_1'}$ (22)

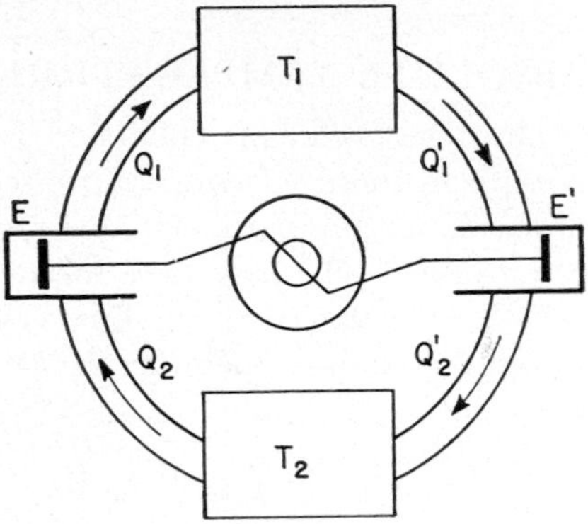

FIG. 12.8.   Connected pair of heat engines.

where the work W' done per cycle by the irreversible engine equals the work W done on the reversible engine. From the first law of thermodynamics

$$Q_1 - Q_2 = Q_1' - Q_2' \tag{23}$$

From the expressions for efficiencies

$$EQ_1 = E'Q_1' \tag{24}$$

Suppose that, contrary to the theorem being proved, $E' > E$. Then $Q' > Q_1'$ from Eq. (24) and $Q_2 > Q_2'$ from Eq. (23). The result would be that the two engines constituting together a self-acting engine would transfer heat from the low temperature reservoir to the high temperature reservoir. But this would be a contradiction of the second law of thermodynamics. Hence we conclude that

$$E'_{irrev} \le E_{rev} \tag{25}$$

All reversible engines operating between the same two temperatures have the same efficiency, regardless of the nature of the working substance. Consider two reversible engines that employ different working substances and that have efficiencies E_1 and E_2, respectively. If the first engine is used to operate the second engine in reverse, as in Fig. 12.8, we have from the previous discussion $E_2 \leq E_1$, and if the engines are interchanged, $E_1 \leq E_2$. These conditions can both be satisfied only if

$$E_1 = E_2 \tag{26}$$

ABSOLUTE TEMPERATURE SCALES

In 1848, William Thomson (Lord Kelvin) showed that it was possible to construct temperature scales that were independent of the properties of any particular thermometric substance such as mercury or nitrogen. The basis for a thermodynamic temperature scale is the fact that the efficiencies of all reversible Carnot engines, whatever the working substance, operating between the same two temperatures, are the same

$$E = \frac{W}{Q_1} = \frac{Q_1 - Q_2}{Q_1} = 1 - \frac{Q_2}{Q_1} \tag{27}$$

The absolute temperatures of the reservoir and the source between which a reversible engine operates are defined by the relation

$$\frac{Q_2}{Q_1} = \frac{T_2}{T_1} \tag{28}$$

where Q_2/Q_1 is the ratio of heats rejected and absorbed, and T_2/T_1 is the ratio of the absolute temperatures of the reservoir and the source. If, further, we arbitrarily set the difference between the absolute temperatures of the steam point and the ice point at 100°, we have completely defined the centigrade absolute scale usually called the Kelvin scale and designated by °K. If, however, the fundamental interval is divided in 180°, we have the Fahrenheit absolute scale, called the Rankine scale and designated by °R.

From Eqs. (27) and (28) we see that the efficiency of a Carnot engine is

$$E_t = 1 - \frac{T_2}{T_1} \tag{29}$$

This equation indicates the conditions which a real engine, such as a steam engine, must fulfill to approach as closely as possible the thermodynamic (theoretical maximum) efficiency. These conditions are that the intake temperature T_1 be as high as possible and the exhaust temperature T_2 be as low as possible.

We may now satisfy ourselves that the absolute gas scale, Eq. (15), and the thermodynamic scale of temperatures are identical. Consider a Carnot engine employing an ideal gas. Since no internal work is done by an ideal gas on expanding, the heat added, Q_{AB}, during the isothermal process, AB in Fig. 12.7, equals the work W_{AB} done by the gas

$$Q_{AB} = W_{AB} = \int_{V_A}^{V_B} p \, dV = nRT_1 \log_e \frac{V_B}{V_A} \tag{30}$$

For the isothermal compression CD

$$Q_{CD} = W_{CD} = nRT_2 \log_e \frac{V_D}{V_C} = -nRT_2 \log_e \frac{V_B}{V_A} \tag{31}$$

The net result of the work done during the two adiabatic processes is zero. For the cycle as a whole, however, the work performed is

$$\Sigma W = Q_{AB} + Q_{CD} = nR(T_1 - T_2) \log_e \frac{V_B}{V_A} \tag{32}$$

which is represented in Fig. 12.7 by the enclosed area $ABCDA$. The efficiency for this Carnot cycle is

$$E_t = \frac{Q_1 - Q_2}{Q_1} = \frac{nR(T_1 - T_2) \log_e (V_B/V_A)}{nRT_1 \log_e (V_B/V_A)} = \frac{T_1 - T_2}{T_1}$$

$$= 1 - \frac{T_2}{T_1} \tag{33}$$

By a comparison of Eqs. (29) and (33) we see that the thermodynamic and the ideal-gas temperature scales are identical.

EXAMPLE: A simple steam engine receives steam from the boiler at 180°C (about 150 lb/in.² gauge pressure) and exhausts directly into the air at 100°C. What is the upper limit of its efficiency?

$$\text{Ideal efficiency} = \frac{(180 + 273)°\text{K} - (100 + 273)°\text{K}}{(180 + 273)°\text{K}} = 0.176 = 17.6 \text{ per cent}$$

ABSOLUTE ZERO

Consider a series of Carnot engines operating in the following way. The first engine absorbs heat Q_1 from a source, does work W, and discharges a smaller amount of heat Q_2 at a lower temperature. The second engine receives the heat Q_2 rejected by the first, at the temperature at which it was rejected, does work W, and rejects a still smaller amount of heat Q_3 at a still lower temperature; and so on. If each engine is adjusted to do the same work W, then the heats Q_2, Q_3, $\cdots$ rejected by successive engines are represented by a set of decreasing positive numbers. By definition of the Kelvin scale, the temperatures T_2, T_3, $\cdots$, at which each succeeding engine rejects its heat, get lower and lower. A final engine can be imagined which will reject no heat at a temperature which will be absolute zero. Absolute zero is the temperature of a reservoir to which no heat will be discharged by a reversible (Carnot) engine operating between this reservoir and a source at a higher temperature.

SUMMARY

The interchangeability of heat and mechanical energy is expressed in the *first law of thermodynamics*

$$Q = \Delta U + W$$

The accepted value of the *mechanical equivalent of heat* is 4.180 joules/cal.

The conservation principle has been extended to include interchange of mass and energy

$$U = mc^2$$

An *isothermal* process is one occurring at constant temperature. For an ideal gas

$$p_1 V_1 = p_2 V_2$$

An *adiabatic* process is one in which there is no exchange of energy with the surroundings. For an ideal gas

$$pV^\gamma = \text{constant.}$$

A *reversible process* is one that is in equilibrium at each instant.

An *ideal gas* is one whose internal energy is independent of pressure and volume, depending only on temperature. Its equation of state may be written

$$pV = nRT$$

The specific heat of a gas at constant pressure is greater than its specific heat at constant volume

$$c_p - c_v = R$$

The *triple point* is the condition of pressure and temperature at which the solid, liquid, and vapor phases of a substance can coexist in equilibrium.

The *critical point* is the condition of pressure and temperature at which a liquid and its vapor are indistinguishable. The critical temperature is the highest temperature at which a gas can be liquefied by pressure alone.

Absolute humidity is the mass of water vapor per unit volume of air.

Relative humidity is defined as the ratio of actual partial pressure of water vapor to the saturated vapor pressure at that temperature.

The *dew point* is the temperature to which the air must be cooled, at constant pressure, to produce saturation.

The *second law of thermodynamics* states that a heat engine cannot transfer heat from a body to another at higher temperature unless external energy is supplied to the engine.

Heat engines transform heat into mechanical energy.

Work can be obtained from a source of thermal energy only by a process that transfers some of the heat to a reservoir at a temperature lower than that of the source.

$$\text{Thermodynamic efficiency} = \frac{\text{output work}}{\text{input work}} = \frac{Q_1 - Q_2}{Q_1}$$

The *Kelvin* or absolute temperature scale is independent of the thermometric substance, being based on the efficiency of an ideal heat engine.

$$\text{Thermodynamic efficiency} = \frac{T_1 - T_2}{T_1} \qquad \text{or} \qquad \frac{Q_2}{Q_1} = \frac{T_2}{T_1}$$

The temperature at which a Carnot engine ejects no heat would be the *zero* on the absolute temperature scale.

REFERENCES FOR SUPPLEMENTARY READING

1. Barnett, M. K., "The Temperature Concept," *J. Phys. Chem.*, **46,** 715 (1942).
2. Becher, H., "A Method of Teaching Thermodynamic Functions," *J. Chem. Education*, **19,** 5 (1942).
3. Bridgman, P. W., *A Condensed Collection of Thermodynamic Formulas*, Harvard University Press, 1925.
4. Buckingham, E., "The Definition of the Ideal Gas," *Bull. Bur. Standards*, **6,** 409 (1910).
5. Coffin, C. C., "A Presentation of the Thermodynamic Functions," *J. Chem. Education*, **23,** 584 (1946).
6. Darrow, K. K., "Entropy," *Bell Syst. Tech. J.*, **21,** 51 (1942); also as Monograph B-1347.
7. Donald, M. B., "The Logarithmic Temperature Scale," *Chemistry and Industry*, **37,** 342 (1946); *Nature*, **157,** 624 (1946).
8. Fernald, E. M., "Basic Qualitative Thermodynamics," *J. Eng. Education*, **34,** 418 (1944).
9. Joule, J. P., "Scientific Works of Joule," *Nature*, **43,** 111 (1890).
10. MacRae, Duncan, "The Introduction to Thermodynamics," *J. Chem. Education*, **23,** 366 (1946).
11. Martell, A. E., "Entropy and the Second Law of Thermodynamics," *J. Chem. Education*, **23,** 166 (1946).
12. Osgood, T. H., "Physics in 1936" (sec. V), *Rev. Sci. Instruments*, **8,** 1 (1937).

224   *THERMODYNAMICS*

13. Rechel, E. R., "The Reversible Process in Thermodynamics," *J. Chem. Education*, **24**, 298 (1947).
14. Rumford, Count Benjamin Thompson, "Enquiry Concerning the Source of Heat Which Is Excited by Friction," *Phil. Trans. Roy. Soc., London*, **88**, 80 (1798).
15. Shedd, J. C., "A Mechanical Model of the Carnot Engine," *Phys. Rev.*, **8**, 174 (1899).
16. Tunell, G., "The History and Analytical Expression of the First and Second Laws of Thermodynamics," *J. Phys. Chem.*, **36**, 1744 (1932).

QUESTIONS AND PROBLEMS

1. Show that areas in the p–V diagram of Fig. 12.7 represent energy.

2. When is the conduction of heat a reversible process? when an irreversible process?

3. What is the heat of vaporization of a liquid at its critical temperature?

4. What is the dew point and what does it indicate? Is the dew point a fixed point in the sense that the freezing point is?

5. Heat is transferred from the cool interior of an electric refrigerator to warmer surroundings. Show that this is not a violation of the second law of thermodynamics.

6. What determines the efficiency of heat engines? Why is it generally so low?

7. What advantage results from using mercury vapor instead of steam in driving turbines?

8. List in outline form the steps necessary in defining the thermodynamic (Kelvin) scale of temperature. Can there be more than one absolute scale of temperature?

9. It has been asserted that the temperature of interstellar space is 2°K. What meaning is to be attributed to this statement?

10. How hot can a given mass be heated? How cold can a given mass be cooled?

11. In a certain process, 700 cal of heat are supplied to a system and 250 joules of work are done on the system. What is the increase in its internal energy?

12. When 1.0 lb of water is boiled at 212°F and atmospheric pressure, it becomes 26.8 ft³ of steam. The heat of vaporization is 970 Btu/lb. Compute (a) the external work in foot-pounds, (b) the increase in internal energy in Btu. *Ans.* 2120 ft-lb, 969 Btu.

13. An air conditioning system is required to raise the relative humidity of 7.5 ft³ of air per second from 15 to 45 per cent. The temperature is 68°F. How many pounds of water must be evaporated per hour?

14. A closed room 6.0 by 5.0 by 3 0 m is kept at a temperature of 20°C. The relative humidity in the room is 12 per cent. If a pan of water is placed in the room, how much will evaporate? *Ans.* 14 kg

15. (a) What is the relative humidity in a room when the temperature is 72°F and the dew point is 50°F? (b) What is the partial pressure of water vapor in the atmosphere? (c) What is the absolute humidity?

16. (a) What is the dew point temperature on a day when the air temperature

is 25°C and the relative humidity is 65 per cent?   (b) What is the absolute humidity?
Ans. 18°C, 15.4 × 10⁻⁶ gm/cm³.

17. A Carnot engine takes in 200 cal of heat in each cycle from a reservoir at 125°C and gives up 150 cal to the low temperature reservoir.   Find the temperature of the latter reservoir.

18. What is the thermodynamic efficiency of a noncondensing steam engine which receives steam at 150 lb/in.² (358°F) and exhausts it to the atmosphere?
Ans. 18 per cent.

19. A Carnot engine whose low temperature reservoir is at 5°C has an efficiency of 30 per cent.   An efficiency of 50 per cent is desired.   By how much must the temperature of the high temperature reservoir be increased?

20. An ideal heat engine has an efficiency of 25 per cent when its condenser temperature is 25°C.   It is desired to increase the efficiency to 35 per cent.   What change should be made in either (a) the condenser temperature, or (b) the boiler temperature?   *Ans.* −39 C°, 61 C°.

21. A Carnot refrigerator removes heat from a reservoir at −10°C and delivers heat to a reservoir at 25°C.   How many kilowatt-hours of energy would have to be supplied to the refrigerator to freeze 100 lb of water initially at 15°C?

22. (a) What is the coefficient of performance, $Q_1/(Q_2 - Q_1)$, of a refrigerator which removes heat from a reservoir at 12°F and delivers it to a reservoir at 80°F? (b) How much energy would have to be supplied to the refrigerator to make 1.0 lb of ice cubes from water at 60°F?   *Ans.* 7.95, 0.048 kw-hr.

23. Compare the heating effects produced in a room at 17°C by a given quantity of electrical energy, (a) if the electrical power is dissipated in a resistance heater, and (b) if the electrical power is used to operate an ideal heat engine to transfer heat from the outside (−5°C) to the room.   Comment on the practical possibility of such a scheme.

Chapter 13

IIIIIIIIIIIIIIIIIIIIIIIII

EXTREME TEMPERATURES

LIQUEFACTION OF GASES IIIIIIII
APPROACH TOWARD ABSOLUTE ZERO
IIIIIIII *HIGH TEMPERATURE FURNACES*

LOW TEMPERATURES

The existence of a theoretical lower limit of temperature (p. 222) is a challenge to produce successively lower temperatures in the laboratory. Progress toward the absolute zero is for the purpose of studying phenomena that involve energy changes of such small magnitude that they can be observed only in this region. One hopes to obtain important new information about the structure and forces within matter from the study of low-temperature specific heats, supraconductivity, magnetic and mechanical properties, surface phenomena, and the many unique properties of helium. Herein lies the incentive to obtain experimentally temperatures of the order of 0.001°K, lower even than the temperature of interstellar space (about 2°K).

Processes used to produce cooling are: (1) solution of salts, acids, or gases in water or ice; (2) evaporation of a liquid; (3) adiabatic expansion of a gas with performance of external work; (4) controlled expansion of a gas utilizing the Joule-Thomson effect; (5) absorption and desorption of a gas; and (6) adiabatic demagnetization.

The behavior of a freezing solution is represented by Fig. 13.1. When salt comes in contact with ice in an excessive quantity it forms a solution which in turn dissolves more ice.   If the mixture is thermally insulated, the heat required to transform the ice comes from the internal energy of the mixture itself, lowering its temperature.

When a thermally insulated liquid is allowed to evaporate, the heat of vaporization is supplied by the liquid itself and its temperature

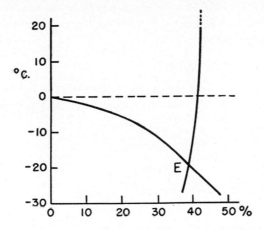

FIG. 13.1.   Equilibrium diagram for ice and ammonium sulfate.

is reduced.   If the vapor is carried away, more liquid evaporates and its temperature decreases further.   Although the boiling point of helium is 4.2°K, by continually pumping the vapor from liquid helium contained in a Dewar flask a temperature as low as 0.7°K is reached.

The liquefaction of gases is the most important process in the attainment of low temperatures.   We shall examine the conditions that must be met in the practical, efficient liquefaction of gases.

VAN DER WAALS' EQUATION OF STATE

Dozens of empirical equations have been proposed for the p-v-T relationships of real gases.   One of the simplest and most successful relations was suggested by J. D. van der Waals (1837–1923)

$$\left(p + \frac{a}{v^2}\right)(v - b) = RT \qquad (1)$$

in which a and b are constants that can be determined experimentally, and v is expressed in volume units per mole.   This equation holds fairly well in the gas, vapor, and even liquid regions, and in the neighborhood of the critical point. A limited physical significance may be associated with the constants. In the ideal gas we tacitly assumed point molecules and the absence of intermolecular forces. In a real gas b is related to the volume occupied by the molecules per unit mass; and a is related to internal forces, in consequence of which the gas behaves as if it were subjected to a pressure greater than the externally applied pressure p.

THE CRITICAL STATE

The criteria which determine the values of temperature, pressure, and molar volume at the critical point are that at the critical point

$$\left(\frac{dp}{dv}\right)_T = 0 \tag{2}$$

and

$$\left(\frac{d^2p}{dv^2}\right)_T = 0 \tag{3}$$

The first condition expresses the fact that on a p-v diagram (Fig. 12.3) the critical isotherm is a horizontal line at the critical point. The second condition arises from the fact that the critical point is a point of inflection of the isothermal.

To apply these conditions to van der Waals' equation, we may rewrite it in the form

$$p = \frac{RT}{v - b} - \frac{a}{v^2} \tag{4}$$

Setting the first and second derivatives equal to zero we have

$$\left(\frac{dp}{dv}\right)_T = \frac{-RT}{(v_c - b)^2} + \frac{2a}{v_c^3} = 0 \tag{5}$$

$$\left(\frac{d^2p}{dv^2}\right)_T = \frac{2RT_c}{(v_c - b)^3} - \frac{6a}{v_c^4} = 0 \tag{6}$$

from which

$$v_c^3 = \left(\frac{2a}{RT}\right)(v_c - b)^2 \tag{7}$$

$$v_c^4 = \left(\frac{6a}{2RT}\right)(v_c - b)^3 \tag{8}$$

Dividing Eq. (8) by Eq. (7) we obtain

$$v_c = 3b \tag{9}$$

By substitution in Eq. (5) and then in Eq. (4), we get

$$T_c = \frac{8a}{27bR} \tag{10}$$

$$p_c = \frac{a}{27b^2} \tag{11}$$

It is of interest to use the three critical values to calculate the test quantity $RT_c/p_c v_c$. This dimensionless quantity should have the same value for all gases that obey a van der Waals equation

$$\frac{RT_c}{p_c v_c} = \frac{8a}{27b} \frac{1}{3b} \frac{27b^2}{a} = 2.67 \tag{12}$$

The experimental results listed in Table 13.1 are higher than this predicted value. The agreement is worse for the more complex molecules, nevertheless, the approximate constancy of $RT_c/p_c v_c$ is significant.

TABLE 13.1 CRITICAL CONSTANTS FOR VARIOUS SUBSTANCES

	T_c in °C	p_c in atm	$1/V_c$ in gm/cm³	$\frac{RT_c}{p_c v_c}$
Ammonia (NH₃).........	132.4	111.5	0.235	4.11
Carbon dioxide (CO₂)....	31.1	73.0	0.460	3.57
Ethyl alcohol (C₂H₅OH) ..	243.1	63.1	0.2755	4.09
Helium (He)............	−267.9	2.26	0.0693	3.31
Hydrogen (H₂)..........	−239.9	12.8	0.0310	3.28
Nitrogen (N₂)..........	−147.1	33.5	0.3110	3.43
Oxygen (O₂)	−118.8	49.7	0.430	3.43
Water (H₂O)...........	374.0	217.7	0.4	

JOULE-THOMSON EXPERIMENT

James Joule in collaboration with William Thomson (Lord Kelvin) investigated the forces between gas molecules by means of a throttled expansion of the gas through a porous plug. As the gas passes through the plug (Fig. 13.2) work equal to $p_1 V_1$ is done on a chosen sample of gas by the gas back of it on the high pressure side. As it passes through the plug, the gas does work equal to $p_2 V_2$ on the gas ahead of it.

Assuming that the expansion takes place in a thermally insulated chamber and that the stream velocities on the two sides of the plug are the same, the first law of thermodynamics gives

$$Q = \Delta U + W = 0 \tag{13}$$

The changes of energy that occur involve only ΔU and W. For the throttled expansion indicated by Fig. 13.2

$$W = p_2V_2 - p_1V_1 \tag{14}$$

and $$\Delta U = U_2 - U_1$$

By substituting these relations in Eq. (13), we see that

$$U_1 + p_1V_1 = U_2 + p_2V_2 = \text{constant} \tag{15}$$

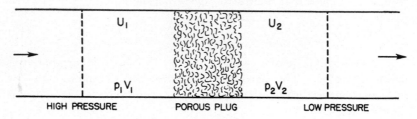

FIG. 13.2.   The porous-plug expansion process.

Expressed in terms of unit mass, the quantity $u + pv$ is called the *enthalpy*, per unit mass. The porous plug experiment involves an irreversible, throttled expansion in which the enthalpy h remains constant.

By experiment it is found that a Joule-Thomson expansion may result in either a *cooling* or a *heating* of the gas, depending on the gas used and the initial conditions. Cooling is readily interpreted as due to the fact that work is done against the attractive forces between molecules. Heating is associated largely with changes that occur in pv during flow through the plug. The work p_1V_1 done on the gas about to enter the plug may be greater than the work p_2V_2 done by it on emerging from the plug.

From the first and second laws of thermodynamics it may be shown that the Joule-Thomson effect, dT/dp at constant enthalpy h, is given by the expression

$$\left(\frac{dT}{dp}\right)_h = \frac{1}{c_p}\left[T\left(\frac{dv}{dT}\right)_p - v\right] \tag{16}$$

For a van der Waals gas this becomes

$$\left(\frac{dT}{dp}\right)_h = \frac{1}{c_p}\left(\frac{2a}{RT} - b\right) \tag{17}$$

The term in parentheses in Eq. (17) can be positive or negative. It is apparent that the inversion temperature at which the sign of dT/dp changes is that for which $2a/RT_i = b$ or $T_i = 2a/bR$.

A gas can be liquefied if we compress it, cool it below the inversion temperature, and then allow an adiabatic throttled expansion to produce further cooling. An additional requirement for practical efficiency of this process is that the gas be cooled initially below the temperature at which $d(pv)/dp = 0$. This is the so-called Boyle point T_B. From van der Waals' equation $T_B = a/bR$. Hence, the Boyle temperature is half the inversion temperature.

LIQUEFACTION OF GASES

Carl von Linde first liquefied air on a commercial scale (1896) in an apparatus that utilized Joule-Thomson cooling and was provided with heat exchangers to minimize thermal losses. Such a process is

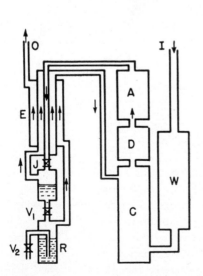

Fig. 13.3. Linde air liquefier.

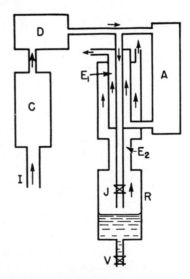

Fig. 13.4. Claude and Heylandt air liquefier.

represented in Fig. 13.3. Air at atmospheric pressure enters the intake *I*. Dust and carbon dioxide are removed at *W*. The air is compressed to 200 atm in compressor *C* from which it passes through a dryer *D* into chamber *A*, which is surrounded by an ammonia freezing mixture that cools the air to $-50°C$. It then passes the throttling valve *J* where the pressure is reduced to 20–50 atm. Much of the cooled, expanded air returns through the heat exchanger *E* to the compressor, but some is liquefied and passes through valve V_1 into reservoir *R*. Liquid air can be removed from the reservoir by tap V_2, while air evaporating in the reservoir flows through the exchanger *E* and passes into the atmosphere at outlet *O*.

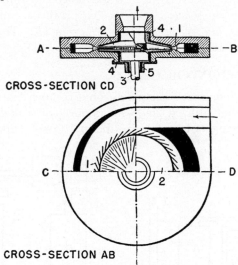

CROSS-SECTION CD

CROSS-SECTION AB

FIG. 13.5. Construction of turbine for cooling of gas by performance of work.

In the type of plant used by Claude and Heylandt (Fig. 13.4) purified air enters *C* where it is compressed to 200 atm. After passing through dryer *D*, the current branches. Part goes into engine *A* where it performs work during an adiabatic expansion to 1 atm, during which it is cooled, and then passes through heat exchanger E_1. The other part goes through E_1 where it is cooled and then is expanded to 1 atm at valve *J*. During this expansion some of the air is liquefied and remains in reservoir *R*. The rest passes through E_2 and escapes into the atmosphere.   About 25 per cent of the air compressed is liquefied.

Kapitza investigated the thermodynamic conditions under which liquefaction might be carried out at low pressures (5–6 atm).   This can be accomplished, for air, by the use of an expansion turbine, whose efficiency is improved by use of centrifugal forces.   The original liquefier constructed on these principles had an efficiency of 83 per cent, a short starting period (18–20 min), and produced 30 kg of liquid air per hour.

The turbine is illustrated in Fig. 13.5, which shows the shape of the nozzles 1 and the rotor blades 2.   The monel rotor has a diameter of 8 cm and is normally run at 41,000 rev/min.   To prevent air flowing past the blades, two labyrinth glands 4, with a 0.15-mm clearance, are provided.

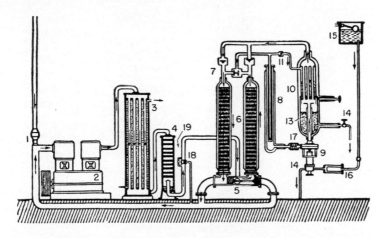

Fig. 13.6.   Liquid-air plant using turbine expansion engine.

Figure 13.6 shows the general arrangement of the liquefier.   Air is admitted through the filter 1 to the compressor 2 where it is compressed to about 6 atm.   The compressed air passes through the water cooler 3, the oil remover 4, and enters the valve system 5 of the regenerators 6.   The slide valve is actuated by electromagnets and reverses its stroke every 25 sec.   Passing valves 7, the compressed air divides. The main bulk of air, after passing a filter and a temperature equalizer 8, enters turbine 9 where it expands, and then returns through condenser 10 into the other exchanger and escapes into the atmosphere.

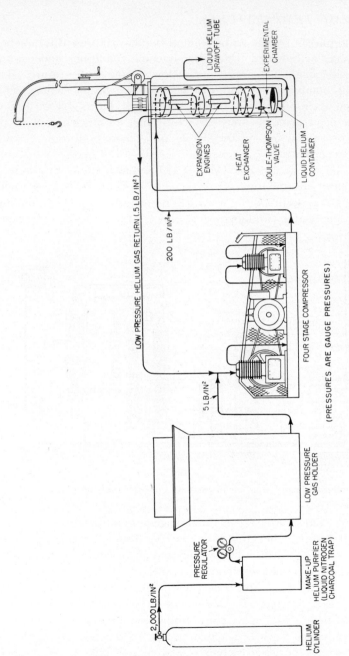

LIQUID HELIUM
DRAWOFF TUBE

EXPERIMENTAL
CHAMBER

EXPANSION
ENGINES

HEAT
EXCHANGER

JOULE-THOMPSON
VALVE

LIQUID HELIUM
CONTAINER

LOW PRESSURE HELIUM GAS RETURN (.5 LB/IN²)

200 LB/IN²

5 LB/IN²

FOUR STAGE COMPRESSOR

(PRESSURES ARE GAUGE PRESSURES)

LOW PRESSURE
GAS HOLDER

PRESSURE
REGULATOR

MAKE-UP
HELIUM PURIFIER
(LIQUID NITROGEN
CHARCOAL TRAP)

2,000 LB/IN²

HELIUM
CYLINDER

Fig. 13.7. Schematic layout of Collins helium cryostat.

Work performed by the gas expanding in the turbine is absorbed by a water brake at the rate of 4 kw. The remaining flow of compressed air is delivered through the check valve 11 to the condenser 10 where it liquefies. The liquid air is drawn off into container 13, from which it may be removed through tap 14.

A helium cryostat is commercially available which provides a cold chamber for experiments at any temperature down to 2°K. The helium is cooled by expansion, without the aid of liquid air or other refrigerants. One expansion device is a diaphragm engine, the other two are piston-cylinder-crankshaft assemblies in which leakage is controlled by extremely close fitting of piston to cylinder. The steps in the liquefaction process are shown in Fig. 13.7.

COOLING BY ABSORPTION AND DESORPTION

In Simon's process for liquefying helium, the helium comes in contact with an absorbent substance, such as charcoal or chabazite, at the temperature of liquid hydrogen. The heat of absorption of helium is removed by a liquid hydrogen bath. The system is then thermally insulated and the helium pumped off the absorbing surface. Desorption cools the helium below its critical temperature and expansion results in its liquefaction.

MAGNETIC APPROACH TO ABSOLUTE ZERO

The smallest molecular attraction known is that between helium atoms. As a result helium is the gas that is hardest to liquefy and that, after liquefaction, will boil at the lowest temperature. At 1 atm pressure its boiling point is 4.2°K. It is possible to go below 4.2°K by reducing the pressure of the boiling helium. In 1932 Keesom attained a temperature of 0.7°K by rapid pumping of boiling helium. But as seen from the first and fifth lines of Table 13.2, a factor of 1/300,000 in

TABLE 13.2 VAPOR PRESSURE OF LIQUID HELIUM

°K	Mm of Mercury
4.219	760
1.714	10
1.237	1.0
1.00	1.5×10^{-1}
0.50	2.5×10^{-5}
0.30	7×10^{-10}
0.10	3×10^{-31}
0.03	6×10^{-103}

the pressure gives a factor of only ⅛ in the temperatures, and 0.7°K is practically the limit by this method.

In 1926–27 Debye and Giaque independently proposed the use of a magnetic process instead of the mechanical process for gas liquefaction. If a paramagnetic substance is magnetized in a magnetic field, heat is developed during the process analogous to the heat produced in compressing an ideal gas. The heat produced at ordinary temperatures is very small even for the strongest fields obtainable. However, Curie and Langevin showed that the magnetization obtainable in a given magnetic field becomes steadily stronger the more the temperature decreases. Some paramagnetic substances show this increase in their susceptibility χ in accord with Curie's law

$$\chi = \frac{C}{T} \tag{18}$$

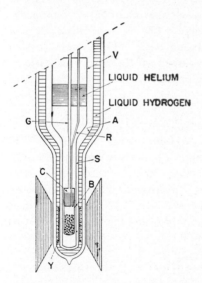

FIG. 13.8. Cryostat for cooling by adiabatic demagnetization.

even down to liquid-helium temperatures. Such ideal magnetic substances are used in the magnetic process.

In the first step a paramagnetic sample at about 1°K is placed in a magnetic field increasing in strength up to a final value. During this period heat is produced and provision is made to let this heat escape into the surrounding bath of liquid helium. We then have the sample magnetized and in the final field at 1°K. Next, contact between the sample and the helium bath is broken by evacuating the intermediate jacket (Fig. 13.8), and from now on every appreciable heat transfer is prevented. Finally, we remove the magnetic field. Thereupon, the sample goes back to its original unmagnetized state. In doing so it has to absorb heat, but since it cannot take this heat from its surroundings, it cools off to some temperature lower than 1°K. Results obtained by deHaas are listed in Table 13.3, where H_i and T_i represent initial values of magnetic field strength and temperature, and H_f and T_f represent the final values.

We may next consider why the process stops at some definite low temperature and where on the temperature scale this point has to be expected. The liquefaction of gases is associated with their deviations from the ideal state, due to intermolecular actions. In an analogous way the limits of the magnetic process are associated with deviations from ideal magnetic behavior caused by interactions of the magnetic electrons in the atoms of the substance with their surroundings and with each other.

TABLE 13.3 COOLING PRODUCED BY DEMAGNETIZATION

Substance	H_i oersted	H_f oersted	T_i °K	T_f °K
CeF$_3$	27,600 27,600 27,600	4,500 2,200 850	1.314 1.314 1.314	0.27 .19 .13
Ds(C$_2$H$_2$SO$_4$)$_3$·9H$_2$O	19,500	200	1.314	.12
Ce(C$_2$H$_5$SO$_4$)$_3$·9H$_2$O	27,600	850	1.314	.09
K$_2$SO$_4$Cr$_2$(SO$_4$)$_3$·24H$_2$O	19,500	350	1.314	.05
Cs$_2$SO$_4$Ti$_2$(SO$_4$)$_3$·24H$_2$O	25,075	1.0	1.314	.0055
1 [K$_2$SO$_4$Cr$_2$(SO$_4$)$_3$·24H$_2$O] + 14.4 [K$_2$SO$_4$Al$_2$(SO$_4$)$_3$·24H$_2$O] ···	24,075	1.0	1.92	.0044

Cooling represents essentially a decrease in thermal molecular disorder. On cooling a substance through gaseous, liquid, and solid phases, its molecules approach a state of highest possible order. At temperatures around 1°K the disorder connected with the motions of the atoms or molecules has been removed to a large extent. This is shown by the fact that at such temperatures the specific heat of solids (due to atomic motion) is very small. However, paramagnetic atoms have interior spinning electrons which are in disorder with respect to the directions of their magnetic axes. We are able to influence the amount of this disorder by an externally applied magnetic field. In cooling through the interval from 1°K to 0.001°K, we are removing the inner atomic disorder of the spinning electrons.

MEASUREMENT OF EXTREME LOW TEMPERATURES

The temperature coefficient of resistance of most metals approaches zero at the liquid helium region. However, resistance thermometers made from an alloy of 5 per cent lead in silver are usable for the range from 7 to 3°K, and unannealed phosphor bronze for the range from 4.2 to 1°K. In the range from 5 to 0.7°K the vapor pressure of helium gives the temperature, using various empirical formulas.

The paramagnetic substances used in attaining the lowest temperatures can be made to indicate their own temperatures in terms of magnetic susceptibility, Eq. (18). In Simon's method, two coils are placed around the specimen. An alternating current is produced in one and the other is connected to a galvanometer. The electric circuit is so compensated that the galvanometer deflection varies inversely as the temperature.

DeHaas used a sensitive balance to measure the force on the specimen when placed in a non-homogeneous field, given by

$$F = MV\chi H \frac{dH}{dx} \tag{19}$$

where M is the mole number, V the volume, and χ the susceptibility of the specimen; and the field H and its gradient dH/dx are constant. From Eqs. (18) and (19), it is evident that the force is inversely proportional to the absolute temperature.

CLOSER APPROACH TO 0°K

Suggestions have been made to use the magnetic properties of the nucleus of the atom instead of its spinning electrons in much the same type of magnetic process to attain still lower temperatures. This would mean that around 0.001°K, having removed all the disorder of atoms in bulk and the disorder inside their electronic structure, we should begin attacking the disorder hidden in the nucleus. So far no actual experiments of this sort have been reported.

HIGH TEMPERATURES

There is no generally accepted upper limit to temperature. Various limiting values of the order of 10^{12}°K have been suggested on theoretical grounds, based upon assumptions of questionable validity. The attainment of high temperatures for useful purposes is limited by the materials available for constructing furnaces and the difficulty of securing a controlled, uniform temperature. The temperature in industrial metallurgical processes seldom exceeds 1700°C, while temperatures above 3000°C are seldom used in the laboratory.

REFRACTORY MATERIALS

There is a progressive failure of all construction materials at high temperatures by (1) decomposition or alteration, (2) oxidation, (3) fracture or flow, or (4) fusion. Asbestos disintegrates by loss of water with the formation of powdery silicate of magnesia. Vitreous silica crystallizes at 1200°C and higher to become powdery white cristobalite. Oxidation of metals is avoided by the use of a protecting atmosphere of hydrogen, nitrogen, or helium, or by the use of iron-nickel-chromium alloys and such high-melting metals as tungsten and molybdenum. Silicon carbide is the only common refractory material which fails by oxidation rather than by fusion. Fracture is important in large industrial apparatus, while for laboratory apparatus slow flow or shrinkage is usually more bothersome. This is due to the objectionable practice of adding plastic clay to some refractory materials. At the eutectic temperature (1545°C for the mullite-cristobalite eutectic) a small amount of liquid is produced with consequent flow or shrinkage of the material. Some refractory materials of commercial importance are listed in Table 13.4.

TABLE 13.4 SOFTENING RANGE OF SOME MINERALS AND CERAMIC PRODUCTS

Material	Softening Temperature (°C)
Alumina brick	1750–2050
Bauxite brick	1730–1850
Carbon brick	2000
Chrome brick	1950–2200
Fireclay brick	1580–1880
Magnesite brick	2200
Mullite	1827
Porcelain, technical	1670–1920
Silica brick	1700–1750
Spinel	2135
Zircon brick	2200–2700

COMBUSTION FURNACES

The burning of city gas in about six times its volume of atmospheric oxygen yields a temperature of about 1800°C. A burner for the combustion of oil in oxygen provides a temperature of 2600°C. In order to minimize heat losses, combustion furnaces often are designed to direct the flame on the sample. Combustion furnaces generally do not have the ease of control of electric furnaces.

The Langmuir atomic-hydrogen flame produces a temperature of 3800°C. It is strongly reducing, which is an advantage when melting tungsten or molybdenum. Molecular hydrogen is circulated around the tungsten electrode of an electric arc where it is dissociated. Recombination occurs in the flame with the evolution of heat.

ELECTRIC-RESISTANCE FURNACES

Carbon granule furnaces utilize the heating effect of a current through pulverized carbon surrounding the specimen. Above 1750°C the carbon reacts appreciably with the protecting tube. Uniformity of temperature is difficult to attain, since the region of highest temperature offers least resistance to the current. In some furnaces the substance to be heated is in powdered or liquid form and is itself the conductor of the heating current.

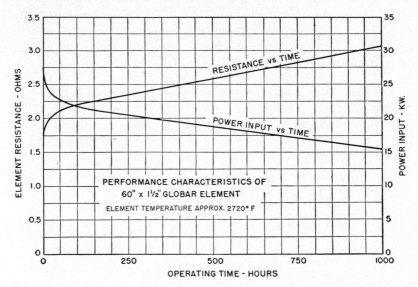

FIG. 13.9.   Performance characteristics of SiC heating elements.

Wire-wound furnaces commonly have nichrome resistors for use up to 1100°C or platinum for temperatures up to 1400°C. Heat transfer is facilitated by the use of large (1 to 3 mm diameter) wire wound on the inside of a magnesia cylinder. Reaction occurs between a tungsten or molybdenum heating wire and the refractory support above 2000°C. Using self-supporting spirals of molybdenum or tungsten wire one can attain temperatures of 2300°C and 2800°C, respectively. A wire-wound furnace is easily constructed and has a long life if the heater is in a reducing or neutral atmosphere. If an oxidizing atmosphere is required for the sample, the heating coil is wound on the outer surface of a refractory shell, such as alundum, which is a good thermal conductor. The furnace cannot be used above 2000°C without having the refractory tube become sufficiently permeable to gas to damage the heater.

Tubular furnaces are efficient for heating small volumes. The conducting tube may be made of platinum, iridium, molybdenum, or tungsten. This type is sturdy, but requires large current owing to its low resistance. Tubes of the Nernst type, made of 85 per cent Zr_2O_3 and 15 per cent Ti_2O_3, have higher resistivity and are convenient for use to 2300°C.

There are various designs of tubular furnaces. One consists of rods laid parallel to the axis of the tube and welded at their ends. Another is a graphite tube in which a helix is cut to increase the resistance. The latter type attains 3000°C in air, and can be used equally well in a vacuum where its useful temperature is limited to 2400 to 2800°C by the evaporation of carbon.

Rod furnaces use resistance rods of recrystallized silicon carbide which radiate directly into the volume to be heated. The elements have a negative temperature coefficient of resistivity up to about 450°C, and a positive coefficient at higher temperatures. Other performance characteristics are illustrated in Fig. 13.9. This shows, for example, that since the resistance of the elements increases with time, a furnace requiring 15 kw to operate must have elements with an initial power capacity of 27.5 kw to obtain about 1000 hr service from them. Silicon carbide elements are used for furnace temperatures up to 1500°C. Since the heat is radiated from a small surface, care must be taken in designing the furnace to secure uniformity of temperature.

Arc furnaces are most convenient for concentrating a large amount of heat in a small volume. This permits heating operations of short duration, an advantage for volatile substances. Temperatures up to 3000°C may easily be maintained in an industrial furnace by the use of one or more arcs. The temperature of the arc itself may vary from 3400 to 4000°C, depending on current density, atmospheric pressure, and electrode material. The furnace atmosphere may be varied from

oxidizing to reducing.   Industrial arc furnaces are used in the preparation of calcium carbide and steel, while in the laboratory they are
used for fusing oxides of manganese, zirconium, and thorium.   Arc
furnaces are not susceptible of precise control.

Thermocouples serve to measure furnace temperatures up to
1600°C.   Optical pyrometers or radiation pyrometers are generally
used to determine temperatures above 1100°C, without upper limit.

INDUCTION AND RADIATION FURNACES

The high frequency induction furnace consists of a solenoid to
produce an alternating magnetic field which can induce a current in a
conducting substance of any shape placed inside it.   The uniformity of
temperature is best when the sample is a liquid metal, since it is then
stirred electromagnetically.   Uniformity is poorest when the sample
is a solid of low thermal conductivity.   Electrical nonconductors, such
as refractory oxides, are surrounded by a conducting cylinder of
tungsten or graphite and are heated indirectly.   Induction furnace
temperatures are not limited by the characteristics of refractory materials.   With an induction furnace one can maintain conditions of high
purity.

Cathode ray furnaces employ electron bombardment of the sample
to produce heating.   Since they operate only in a vacuum they are
essentially laboratory apparatus.

Concentrated radiation furnaces use mirrors to focus radiation on
the specimen.   By this method a carbon arc may be used to heat a
sample without contaminating it.   In the furnace developed by
Straubel, solar radiation (about 1 kw/m² at the earth's surface) is
concentrated by a heliostat and mirrors about 3 m in diameter.   A
small tungsten cylinder placed at the focus is brought to 3000°C in
0.5 min.   Since the maximum energy of the sun's spectrum lies just
below 1 micron, it can be transmitted through walls of vitreous silica
into an evacuated chamber without heating the walls.   Rapid heating,
conditions of purity, and, for some experiments, the absence of electric
and magnetic fields, are the advantages of the sun furnace.   Its
obvious disadvantages are cumbersome dimensions and an unreliable
source of heat.

Very high temperatures have been produced by exploding a wire
electrically with the discharge from a condenser.   The extreme temperature is produced only momentarily.   So far the temperature cf

the exploding wire, originally thought to be as high as 20,000°K, has not been determined accurately.

SUMMARY

Owing to intermolecular forces, it is possible to change the internal energy of real gases by changing pressure or volume, as well as by temperature changes.

The behavior of most gases can be represented by a van der Waals equation of state

$$\left(p + \frac{a}{v^2}\right)(v - b) = RT$$

A Joule-Thomson throttled expansion of a gas results in cooling, provided the temperature is below the inversion temperature

$$T_i = 2a/bR$$

Gases are liquefied by processes which utilize adiabatic expansion of the gas with performance of mechanical work, or by throttled expansion of the gas under such conditions that the Joule-Thomson effect produces cooling.

The lowest temperatures have been produced by the use of magnetic fields to remove the disorder of spinning electrons in paramagnetic atoms.

Temperatures are measured by resistance thermometers to 14°K, by helium thermometers as low as 0.7°K, and in terms of paramagnetic susceptibilities to yet lower temperatures.

The high temperatures attainable with flames, electric resistance furnaces, and radiation furnaces are limited chiefly by the refractory materials available and by the uniformity of control required.

Optical pyrometer measurements based on the radiation laws are possible to the highest attainable temperatures.

REFERENCES FOR SUPPLEMENTARY READING

1. Am. Inst. of Physics, *Temperature—Its Measurement and Control in Science and Industry*, pp. 764–772; W. M. Cohn, "The Field of Extreme High Temperatures," Reinhold Publishing Corp., 1941.
2. Beattie, J. A., "A Simple Equation for the Joule-Thomson Effect in a Real Gas," *Phys. Rev.*, **35,** 643 (1930).
3. Brucksch, W. F., Jr., and W. T. Ziegler, "Studies in Superconductivity, II Evaporated Lead Films," *Phys. Rev.*, **60,** 348 (1942).
4. Collins, S. C., "A Helium Cryostat," *Rev. Sci. Instruments*, **18,** 157 (1947).
5. Cork, J. M., "A Method for Determining Critical Constants . . .," *Rev. Sci. Instruments*, **1,** 563 (1930).
6. Darrow, K. K., "Helium the Superfluid," *Rev. Modern Phys.*, **12,** 257 (1940).
7. Giaque, W. F., "A Proposed Method of Producing Temperatures Considerably Below 1° Absolute," *J. Am. Chem. Soc.*, **49,** 1864 (1927).
8. Jackson, L. C., *Low Temperature Physics*, 2nd ed., Methuen & Co., 1948.
9. Kanolt, C. W., "Production of Cold," *J. Optical Soc. Am.*, **9,** 411 (1924).

10. Kapitza, P., "Expansion Turbine Producing Low Temperatures Applied to Air Liquefaction," *J. Phys. (USSR)*, **1,** 7 (1939).
11. Roebuck, J. R., "A Porous Plug Method for the Mechanical Equivalent of Heat," *Phys. Rev.*, **2** (2), 79 (1913).
12. Roebuck, J. R., and H. Osterberg, "The Joule-Thomson Effect in Nitrogen," *Phys. Rev.*, **48,** 450 (1935).
13. Ruhemann, M., and B. Ruhemann, *Low Temperature Physics*, Cambridge University Press, 1938.
14. Taft, R., and J. Stareck, "Relationships between Melting Points, Normal Boiling Points and Critical Temperatures," *J. Phys. Chem.*, **34,** 2307 (1930).
15. Walden, L., "The Construction of Laboratory Electric Furnaces . . .," *J. Sci. Instruments*, **16,** 1 (1939).

QUESTIONS

1. Distinguish between a gas and a vapor. Explain what is meant by the critical temperature of a gas.

2. Why is the liquefaction of air important in the production of oxygen for industrial use and medical use, the separation of argon for gas-filled electric lamps, and the preparation of neon for advertising signs?

3. What methods would you employ to measure temperatures of approximately the following values: 6000°K, 1700°K, 300°K, 20°K, 2°K, and 0.2°K?

4. Liquid air boils at $-196°C$, yet a vacuum flask filled with liquid air and left open in a warm room may still contain some liquid a day later. Explain.

5. Discuss the possibility of a substance having a boiling point at a lower temperature than its melting point.

6. Show that there is no temperature change when an ideal gas performs a throttling process.

7. Which of the gases listed in Table 13.1 would you expect to have the smallest values of the van der Waals constants a and b?

8. Prove that when an ideal gas is expanded in a throttling process the net work done is zero.

Chapter 14

||||||||||||||||||||||||||

SPECIAL METHODS OF TEM-
PERATURE MEASUREMENT

FLAME TEMPERATURES |||||||| *SPECTRAL LINE
REVERSAL* |||||||| *PYROMETRIC CONES* |||||||| *THER-
MOCOLORS* |||||||| *INTERFEROMETER* ||||||||

DETERMINATION OF GAS TEMPERATURES

The temperature of a gas placed in an isothermal enclosure can be measured easily. Any measuring device placed in the gas attains the equilibrium temperature and indicates correctly the temperature of the gas.

In problems of practical interest, however, the gas temperature is often quite different from that of its surroundings and any pyrometer measurements made in the gas without suitable precautions are liable to large errors. The desirability of shielding the thermometer from radiation and of increasing the heat transfer from gas to thermometer by forced convection has long been recognized in the design of the aspiration thermometers used for meteorological measurements.

Gas temperature measurements are of considerable industrial importance in the control of boiler furnaces, heat exchangers, glass furnaces, etc. An outline of the principal methods and precautions used may suggest designs for particular applications.[1]

(a) *Radiation protecting shield.* If a stream of gas at temperature T is passing through a tube whose walls are at a lower temperature T_w, a

245

pyrometer placed in the gas assumes a temperature T_p intermediate to T_w and T. If a is the coefficient for energy exchange by conduction and convection between the pyrometer and the gas, and b is the radiation coefficient, one can write for unit area

$$a(T - T_p) = b(T_p^4 - T_w^4)$$ (1)

If shield S (Fig. 14.1) is interposed between the pyrometer and the wall, it will assume a temperature T_1 lower than T but higher than T_w. The equation for thermal equilibrium then becomes

$$a(T - T_p') = b(T_p'^4 - T_1^4)$$ (2)

where T_p' is the new temperature of the pyrometer. Since T_1^4 is much greater than T_w, T_p' is greater than T_p and the accuracy of the pyrometer indication is improved. A second shield S_2 may be added to make T_p'' approach more nearly the true gas temperature. But unless the gas velocity through the shields is appreciable, considerable error remains.

(b) *Thermocouples with different diameters*. The radiation error of a thermocouple decreases as the diameter of the wire is made smaller. Because of the existence of a gas film, the effective area receiving heat by convection is larger than the actual surface of the wire losing heat by radiation. The use of very small thermocouples is impractical because of their fragility. However, if measurements are made with a number of thermocouples of different diameters, a curve of indicated temperature against wire diameter may be drawn and extrapolated to zero diameter to obtain an estimate of the gas temperature.

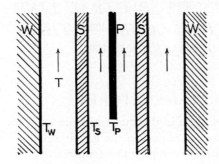

FIG. 14.1.   Radiation shields for a pyrometer.

(c) *Radiation, optical, or color pyrometers* are subject to large errors when used to indicate gas temperatures directly. They generally measure a surface temperature. Their readings require corrections, usually unknown, for emissivity and for thickness of the gas layer.

(d) *High velocity thermocouple.* A thermocouple using a radiation shield and forced convection appears to be the most satisfactory method of measuring gas temperatures in many industrial applications. Figure 14.2 shows a pyrometer of this design for measuring temperatures in slag-bearing gases up to 3100°F. The gases are drawn through a

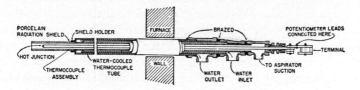

FIG. 14.2. Water-cooled high-velocity aradiant thermocouple.

water-cooled tube by means of an aspirator operating by compressed air. At the furnace end, a thermocouple hot junction surrounded by a porcelain radiation shield is heated by the high-velocity gases flowing past, thus giving the gas temperature. The construction facilitates replacement of the shield or the thermocouple junction when the instrument becomes plugged or damaged by slag. Similar instruments have been variously called suction, aspiration, and aradiant-

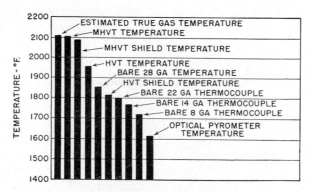

FIG. 14.3. Gas temperature measured by various pyrometers.

convection pyrometers. It is obvious that the principles of this type of pyrometer can be used with temperature-indicating instruments other than thermocouples. Figure 14.3 shows the gas temperatures indicated in a certain test by an optical pyrometer, various bare thermocouples, a high-velocity thermocouple, and a high-velocity thermocouple with multiple shields. Such a comparison is an example of the misinformation supplied by even good instruments when used under conditions other than that for which they were calibrated.

(e) *Heated-shield high velocity thermocouple.* Consider that Fig. 14.1 had two shields, co-axial alundum tubes, the outer one S_2 provided with a heating coil. When the gas is aspirated through the tubes, the heating of S_2 is varied until its temperature T_2 (read on an auxiliary thermocouple) is equal to the temperature T_p indicated by the pyrometer. The temperature T_p is then taken as an accurate indication of the gas temperature, since there is no net radiation from the pyrometer.

(f) *Resistance thermometers, glass thermometers, and expansion thermometers* are usually limited to measuring gas temperatures below 500°C. They are usually less accurate than thermocouples and more difficult to install.

(g) *Dynamic gas thermometers.* The rate of flow of gas through an orifice varies as the square root of its absolute temperature.

(h) *Calorimetric method.* The initial temperature of a gas is calculated by measuring the heat content of a sample. The method is difficult and slow.

(i) *Gas temperature from velocity of sound.* The fact that the velocity of sound varies as the square root of the absolute temperature of a gas offers an attractive but little-used method of measuring gas temperature.

(j) *Interference* and *photography* provide methods of measuring gas temperature which are described below.

FLAME TEMPERATURES

The temperature of a flame may be defined and measured as the temperature of a solid body that is in thermal equilibrium with it. In using a thermocouple or a resistance thermometer to measure a flame temperature directly, one encounters the same sort of difficulties as outlined under gas temperature measurements. A more desirable method is one that does not disturb conditions in the flame and that takes account of radiation losses from the measuring element.

One useful method of measuring flame temperature makes use of a wire, heated electrically, which is placed in the flame.[5] The wire loses heat by radiation, by conduction to its supports, and by convection to the surrounding gas. If the wire is at the temperature of the gas, no heat loss occurs by convection, but only by radiation and con-duction. Similar conditions prevail if the wire is placed in a vacuum. From a current-temperature graph, the point is found at which both the current and the temperature are the same for the wire in the flame as in a vacuum. This wire temperature is determined by a thermocouple or by an optical pyrometer and is taken as being the temperature of the gas.

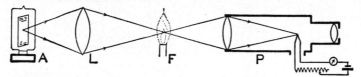

FIG. 14.4.   Optical measurement of flame temperature, Kurlbaum's method.

If the gases that comprise a luminous flame are in chemical equilib-rium at the temperature of the flame and are the only source of radia-tion (assumptions which are not always justified), then Kirchhoff's law may be applied to measure the flame temperature by an optical method. Light from an auxiliary source A (an incandescent tungsten foil, an arc, or a blackbody) is directed through the flame and on the objective of an optical pyrometer P, Fig. 14.4. The brightness observed in the pyrometer is the brightness $b_{\lambda T}$ of the flame at tem-perature T and in addition the brightness of the auxiliary source at temperature T' that is transmitted by the flame, $B_{\lambda T'}(1 - \alpha_\lambda)$. This will be equal to the brightness of the auxiliary source $B_{\lambda T'}$ alone, provided $b_{\lambda T} = B_{\lambda T'}\alpha_\lambda$, that is if $T' = T$. Observations are made by regulating the auxiliary source until the indication of the optical pyrometer does not change when the flame is interposed. The reading of the optical pyrometer then gives the flame temperature.

The method of spectral line reversal is widely used for measuring temperatures of nonluminous flames. A lens L_1 (Fig. 14.5) forms an image of an auxiliary light source A in the flame. A second lens L_2 projects the image of the source and the flame on the slit S of a spectro-scope. The flame is colored by the addition of a small amount of a metallic salt (usually sodium) which furnishes radiation of wavelength λ. If B_λ is the spectral brightness of the source A and b_λ is the spectral brightness of the flame, the image seen in the spectroscope has a brightness $B_\lambda + b_\lambda(1 - \alpha_\lambda)$. The brightness matches that of the continuous background illumination from A provided $B_\lambda/\alpha_\lambda = b_\lambda$. From Kirchhoff's law, $B_{T\lambda}/\alpha_\lambda$ represents the brightness of a blackbody at the temperature of the radiating particles. Hence the flame temperature is determined by adjusting A until the sodium line matches the background illumination, and then measuring the temperature of A with an optical pyrometer.

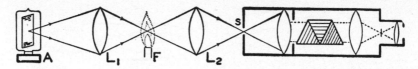

FIG. 14.5. Flame temperature by Féry's sodium line-reversal method.

The sodium line reversal method has been extensively applied to measuring internal combustion engine temperatures.[3, 16] A quartz window is placed in the cylinder and a stroboscopic shutter permits temperature measurements to be made during any desired part of the operating cycle.

PYROMETRIC CONES

Pyrometric "cones" are slender trihedral pyramids made from mixtures of china clay, feldspar, whiting, flint, and fluxes, which by their softening and deformation indicate the heat treatment to which they have been subjected. The cones are particularly useful guides to the proper firing of ceramic products since they behave thermochemically much like the ware. The term "pyrometric cone equivalent" (*PCE*) is used to designate the temperature (strictly, the heat treatment) indicated by pyrometric cones.

Pyrometric cones were made for private use by Lauth and Vogt at the Sèvres Pottery in 1882. They were made commerically over an extended temperature range by Seger in 1886. The cone series has subsequently been extended to indicate temperatures over the range from 600 to 2000°C in intervals of about 20 C°.[15] Table 14.1 lists a series of standard cones.[14]

Cones are mounted on a plaque at a slight inclination, with the aid of a template, 8° from the vertical being taken as the standard. They are so placed in the kiln as to be subject to a representative heat condition, and are protected from flame or radiation from surfaces

TABLE 14.1 TEMPERATURE EQUIVALENTS OF CONES

Cone Number	When Fired Slowly, 20C°/hr		When Fired Rapidly, 150C°/hr	
	°C	°F	°C	°F
The Soft Series				
022	585	1085	605	1121
021	595	1103	615	1139
020	625	1157	650	1202
019	630	1166	660	1220
018	670	1238	720	1328
017	720	1328	770	1418
016	735	1355	795	1463
015	770	1418	805	1481
014	795	1463	830	1526
013	825	1517	860	1580
012	840	1544	875	1607
011	875	1607	905	1661
The Low-temperature Series				
010	890	1634	895	1643
09	930	1706	930	1706
08	945	1733	950	1742
07	975	1787	990	1814
06	1005	1841	1015	1859
05	1030	1886	1040	1904
04	1050	1922	1060	1940
03	1080	1976	1115	2039
02	1095	2003	1125	2057
01	1110	2030	1145	2093
1	1125	2057	1160	2120
2	1135	2075	1165	2129
3	1145	2093	1170	2138
4	1165	2129	1190	2174
5	1180	2156	1205	2201
6	1190	2174	1230	2246
7	1210	2210	1250	2282
8	1225	2237	1260	2300
9	1250	2282	1285	2345
10	1260	2300	1305	2381
11	1285	2345	1325	2417
12	1310	2390	1335	2435
13	1350	2462	1350	2462
14	1390	2534	1400	2552
15	1410	2570	1435	2615
16	1450	2642	1465	2669
17	1465	2669	1475	2687
18	1485	2705	1490	2714
19	1515	2759	1520	2768
20	1520	2768	1530	2786

TABLE 14.1 TEMPERATURE EQUIVALENTS OF CONES (*Continued*)

Cone Number	When Heated at 100C°/hr	
	°C	°F
The High-temperature Series		
23	1580	2876
26	1595	2903
27	1605	2921
28	1615	2939
29	1640	2984
30	1650	3002
31	1680	3056
32	1700	3092
32½	1725	3137
33	1745	3173
34	1760	3200
35	1785	3245
36.	1810	3290
37	1820	3308
38	1835	3335
*39	1865	3389
40	1885	3425
41	1970	3578
42	2015	3659

* The last four cones were heated 600C°/hr.

markedly hotter than the rest of the kiln.   Reducing or sulfurous atmospheres have a detrimental effect on the proper deformation of some cones.

Cones are not pyrometers, and should not be so used.   Through the use of radiation pyrometers and modern automatic control, an increasing number of ceramic furnaces are now being held within temperature limits that were not feasible so long as the cone was the only practical method of measuring temperature.   Cones, however, measure the maturity of the ware in an accurate manner and in a way that can be compared from plant to plant.

THERMOCOLORS

Temperature-sensitive paints indicate, by a change of color, when the temperature of the surface has exceeded a predetermined value. This chemical method of temperature measurement has certain obvious advantages over more exact physical methods.   It gives information about an entire surface at a glance. Indications are independent of the distance. It provides a simple and inexpensive way of safeguarding bearings, motors, circuit breakers, radiators, drying chambers, and the like from overheating. It makes possible the quick determination of isothermals on airplane motor cylinders, indication of faulty insulation on heating tanks, and the detection of burners which have "struck back."

Thermocolors are made of salts of different metals (particularly copper, cobalt, nickel, chromium, molybdenum, and uranium) in compounds which change color at certain temperatures through loss of water, ammonia, carbon dioxide, in changing from orthosalts to pyrosalts. Many thermocolors are organic or inorganic compounds with ammonia which contain colored ions. Some pigments show multiple color changes. This suggests the goal of a thermocolor paint that can be sprayed on a surface to indicate at a glance its temperature over a wide range of values.

For some applications reversible color changes are suitable, but more often irreversible changes are desired for permanent indications. It is difficult to find colors whose changes are stable at low temperatures. The color change is somewhat dependent on time as well as temperature. For rapid heating it occurs at higher temperature.

SURFACE TEMPERATURES

Surface temperatures may be measured with the aid of substances which melt at specific temperatures. A series of such substances is available commercially in the form of crayons, pellets, and lacquers. These Tempil° products permit measurements of some fifty temperatures in the range 125 to 1700°F, each with a mean accuracy of 1 per cent of the stated value. They provide indications at lower temperatures where pyrometric cones and optical pyrometers are not applicable. While pyrometric cones are primarily for use in furnaces, Tempilstiks can be used whenever there is a surface upon which a mark can be made. The mark made with a Tempilstik melts and becomes shiny in appearance when its melting point is reached. The Tempil° indicators are used to signal desired preheating temperatures in welding metals or in the molding of glass, rubber, or plastics; to check the approach of safe temperature limits in the machining of castings; and to warn of dangerously high temperatures in the bearings or insulation of machinery.

PHOTOTHERMOMETRY

With the development of infrared-sensitive photographic plates it has become possible to photograph hot bodies by their own radiation and from the photographs to determine temperatures.[13] The blackening of the photographic plate depends on the temperature of the source since each temperature is characterized by a definite radiation energy. The lower limit of usefulness for photothermometry is determined by plate sensitivity and intensity of radiation. It is approximately 250 to 270°C for large aperture lenses and 15-hr exposures. There is no upper limit. There is a rapid increase in radiant energy with temperature. As the temperature increases from 275 to 400°C the radiant energy (for $\lambda = 0.85\mu$) increases from 3.23×10^{-6} to 933×10^{-6} cal cm^{-3}. The method of photothermometry is not good for absolute measurements. Uncertainties may be of the order of 60 to 120C°. It does, however, determine temperature ratios with good accuracy, and is particularly useful in obtaining quickly the isothermals of engine cylinders, furnaces, insulating jackets, and the like.

The monochromatic radiant intensities J_1 and J_2 corresponding to source temperatures T_1 and T_2 are related by

$$\log J_1 - \log J_2 = \frac{c_2}{\lambda}\left(\frac{1}{T_2} - \frac{1}{T_1}\right) \tag{3}$$

For small temperature differences the quantity in parentheses may be replaced by $b(T_1 - T_2)$. In calibrating the photographic plate, temperature differences, proportional to logarithms of energy, are plotted as abscissas and plate darkening as ordinates, giving curves similar to the familiar density—log intensity curves of ordinary photography.[12]

The standard used in calibrating the plate may be an electrically heated nickel cylinder whose temperature is measured with a thermocouple. Rapid calibration from a single exposure is made by photographing the temperature parabola existing in an aluminum or silver rod heated at one end.

Commercial infrared plates are available for photothermometry. These are best stored in a refrigerator and used within a few months. They may be sensitized with ammonia immediately before use. Rodinal developer is used for steep gradation, or metol-hydroquinone or glycine for smaller γ.

Photothermometry in a darkened room requires no filters. If extraneous light is present it is kept from the plate by a red or "black" filter, such as a cobalt oxide glass which has been heated to blackness.

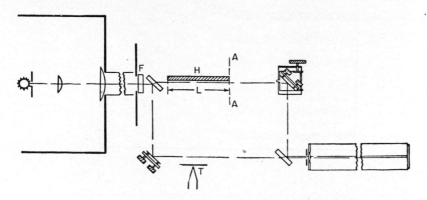

FIG. 14.6. Interferometer for temperature measurement.

INTERFEROMETER MEASUREMENT OF TEMPERA-TURE

The "heat waves" often seen near a hot surface suggest a possible method of measuring temperature.   Schmidt demonstrated that photographs of the atmospheric streaks in a temperature field near a hot body were susceptible of quantitative measurement.   Kennard[8] used a more sensitive interferometer method to investigate isothermal patterns, to calculate convective heat transfer, and to investigate how closely film theory agreed with experiment.

The Mach interferometer used by Kennard is represented in Fig. 14.6, where H is the test body (plate or cylinder) of length L, AA is the plane in which the fringes were brought to virtual focus, and F is a filter which transmits only the green mercury light.   A shielded thermocouple is at T.

The method of measuring temperature from fringe shift can be indicated with the aid of Fig. 14.7.   Let A and B be two adjacent fringes formed by monochromatic light passing through the column of air adjacent to the heated surface H.   The shift of one fringe at P relative to Q indicates that there is one less light wave in the path through P than there would be if the temperature of P were the same

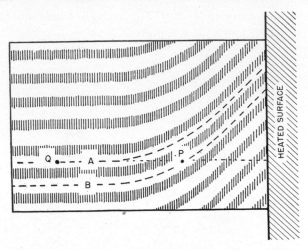

Fig. 14.7.   Method of measuring temperature from fringe shift.

as at Q.   The temperature of the air is obtained from its density which is related to the refractive index by the Lorenz-Lorentz equation

$$\frac{n^2 - 1}{n^2 + 2} = C\rho \qquad (4)$$

Fig. 14.8.   Fringes about horizontal heated cylinders: left, diameter = 1.27 cm; right, diameter = 5 mm.

where n is the index of refraction, ρ the density, and C is a constant. For an index of refraction of the order of 1.0003 this reduces approximately to

$$n - 1 = \tfrac{3}{2}C\rho \qquad (5)$$

If, under one set of conditions, N_1 and n_1 are the number of light waves over a given path and the index of refraction, respectively, and N_2 and n_2 are the same quantities for a second set of conditions

$$n_1 = \frac{N_1}{N_0} \qquad \text{and} \qquad n_2 = \frac{N_2}{N_0} \qquad (6)$$

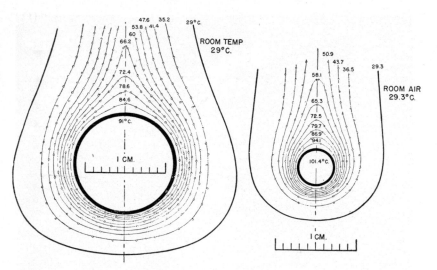

FIG. 14.9.   Isothermals about horizontal heated cylinders.

where N_0 is the number of light waves in the same path in a vacuum.

If L is the length of path under consideration, which is the length of the heated surface L_0 plus a small end correction ΔL, and if λ_0 is the wavelength in a vacuum of the light used

$$N_0 = \frac{L}{\lambda_0} \qquad (7)$$

From Eq. (5) the change of index of refraction for a given change in density is

$$n_1 - n_2 = \tfrac{3}{2}C(\rho_1 - \rho_2) \qquad (8)$$

Inserting the values given in Eqs. (6) and (7) and rearranging yields

$$\mathcal{N}_1 - \mathcal{N}_2 = \frac{3}{2} C\rho_1 \frac{L}{\lambda_0}\left(1 - \frac{\rho_2}{\rho_1}\right) = (n_1 - 1)\frac{L}{\lambda_0}\left(1 - \frac{\rho_2}{\rho_1}\right) \qquad (9)$$

If the change in density is caused by a change in temperature only

$$\frac{\rho_2}{\rho_1} = \frac{T_1}{T_2} \qquad (10)$$

whence
$$\mathcal{N}_1 = \mathcal{N}_2 = (n_1 - 1)\frac{L}{\lambda_0}\frac{T_2 - T_1}{T_2} \qquad (11)$$

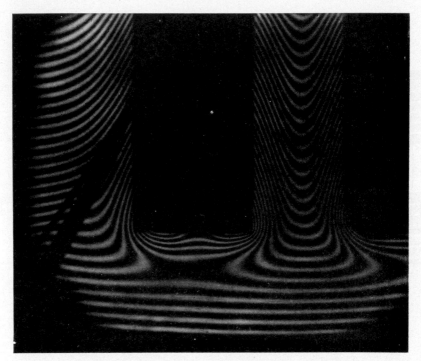

Fig. 14.10.   Fringes about parallel vertical heated plates.

Since in the interferometer the change in number of light waves in a given path is equal to the fringe displacement, Eq. (11) gives the fringe displacement as measured in fringe widths that takes place when the temperature is changed from T_1 to T_2. Letting T_1 and n_1 be the temperature and index of refraction of room air, Eq. (11) may be solved explicitly for the temperature rise above the room temperature giving

$$T_2 - T_1 = T_1 \frac{\Delta \mathcal{N}}{(n_1 - 1) \dfrac{L}{\lambda_0} - \Delta \mathcal{N}} \tag{12}$$

The quantity $(n_1 - 1)$ is given in the International Critical Tables for standard conditions and may be calculated for any conditions by using the gas laws, making proper correction for humidity.

Figure 14.8 is a photograph of the interference fringe pattern observed in the air near two horizontal heated cylinders of diameters 1.27 cm. and 5 mm. respectively. Figure 14.9 shows the isothermals for free convection calculated from the fringe pattern. In practice, heating surfaces are often in the form of parallel plates. Figure 14.10 shows the interference fringes about the lower portion of two vertical parallel plates, 11 cm wide and 21.4 cm high, separated by 0.67 cm. Such a pattern can be used to measure heat flux.

SUMMARY

Experience in measuring gas temperatures emphasizes the necessity of securing thermal equilibrium between pyrometer and gas. Accuracy is enhanced by adequate convection, by prevention of or compensation for radiation losses, and by using a pyrometer only under the conditions for which it has been calibrated.

The spectral line reversal method uses Kirchhoff's law to measure the temperature of luminous and nonluminous flames, being applicable in particular to the study of internal-combustion engine temperatures.

Pyrometric cones indicate heat treatment, in which factors other than temperature must be considered.

Thermocolors and Tempil° materials provide visual indication of surface temperatures, chiefly valuable in warning of overheating.

Photothermometry, based on laws of radiation and photography, permits rapid determination of temperature and isothermals over extended surfaces.

Another photographic method uses an interferometer to measure temperature in terms of refractive index, a method useful in designing radiating surfaces for optimum heat transfer.

REFERENCES FOR SUPPLEMENTARY READING

1. Am. Inst. of Physics, *Temperature—Its Measurement and Control in Science and Industry*, pp. 775–804; Mullikin, H. F., "Gas Temperature Measurements and the High-Velocity Thermocouple," Reinhold Publishing Corp., 1941.
2. Andrews, D. H., and others, "Attenuated Superconductors, I. For

Measuring Infrared Radiation," *Rev. Sci. Instruments*, **13**, 281 (1942); "A Fast Superconducting Bolometer," *J. Optical Soc. Am.*, **36**, 518 (1946).

3. David, W. T., "Temperature of Flame Gases," *Nature*, **152**, 278 (1943); **150**, 320 (1942); **139**, 67 (1937); *Phil. Mag.*, **23**, 345 (1937); **21**, 280 (1936).

4. Glasser, O., *Medical Physics*, Chicago: The Year Book Publishers, Inc., 1944.

5. Griffiths, E., and J. H. Awberry, "The Measurement of Flame Temperatures," *Proc. Roy. Soc., London*, **123**, 401 (1929).

6. Hall, J. A., "Photographic Photometry Applied to the Measurement of Liquid Steel Temperatures," *Phot. J.*, Sec. B, **86B**, 117 (1946).

7. Hottel, H. C., and A. Kalitinsky, "Temperature Measurements in High-Velocity Air Streams," *J. Applied Mechanics*, **12**, A25–A32 (1945).

8. Kennard, R. B., "An Optical Method for Measuring Temperature Distribution and Convective Heat Transfer," *Bur. Standards J. Research*, **8**, 787 (1932).

9. Larsen, B. M., and W. E. Shenk, "Temperature Measurement with Blocking-layer Photo-cells," *J. Applied Phys.*, **11**, 555 (1940).

10. Lee, E., and R. C. Parker, "Use of Lead Sulphide Photo-conductivity Cells for High-speed Pyrometry," *Nature*, **158**, 518 (1946).

11. Lewis, B., and G. von Elbe, "Flame Temperature," *J. Applied Phys.*, **11**, 698 (1940); "Stability and Structure of Burner Flames," *J. Chem. Phys.*, **11**, 75 (1943).

12. Mack, J. E., and M. J. Martin, *The Photographic Process*, Chap. 6, McGraw-Hill Book Co., Inc., 1939.

13. Neubert, P., "Photothermometry," *Arch. Warmewirt*, **19**, 30 (1938) Contains bibliography.

14. *The Properties and Uses of Pyrometric Cones*, The Edward Orton Jr. Ceramic Foundation, Columbus, Ohio.

15. Rea, R. F., "Temperature-measuring Cones," *J. Am. Ceram. Soc.*, **21**, 98 (1938).

16. Watts, S. S., B. Evans, and J. Lloyd, "Flame Travel in an I. C. Engine," *Engineering*, **143**, 713 (1937).

QUESTIONS

1. How do radiation shields around a thermometer element in a stream of hot gas enable the element to indicate more closely the temperature of the gas?

2. What equipment would you use to measure the temperature of the exhaust gas from an aircraft engine in flight?

3. Design a resonance tube apparatus that might be used to measure the temperature in an oven in terms of the speed of sound in the gas.

4. What equipment and procedure would you use to calibrate a set of pyrometric cones for use under conditions of rapid (500 C°/hr) heating? How would you expect this calibration to compare with that of Table 14.1?

5. Sketch an apparatus with which the melting points of crayons designed for surface temperature measurements might be checked against a standard thermo-

couple. State clearly how the crayons might be calibrated and the uncertainties estimated.

6. It is desired to map isothermal lines on the cooling fins of an aircraft internal combustion engine while operating under test conditions. Suggest two methods that might be used and compare them as to accuracy and convenience.

Chapter 15

||||||||||||||||||||||||||||

INTERNATIONAL TEMPERA-
TURE SCALE

*INTERNATIONAL AGREEMENTS ON THE
TEMPERATURE SCALE* |||||| *EXPERIMENTAL
PROCEDURES RECOMMENDED* ||||||

INTERNATIONAL STANDARDS

The General Conference on Weights and Measures is the diplomatic body, representing 33 participating nations, that has power to adopt recommendations concerning standards of weights and measures for international use. The recommendations are made by the International Committee on Weights and Measures which nominally consists of 18 scientists (not more than one from any nation) elected by the General Conference. The General Conference is scheduled to meet at intervals of 6 years and the International Committee at intervals of 2 years.

1927 SCALE

The Kelvin scale is recognized as the fundamental scale to which all temperatures should ultimately be referable. There is considerable experimental difficulty, however, in the measurement of temperature on any thermodynamic scale. Hence the first International Temperature Scale was adopted by the Seventh General Conference on Weights and Measures in 1927 and is now known as the International

Temperature Scale of 1927.[2] This scale agreed with the thermo-dynamic centigrade scale as closely as possible for the knowledge then available. It specified (a) the values for the fixed temperatures at which instruments are to be calibrated, (b) the types of instruments to be used in realizing the scale, (c) the equations to be used for inter-polating or extrapolating from fixed points, and (d) the experimental procedures recommended.

REVISIONS

The Seventh General Conference recommended that international thermometric conferences be called by the International Committee to revise the temperature scale as occasion required. The Advisory Committee on Thermometry, created by the International Committee, revised the text of the scale of 1927 in July 1939 for proposal to the International Committee, but no action was taken because World War II began before the date originally scheduled for the Ninth General Conference. During 1948 both the Advisory Committee and the Ninth General Conference met and approved a new text for the International Temperature Scale.

1948 SCALE

The definition of the International Temperature Scale of 1948 appears in the following paragraphs. With it are listed some of the provisions of the 1927 scale, for comparison.

Temperatures on the International Temperature Scale are desig-nated as °C and are denoted by the symbol t. The designation °C should be applied in the future to temperatures on the last scale adopted previous to the time at which the designation is used. When-ever necessary to avoid ambiguity, temperatures may be expressed as °C (Int. 1927) or °C (Int. 1948).

The scale is based upon a number of fixed and reproducible equi-librium temperatures (fixed points) to which numerical values are assigned, and upon specified formulas for the relations between tem-perature and the indications of the instruments calibrated at these fixed points. The fixed points and the numerical values assigned to them are given in Table 15.1. These values, in each case, define the equilibrium temperature corresponding to a pressure of 1 atm (standard), defined as 1,013,250 dynes/cm². The last decimal place given for each of the values of the primary fixed points merely represents the degree of reproducibility of that fixed point.

TABLE 15.1 FUNDAMENTAL AND PRIMARY FIXED POINTS

Fixed point, temperature of equilibrium	Temperature, °C	
	(Int. 1927)	(Int. 1948)
(a) Between liquid oxygen and its vapor (oxygen point)	−182.97	−182.97
(b) Between ice and air saturated water (ice point) (*Fundamental fixed point,* 1948)................	0.00	0.00
(c) Between liquid water and its vapor (steam point) (*Fundamental fixed point,* 1948)...............	100.00	100.00
(d) Between liquid sulfur and its vapor (sulfur point).	444.60	444.60
(e) Between solid and liquid silver (silver point).....	960.50	960.80
(f) Between solid and liquid gold (gold point).......	1063.00	1063.00

The means available for interpolation lead to a division of the scale into four parts.

(a) *From 0°C to the freezing point of antimony* the temperature t is defined by the formula

$$R_t = R_0(1 + At + Bt^2) \tag{1}$$

where R_t is the resistance at temperature t of the platinum resistor between the branch points formed by the junctions of the current and potential leads of a standard resistance thermometer. The constant R_0 is the resistance at 0°C, and the constants A and B are to be determined from measured values of R_t at the steam and sulfur points. The platinum in a standard resistance thermometer shall be annealed, and of such purity that R_{100}/R_0 is greater than 1.3910.

The 1927 scale applied Eq. (1) from 0 to 660°C and required that R_{100}/R_0 should not be less than 1.390.

(b) *From the oxygen point to 0°C* the temperature t is defined by the formula

$$R_t = R_0[1 + At + Bt^2 + C(t - 100)t^3] \tag{2}$$

where R_t, R_0, A, and B are determined in the same manner as in (a) above, and the constant C is calculated from the measured value of R_t at the oxygen point.

The 1927 scale used Eq. (2) to define temperature t from -190 to $0°C$. It specified that a standard thermometer for use below $0°C$ must, in addition to the requirements in (a), satisfy the requirement that $R_{-182.97}/R_0$ not exceed 0.250.

(c) *From the freezing point of antimony to the gold point*, the temperature t is defined by the formula

$$E = a + bt + ct^2 \tag{3}$$

where E is the emf of a standard thermocouple of Pt *vs.* Pt–Rh alloy when one junction is at $0°C$ and the other is at the temperature t. The constants a, b, and c are to be calculated from measured values of E at the freezing point of antimony and at the silver and gold points. The antimony used in determining these constants shall be such that its freezing temperature, determined with a standard resistance thermometer, is not lower than $630.3°C$. Alternatively the thermocouple may be calibrated by direct comparison with a standard resistance thermometer in a bath at any uniform temperature between $630.3°C$ and $630.7°C$.

The platinum wire of the standard thermocouple shall be annealed and of such purity that the ratio R_{100}/R_0 is greater than 1.3910. The alloy wire shall consist nominally of 90 per cent platinum and 10 per cent rhodium by weight. When one junction is at $0°C$, and the other at the freezing point of antimony ($630.5°C$), silver, or gold, the completed thermocouple shall have emf's, in microvolts, such that

$$E_{Au} = 10,300 \pm 50 \, \mu v$$

$$E_{Au} - E_{Ag} = 1185 + 0.158(E_{Au} - 10,310) \pm 3\mu v$$

$$E_{Au} - E_{Sb} = 4776 + 0.631(E_{Au} - 10,310) \pm 5\mu v$$

The 1927 scale specified that the temperature t should be determined by Eq. (3) from 660 to $1063°C$. The purity of platinum of the standard thermocouple was specified by stating that R_{100}/R_0 should not be less than 1.390.

(d) Above the gold point the temperature t is defined by the formula derived from Planck's law

$$\frac{J_t}{J_{Au}} = \frac{e^{\frac{c_2}{\lambda(t_{Au} + T_0)}} - 1}{e^{\frac{c_2}{\lambda(t + T_0)}} - 1} \tag{4}$$

in which J_t and J_{Au} are the radiant energies per unit wavelength interval at wavelength λ emitted per unit time by unit area of a blackbody at the temperature t and at the gold point t_{Au}, respectively. The value of the constant c_2 is 1.438 cm K°; T_0 is the temperature of the ice point in degrees Kelvin; λ is a wavelength of the visible spectrum; and e is the base of Napierian logarithms.

The 1927 scale defined a temperature t above 1063°C by the formula derived from Wien's law

$$\log_e \frac{\mathcal{J}_t}{\mathcal{J}_{1063}} = \frac{c_2}{\lambda} \left(\frac{1}{1336} - \frac{1}{(t + 273)} \right) \tag{5}$$

in which the constant c_2 was 1.432 cm K°. Equation (5) was taken as valid for values of wavelength and temperature that made $\lambda(t + 273)$ less than 0.3 cm degree. The scale thus was not defined for temperatures in excess of about 4300°C.

A comparison of the provisions of the 1948 scale with those of the 1927 scale shows that the experimental procedures are substantially unchanged. Only two of the revisions in the definition of the scale result in appreciable changes in the numerical values assigned to measured temperatures. The change in the value for the silver point from 960.5 to 960.8°C changes temperatures measured with the standard thermocouple. The adoption of a different value for the radiation constant c_2 changes all temperatures above the gold point, while the use of Planck's radiation formula instead of the Wien formula affects the very high temperatures. The Planck formula is consistent with the thermodynamic scale and consequently removes the upper limit which was imposed by Wien's law in the 1927 scale.

Other important modifications, which cause little or no change in the numerical values of temperatures but serve to make the scale more definite and reproducible, are (a) the termination of one part of the scale at the oxygen point instead of at $-190°C$, (b) the division of the scale at the freezing point of antimony (about 630°C) instead of at 660°C, (c) the requirements for higher purity of the platinum of the standard resistance thermometer and standard thermocouple, and for smaller permissible limits for the electromotive force of the standard thermocouple at the gold point.

The scale defined by the resistance thermometer remains substantially identical with the 1927 scale. In the range between 630°C and 1063°C, numerical values of temperature on the 1948 scale are higher than on the 1927 scale, the maximum difference being about 0.4° near 800°C.

RECOMMENDATIONS

The official texts of the 1927 and 1948 International Temperature Scales recommended apparatus, methods, and procedures for temperature measurements. These represented good practice at the time of writing, but the recommendations are advisory rather than mandatory. There is no intention of retarding the development and use of improvements and refinements. The reader who is interested in the experimental procedures recommended can find them in the papers cited.[2, 4]

For the sake of uniformity, the Advisory Committee recommended in 1948 that the temperature of the ice point on the Kelvin scale be taken as $273.15°K \pm 0.2$. In the United States of America, the value $273.16°K$ for the temperature of the ice point has been so generally accepted that its use now prevails in scientific publications and this value will probably continue to be used until a more accurate one has been agreed upon.

SECONDARY FIXED POINTS

In addition to the six fundamental and primary fixed points, certain other fixed points are available and may be useful for various purposes. Some of the more constant and reproducible of these fixed points and their temperatures on the International Temperature Scales of 1927 and 1948 are given in Table 15.2. The temperatures given are those corresponding to a pressure of 1 atm (standard), except for the triple points of water and of benzoic acid. The formulas for the variation of temperature with pressure are intended for use over the range from $p = 680$ to $p = 780$ mm of mercury.

TABLE 15.2 SECONDARY FIXED POINTS

Fixed point	Temperature, °C	
	(Int. 1927)	(Int. 1948)
Temperature of equilibrium between solid carbon dioxide and its vapor .... $$t_p = -78.5 + 0.1443(t_p + 273.2) \log\left(\frac{p}{760}\right) \quad (1927)$$ $$t_p = -78.5 + 12.12\left(\frac{p}{p_0} - 1\right) - 6.4\left(\frac{p}{p_0} - 1\right)^2 \quad (1948)$$	−78.5	−78.5

TABLE 15.2 Secondary Fixed Points (*Continued*)

Fixed point	Temperature, °C	
	(Int. 1927)	(Int. 1948)
Temperature of freezing mercury....................	−38.87	−38.87
Temperature of equilibrium between ice, water, and its vapor (triple point)...............................		+0.0100
Temperature of transition of sodium sulfate decahydrate	32.38	32.38
Temperature of the triple point of benzoic acid..........		122.36
Temperature of equilibrium between naphthalene and its vapor..	217.96	218.0

$$t_p = 217.96 + 0.208(t_p + 273.2) \log\left(\frac{p}{760}\right) \quad (1927)$$

$$t_p = 218.0 + 44.4\left(\frac{p}{p_0} - 1\right) - 19\left(\frac{p}{p_0} - 1\right)^2 \quad (1948)$$

Temperature of freezing tin........................	231.85	231.9
Temperature of equilibrium between benzophenone and its vapor..	305.9	305.9

$$t_p = 305.9 + 0.194(t_p + 273.2) \log\left(\frac{p}{760}\right) \quad (1927)$$

$$t_p = 305.9 + 48.8\left(\frac{p}{p_0} - 1\right) - 21\left(\frac{p}{p_0} - 1\right)^2 \quad (1948)$$

Temperature of freezing cadmium....................	320.9	320.9
Temperature of freezing lead........................	327.3	327.3
Temperature of equilibrium between mercury and its vapor.		356.58

$$t_p = 356.58 + 55.552\left(\frac{p}{p_0} - 1\right) -$$
$$23.03\left(\frac{p}{p_0} - 1\right)^2 + 14.0\left(\frac{p}{p_0} - 1\right)^3 \quad (1948)$$

Temperature of freezing zinc........................	419.45	419.5
Temperature of freezing antimony....................	630.5	630.5
Temperature of freezing aluminum....................		660.1
Temperature of freezing copper in a reducing atmosphere.	1083	1083
Temperature of freezing nickel.......................		1453
Temperature of freezing cobalt.......................		1492
Temperature of freezing palladium....................	1555	1552
Temperature of freezing platinum....................		1769
Temperature of freezing rhodium.....................		1960
Temperature of freezing iridium......................		2443
Temperature of melting tungsten.....................	3400	3380

1948 I.T.S. AND THE THERMODYNAMIC CENTIGRADE SCALE

At the time of the adoption of the International Temperature Scale of 1927, the evidence available was insufficient to establish definite differences between that scale and the thermodynamic centigrade scale. More recently investigations at the Massachusetts Institute of Technology on the intercomparison of two nitrogen gas thermometers with platinum resistance thermometers, in the range from 0° to the sulfur point, have indicated measurable differences between the scales. The differences found between t(thermodynamic scale) and t(International scale) have been formulated as follows

$$t(\text{therm}) - t(\text{int}) = \frac{t}{100}\left(\frac{t}{100} - 1\right)(0.04217 - 7.481 \times 10^{-5}\, t) \qquad (6)$$

The sulfur point on the thermodynamic scale was found to be 444.74°C, the results obtained with the two gas thermometers differing by about 0.05°.

In the range from 0°C to the oxygen point, intercomparisons made by various laboratories indicate that the differences between the International and thermodynamic scales are less than 0.05 C°. The reported differences are of the order of magnitude of the possible uncertainties in the gas thermometer measurements.

In the range extending below the oxygen point, there is evidence that temperatures on the International Temperature Scale of 1927 are progressively higher than those on the thermodynamic scale, by several hundredths of a degree at -190°C. For this reason, and also because it is advantageous to terminate the various parts of the scale at calibration points, the International Temperature Scale of 1948 extends only to the oxygen point.

In the range from the freezing point of antimony to the gold point, there is little evidence relative to the sign or magnitude of departures of the International from the thermodynamic scale. The value 1063.0°C for the gold point has been accepted as a conventional definition and will doubtless remain so until the appearance of new and more accurate basic data. The change from 960.5 to 960.8°C is well within the uncertainty of the location of the silver point on the thermodynamic scale. The change makes the thermocouple scale join more smoothly, not only with the resistance thermometer scale at the freezing point of antimony, but also with the optical pyrometer scale at the gold point when $c_2 = 1.438$ cm K°.

It is of interest to note that, granting the validity of Planck's formula, temperatures above the gold point on the International Temperature Scale of 1948 will differ from those on the thermodynamic centigrade scale only to the extent caused by errors in the constants c_2, t_{Au}, and T_0 used in the formula.

SUMMARY

The International Temperature Scale specifies the procedures to be followed in measuring temperatures in order to yield values which are reproducible and internationally comparable.   Values are assigned to selected fixed points.   Instruments (thermocouple, resistance thermometer, and optical pyrometer) are specified to be calibrated at these fixed points, and the forms of equations for calculating temperatures from the indications of the instruments are defined.   The scale is designed to conform with the thermodynamic centigrade scale as closely as possible with the knowledge available.

The practical importance of the International Temperature Scale is the reproducibility of its values rather than their ultimate accuracy.   Hence it is not desirable to make modifications in the scale that have only a provisional character or to change the scale appreciably at too frequent intervals.

REFERENCES FOR SUPPLEMENTARY READING

1. Brickwedde, F. G., "The Temperature Scale, a Proposed Change in Definition," *J. Applied Phys.*, **11**, 371 (1940).
2.. Burgess, G. K., "International Temperature Scale," *Bur. Standards J. Research*, **1**, 635 (1928).
3. Hoge, H. J., and F. G. Brickwedde, "Establishment of a Temperature Scale for the Calibration of Thermometers between 14° and 83°K," *J. Research Nat. Bur. Standards*, **1**, 351 (1939).
4. Stimson, H. F., "The International Temperature Scale of 1948," *J. Research Nat. Bur. Standards*, **42**, 209 (1949).
5. "Suggestions for New Units in Physics and Engineering," *Nature*, **145**, 597 (1940).
6. Wensel, H. T., "International Temperature Scale and Related Constants," *J. Research Nat. Bur Standards*, **22**, 375 (1939).

QUESTIONS AND PROBLEMS

1. Are the provisions of the International Temperature Scale important chiefly because they assure thermodynamic "correctness" of temperatures so measured, or because temperatures so specified are readily reproducible?

2. Of the instruments specified for the I.T.S., which is assigned the shortest range? the longest?

3. In what region would you expect temperatures measured on the I.T.S. to be subject to the largest experimental errors?   Where would the percentage errors be greatest?

4. The I.T.S. (1948) is not defined below −183°C, yet many experiments are conducted at lower temperatures (see Reference 2).   Suggest reasons why the I.T.S. has not been extended below the oxygen point.

5. Compare the consequences and merits of the following procedures to be followed as precision of temperature measurement increases: (a) the ice and steam

points to be defined as exactly 0°C and 100°C, respectively, or (b) the ice point alone to be defined as, for example, 273.165°K.

6. The freezing point of a sample of aluminum is indicated as 659.87°C using a standard thermocouple, and as 660.01°C using a standard resistance thermometer. What is the freezing temperature on the 1927 I.T.S.? Comment.

7. Taking the density of mercury as 13.5951 gm/cm³ at 0°C and the average pressure existing in a column 760 mm high when subject to a gravitational attraction of 980.665 dynes/gm, find the value of the standard atmosphere of pressure in dynes per square centimeter. *Ans.* 1,013,250 dynes/cm².

PART II

LABORATORY EXPERIMENTS

||||||||||||||||||||||

||||||||||||||||||||||||||

EXPERIMENT 1

GAS THERMOMETER

OBJECT. Determination of the coefficient of expansion of air at constant volume. Measurement of an unknown temperature using the air thermometer.

APPARATUS. Constant-volume air thermometer (Fig. 2.5, p. 26). Ice and steam baths. Scale or cathetometer. Barometer. Mercury thermometer.

DISCUSSION. If a gas confined at constant volume has a pressure p_0 at 0°C and a pressure p_t at temperature t, the pressure coefficient is defined as

$$\beta_v' = \frac{p_t - p_0}{p_0 \, \Delta t} \tag{1}$$

The prime indicates that the value of β_v' is as yet uncorrected for certain errors of measurement.

One source of error in using the air thermometer in the form illustrated (Fig. 2.5, p. 26) is that the bulb expands as the temperature is raised from 0°C to the higher calibrating temperature, usually the steam point. Hence the volume of air in the bulb is not quite constant. To reduce the volume $V(1 + \beta_b t)$ of air in the hot bulb to its value V when the bulb is at 0°C would require a certain pressure x. By Boyle's law

$$\frac{x}{p_t} = \frac{V(1 + \beta_b t)}{V} \tag{2}$$

or

$$x = p_t(1 + \beta_b t) \tag{3}$$

Substituting this for p_t in Eq. (1) we have

$$\beta_v' = \frac{p_t(1 + \beta_b t) - p_0}{p_0 \, \Delta t} = \frac{p_t - p_0}{p_0 \, \Delta t} + \frac{\beta_b p_t}{p_0} \tag{4}$$

275

Hence, to correct the experimental value of β_v' for bulb expansion, we must add the quantity $\beta_b p_t/p_0$, where β_b is the volume expansion of the glass of which the bulb is made.

A second source of error is associated with the capillary tube connecting the thermometer bulb to its manometer. In this so-called dead space, or pressure-transmitting volume v, the gas is at a temperature which differs from that in the bulb. We may write an equation in which the total amount of gas in bulb and dead space at the lower temperature is set equal to the total mass at the higher temperature

$$V_0 p_0 + v \frac{\rho_0}{1 + \beta_v t'} = \rho_0 V_0 \frac{(1 + \beta_b t)}{1 + \beta_v t} \frac{p}{p_0} + \frac{v \rho_0}{1 + \beta_v t'} \frac{p}{p_0} \tag{5}$$

Here V_0, ρ_0, and p_0 denote volume, density, and pressure at 0°C, v is the pressure-transmitting volume, t' its temperature, β_b the expansion coefficient of the bulb, and β_v that of the air. Equation (5) may be solved for either t or β_v to yield more accurate values of these quantities when precision of the experiment warrants.

PROCEDURE. Level the apparatus. Throughout the experiment, keep the mercury adjusted so that its level in the connecting glass tube is close to the reference line. If this is not done, the mercury may be forced into the bulb or completely down into the reservoir, causing trouble.

Carefully surround the thermometer bulb with chipped ice. Add water and, if needed, more ice.

When equilibrium has been attained, determine p_0. This may be calculated as the difference in levels of the mercury columns of the manometer, plus the barometric pressure.

Next remove the ice and water and circulate steam around the thermometer bulb. Measure p_{100}.

From the barometer reading and steam tables, determine the boiling temperature t.

Calculate β_v from Eq. (4).

Use the gas thermometer that you have calibrated to measure an unknown temperature from the relation

$$t = \frac{p_x - p_0}{(p_{100} - p_0) \, \Delta t} 100°C \tag{6}$$

Warm water (30 to 60°C) may be used in the jacket for this measurement. The water temperature may be checked with a mercury thermometer.

IIIIIIIIIIIIIIIIIIIIIIIIIII

EXPERIMENT 2

COEFFICIENT OF EXPANSION OF A LIQUID

OBJECT. Measurement of the absolute coefficient of expansion of a liquid by the method of balanced columns.

APPARATUS. Dulong and Petit type of liquid expansion apparatus. Boiler and burner. Barometer. Thermometer. Cathetometer or meter stick.

DISCUSSION. If a liquid has a volume V_0 at 0°C and V_t at temperature t, the relation between volume and temperature may be expressed, to a good approximation, by the equation

$$V_t = V_0(1 + \beta t) \tag{1}$$

β is characteristic of the liquid and is called the coefficient of cubical expansion. Solving Eq. (1) for β, it is seen that the coefficient of expansion represents the fractional change in volume per centigrade degree

$$\beta = \frac{v_t - v_0}{v_0 \Delta t} \tag{2}$$

The chief difficulty encountered in determining β experimentally is that the volume of the container as well as that of the liquid changes with temperature. This is overcome in a hydrostatic balance method first used by Dulong and Petit (1818) to measure the expansion of mercury, and improved in its present form by Regnault.

The liquid is contained in a tube, rectangular in outline, with an inverted U in the lower horizontal section (Fig. 1a). Branch A is kept at a high temperature by means of a steam jacket. The rest of the apparatus is cooled to a uniform temperature by water jackets.

The liquid columns A and D are connected at the top by tube G which equalizes the pressures in the columns at its level. The liquid surfaces in tubes B and C are separated by compressed air in reservoir R.

Let H_1, H_2, h_1, h_2 and a represent the differences in level indicated

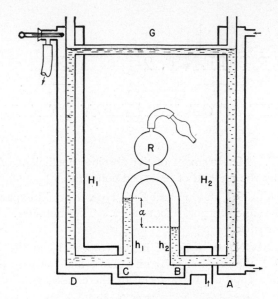

FIG. 1a.   Hydrostatic-balance method of measuring liquid expansion.

in the diagram. Denote the temperature and density of the liquid in column A by t_2 and ρ_2, respectively, and for the rest of the liquid by t_1 and ρ_1. Let P be the atmospheric pressure and P' the pressure of air in R. The pressure at the base of column D is $(P + \rho_1 g H_1)$ and at the base of column C is $(P' + \rho_1 g h_1)$. These are hydrostatic pressures at the same level in the liquid, hence

$$P + \rho_1 g H_1 = P' + \rho_1 g h_1 \qquad (3)$$

In the same manner for columns A and B

$$P + \rho_2 g H_2 = P' + \rho_1 g h_2 \qquad (4)$$

Subtracting Eq. (4) from Eq. (3) and solving for ρ_1/ρ_2

$$\frac{\rho_1}{\rho_2} = \frac{H_2}{H_1 - h_1 + h_2} = \frac{H_2}{H_1 - a} \qquad (5)$$

where a has replaced $(h_1 - h_2)$.

The density of a given mass of liquid is inversely proportional to its volume. From Eq. (1)

$$\frac{\rho_0}{\rho_1} = \frac{V_1}{V_0} = 1 + \beta t_1 \qquad (6)$$

$$\frac{\rho_0}{\rho_2} = \frac{V_2}{V_0} = 1 + \beta t_2 \qquad (7)$$

FIG. 1b.   Hydrostatic balance.

On dividing Eq. (7) by Eq. (6), a value is obtained for ρ_1/ρ_2. If this value be equated to that in Eq. (5), and the resulting equation solved for β, one obtains

$$\beta = \frac{a}{H_2(t_2 - t_1) - at_2} \tag{8}$$

PROCEDURE. Partially fill the apparatus by introducing the liquid at the top of column A or D. Compress air in reservoir R so that the liquid rises in tubes A and D until its surface stands about at the axis of tube G. Connect rubber tubing to circulate steam through the jacket on column A and tap water through the cooling jackets. Temperature t_1 is read on a mercury thermometer. The temperature of the hot jacket is calculated from a barometer reading and steam tables. Measure H_2 with a meter stick and a with a cathetometer. In calculating β use the mean of about five independent determinations of a.

In which type of apparatus would expansion of the container introduce a larger relative error: (a) a gas thermometer, (b) a liquid thermometer? Why?

||||||||||||||||||||||||

EXPERIMENT 3

THERMAL CONDUCTIVITY OF A METAL

OBJECT. Measurement of the thermal conductivity of copper.

APPARATUS. Copper bar conductometer. Four thermometers. Boiler with stand and burner. Constant-level water tank. Beaker. Pan balance. Electric timer.

DISCUSSION. The definition of thermal conductivity k in

$$Q = \frac{kAt(T_1 - T_2)}{L} \tag{1}$$

suggests a simple method of determining the conductivity of a substance. Using a slab of the material of known cross section A and length L, heated on one face, the amount of heat Q that flows through the opposite face in a known time t can be measured, as well as the temperatures T_1 and T_2 of the two surfaces. The conductivity can then be determined from Eq. (1).

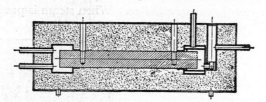

Fig. 2.   Copper conductometer.

Actually, precise measurement of the thermal conductivity of materials is difficult and requires many precautions. There are three principal sources of difficulty in conductivity experiments. It is difficult to measure accurately the temperatures of the two faces of the sample. An unknown, large temperature gradient may exist in the thin films of air or liquid that partially insulate the sample. Finally, although a one-dimensional conduction of heat from the hot to the cold face is assumed, there may be considerable loss of heat by conduction and radiation from the edges of the sample.

Figure 2 illustrates the type of copper conductometer used for this experiment. One end of a cylindrical copper bar is enclosed in a steam chamber. The other end is capped by a container through which cool water circulates, thermometers being provided to give its temperature of entry and exit, T_3 and T_4, respectively. Two thermometers are inserted into holes drilled in the copper rod and are brought into good thermal contact with the metal by the addition of a few drops of mercury. These read the temperatures T_1 and T_2 at cross sections about 10 cm apart, avoiding the necessity of knowing anything about the fluid layers formed on both ends of the sample. The whole rod is wrapped with a nonconducting material to minimize heat losses. In the steady state, if M gm of water flows through the cooling coil in t seconds, the heat conducted by the bar per second is $c_w M(T_4 - T_3)/t$ and this equals $kA(T_1 - T_2)/L$, where L is the distance between the two thermometers T_1 and T_2. Thus the conductivity k is determined from

$$k = \frac{c_w M (T_4 - T_3) L}{t A (T_1 - T_2)} \tag{2}$$

PROCEDURE. Allow water to flow through the cooling coil, using a constant-level water tank to keep the rate of flow constant. Connect the steam jacket to a boiler. When steam is passing through

FIG. 3.   Copper conductometer and accessories.

the jacket, adjust the flow of water through the cooling coil, by adjusting the level of the constant-flow tank (Fig. 3), so that the rise in temperature of the water ($T_4 - T_3$) is about 10 C°. When the readings on the four thermometers have become practically constant, place a weighed beaker below the water outlet, noting the time. Collect water for about 5 min, taking thermometer readings every minute. At a noted instant, remove the beaker and determine the mass M of water collected. Calculate the conductivity of the copper sample from Eq. (2).

||||||||||||||||||||||||||

EXPERIMENT 4

THERMAL CONDUCTIVITY OF HEAT INSULATORS

OBJECT.   Determination of the thermal conductivity of cork, glass, paper, and several commercial insulating materials.   Demonstration of the use of a differential thermocouple.

APPARATUS.   Fitch conductivity apparatus, consisting of source and receiver with embedded thermocouples.   Constantan wire.   Electric immersion heater.   Galvanometer.   Resistance box.   Test samples. Several kilogram weights.

DISCUSSION.   In unidirectional heat flow the quantity of heat transferred by conduction is given by the equation

$$Q = \frac{kAt(T_1 - T_2)}{L} \tag{1}$$

where Q is the quantity of heat transferred in calories, k the thermal conductivity in cgs units, A the area of cross section in square centimeters, L the distance between hot and cold faces in centimeters, T_1, T_2 the temperatures of hot and cold faces, respectively, on the centigrade scale, and t the duration of heat transfer in seconds.

In the case of good conductors, such as metals, the conductivity is measured from samples in the form of rods.   But for heat insulators, such as those investigated in this experiment, the length L must be small and the area A relatively large in order that sufficient heat transfer may occur to permit accurate measurement.

The Fitch conductivity apparatus (Fig. 4) has as the heat source a vessel of boiling water and as a receiver a copper plug of known mass,

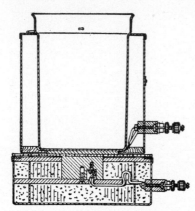

embedded in insulating surroundings. The sample is placed between the polished faces of source and receiver. The quantity of heat transferred is determined from the rise in temperature of the receiver, initially at room temperature. Copper-constantan thermocouples embedded in the bottom of the copper vessel (source) and in the receiver permit measurement of T_1 and T_2. Losses from the copper receiver by radiation and conduction to its surroundings are largely compensated for by the fact that the source has a larger area than

Fig. 4.   Fitch conductivity
apparatus.

the receiver, although the area used in computing k is that of the receiver.

A direct, but rather laborious, way of performing the experiment would be to measure the time rate of increase of T_2, after calibration of the thermocouple, and to compute Q from the thermal capacity of the receiver. An ingenious variation of this, however, simplifies the work.

Equation (1) may be differentiated

$$\frac{dQ}{dt} = \frac{kA(T_1 - T_2)}{L} \tag{2}$$

If M is the mass of the receiver and c the specific heat of copper

$$\frac{dQ}{dt} = Mc\frac{dT}{dt} = \frac{kA(T_1 - T_2)}{L} \tag{3}$$

If now the constantan terminals of the two thermocouples are joined by constantan wire, the galvanometer deflection I_g will measure the temperature difference

$$I_g = c'(T_1 - T_2) \tag{4}$$

where c' is a calibration constant

and
$$\frac{dI_g}{dt} = -c'\frac{dT}{dt} \tag{5}$$

Substituting Eqs. (4) and (5) in (3)

$$Mc\frac{dI_g}{dt} = -\frac{kAI_g}{L} \tag{6}$$

Integrating between the limits $t = 0$ and $t = t$, corresponding to galvanometer deflections I_0 and I, the result is

$$\log_e I = \log_e I_0 - \frac{kA}{MLc}t \tag{7}$$

Changing to logarithms to the base 10

$$t = \frac{2.303MLc}{kA}(\log I_0 - \log I) \tag{8}$$

It is apparent that if values of log I are plotted as ordinates with values of t as abscissas, a straight line will be determined, of slope

$$P = -\frac{kA}{2.303MLc} \tag{9}$$

Measurement of this slope permits evaluation of k. It is convenient to use semilogarithmic paper in making the graph.

PROCEDURE. Start the water heating in the copper-vessel source, using the electric immersion heater. Turn on the heater only when it is in water. Never place the vessel over a flame.

Have the receiver nearly at room temperature and place the source on the sample to be measured. Connect the constantan (gray) terminals of the source and receiver thermocouples with the constantan wire supplied. Join these in series with the galvanometer and sufficient resistance to give nearly full-scale deflection. After the water in the source has been boiling for several minutes and I_g has reached a steady maximum, transfer the source and sample to the receiver. The galvanometer deflection will immediately start to decrease. Record the deflection I_g and time t every 30 sec. The time interval may be made 1 or 2 min for thick samples, or 15 sec for thin ones. A dozen or more readings should be made.

To decrease the air film and to insure good thermal contacts, a load of 2 to 4 kg may be placed on the apparatus during the experiment.

A plot of log I_g vs. t should give a straight line until the copper receiver is warmed appreciably above its surroundings. Measure the slope of the curve, the area A of the receiver, and the thickness L of the specimen. The mass of the receiver is stamped on the side. The specific heat of copper, for the temperature range used, is 0.093 cal/(gm C°).

Calculate the thermal conductivity for each sample tested, expressing k in both metric and British units.

Cool the receiver between tests by placing a copper can filled with ice water on it, but do not wet it. At the conclusion of the experiment, rinse and dry the copper vessel and the heater.

||||||||||||||||||||||||||||

EXPERIMENT 5

THERMAL CONDUCTIVITY, FORBES' BAR METHOD

OBJECT. To determine the coefficient of conductivity for a metal.

APPARATUS. Iron and aluminum bars 100 cm long and a pair 25 cm long. Electric furnace. Transformer. Nine thermometers: one 200°C, one 150°C, three 110°C, and four 50°C. Calipers. Timer. Asbestos twine.

DISCUSSION. When a difference of temperature is maintained between two faces of a block of any solid material, there is a continual flow of heat from the face at higher temperature to that of lower temperature. This process is known as conduction.

The rate of flow of heat, dQ/dt, across the block is directly proportional to (1) the area A of cross section through which the heat flows, and (2) the temperature gradient dT/dL at the section considered

$$\frac{dQ}{dt} \propto A \frac{dT}{dL} \qquad \text{or} \qquad \frac{dQ}{dt} = kA \frac{dT}{dL} \tag{1}$$

where the proportionality constant k is called the coefficient of thermal conductivity.

When a long rectangular bar is heated at one end there is a flow of heat along the bar from that end.   At the beginning of the flow a part

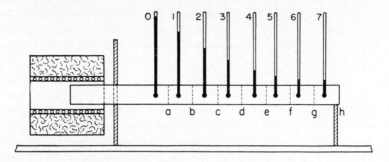

FIG. 5.   Diagram of bar for determining thermal conductivity.

of this heat raises the temperature of the bar and a part is radiated to surrounding objects.   After considerable time the bar reaches a steady state, that is, there is no further change in temperature at any point on the bar.   When the steady state is reached there is equilibrium established between the heat received by each section of the bar from

FIG. 6.   Thermal conductivity from conduction along heated bar.

the preceding section and the heat lost by the section.   The heat lost consists of two parts: that lost to surrounding objects through the exposed surface and that conducted along the bar to the next cooler section. All the heat flowing into any section is eventually lost to surrounding objects since the end of the bar has no cooler section to which it can transmit heat.

Figures 5 and 6 show the apparatus. All the heat flowing through the cross section of the bar at a is radiated from the part of the bar beyond a. Hence the total quantity of heat flowing through the cross section a per unit time will be the sum of the quantities radiated per unit time by the following sections of the bar, ab, bc, cd, etc. Thus

$$\frac{dQ}{dt} = \frac{dq_1}{dt} + \frac{dq_2}{dt} + \frac{dq_3}{dt} + \cdots \qquad (2)$$

The thermometer placed at the midpoint of each section gives approximately the average temperature of the section.

To obtain the values of dq_1/dt, dq_2/dt, etc., we obtain a cooling curve of a second bar similar to the one used for conduction. The bar is heated to a uniform temperature higher than that of the highest reading on the bar of Fig. 5 and is then allowed to cool. The temperature is taken every minute. From these data a curve is plotted of temperature *vs.* time. The slope of the curve at any given temperature is the rate of change of temperature dT/dt at that temperature. Hence

$$\frac{dq_1}{dt} = mc\,\frac{dT_1}{dt} = mc\ (\text{slope of curve at } T_1) \qquad (3)$$

where m is the mass of iron in section ab, c is the specific heat of iron and the subscript 1 refers to the section whose average temperature is given by thermometer 1. The mass may be obtained from the dimensions of the section and the density of iron.

Similarly $\qquad\qquad \dfrac{dq_2}{dt} = mc\ (\text{slope of curve at } T_2)$, etc.

To obtain the temperature gradient at a we plot a curve of temperature with distance along the bar. The slope of this curve at the point corresponding to a is the temperature gradient dT/dL at that point.

PROCEDURE. Heat one end of the bar by means of an electric furnace until each of the thermometers shows a constant reading. (It will require considerable time for the bar to reach a steady state. Perform the remainder of the experiment while the bar is heating.) Record the reading of each thermometer. Plot a curve connecting distance along the bar with temperature. At the point on the curve corresponding to the point *a* on the bar draw a line tangent to the curve. The slope of this line is the temperature gradient.

Place a short bar in an electric furnace and heat it until it reaches a temperature of about 125°C. Remove it and hang it by asbestos strings so that it is not near a source of heat. Insert a thermometer into the hole at the center of the bar and take the temperature every minute until it is approximately at room temperature. Using these values plot the cooling curve for this bar. Get the slopes of this curve at points corresponding to the temperature given by each of the thermometers in the long bar. Measure the width and thickness of the long bar. The length of each section is 10 cm. Using the values for the density and specific heat given below, compute the amount of heat radiated from each section per second and from these the total amount, Q/T, from the whole bar beyond *a*. From these data compute the coefficient of thermal conductivity.

	Density	*Specific heat*
Aluminum alloy....	2.71 gm/cm³	0.212 cal/(gm C°)
Stainless steel......	7.75	0.107

IIIIIIIIIIIIIIIIIIIIIIIII

EXPERIMENT 6

THERMAL CONDUCTIVITY OF GASES

OBJECT. Determination of the thermal conductivity of several gases by a comparison method.

APPARATUS. Conductivity cell. Wheatstone bridge. Galvanometer. Milliammeter. Thermostat. Tank samples of several gases such as CO_2, H_2, He, NH_3.

DISCUSSION. The electrical energy necessary to heat a platinum wire to a given temperature will depend on the nature of the gas in contact with it, other conditions being equal. The constancy of its temperature may be determined by measuring the resistance of the

wire. When a steady state is reached, heat supplied to the wire by electrical energy must equal that lost to the surrounding thermostat
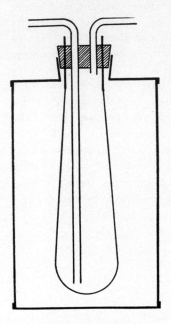
by conduction, convection, and radiation. Radiation loss can be minimized by keeping the wire temperature below 400°C. Heat lost from the wire by conduction through its metal supports is a constant which can be determined for a given apparatus. Then the electrical current necessary to keep the temperature of the wire constant in different gases will be a measure of the thermal conductivity of the gases used.

The heat lost from the wire by conduction

$$Q = \frac{kA(T_2 - T_1)t}{d} + \frac{CA(T_2 - T_1)t}{d} \quad (1)$$

The first term represents heat conducted by the gas. The second term includes heat lost by other means. C is a constant for a given cell. From the current I and resistance R the heat, measured in calories, supplied electrically to the wire may be calculated from

FIG. 7.   Gas conductivity cell.*

$$Q' = 0.239I^2Rt \quad (2)$$

A steady state is represented by equating Q and Q'

$$0.239I^2R = \frac{(k + C)A(T_2 - T_1)}{d} \quad (3)$$

which is independent of time. For two gases of conductivities k_A and k_B placed successively in the cell

$$k_B = (k_A + C)\frac{I_B^2}{I_A^2} - C \quad (4)$$

---

* C. M. Mason and R. M. Doe, *J. Chem. Education*, **14**, 182 (1932).

FIG. 8.   Gas conductivity apparatus.

If the thermal conductivities are known and the corresponding currents are determined for both gases, the cell constant can be evaluated

$$C = \frac{I_A^2 k_B - I_B^2 k_A}{I_B^2 - I_A^2} \qquad (5)$$

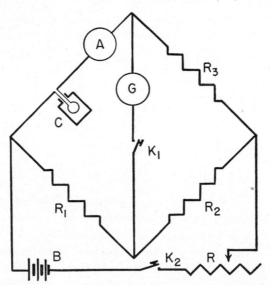

FIG. 9.   Bridge for conductivity measurements.

The conductivity of any other gas can then be obtained by measuring the corresponding current and solving an equation of the form of Eq. (4).

PROCEDURE. Place the cell (Fig. 7) in a thermostat shown at the left in Fig. 8. Flow clean, dry air through the cell. Close inlet and outlet tubes and allow the air to come to thermal equilibrium with the thermostat. Make connections to the Wheatstone bridge as in Fig. 9, and set resistors so $R_1 + R_2 \doteq 1000$ ohms. This is to prevent the burning out of the dial resistance box by excessive current. Close switch K_2 and adjust the heavy-duty resistance R until about 0.15 amp flows through the cell. Then depress key K_1 and adjust R_1 and R_2 (keeping $R_1 + R_2 \doteq 1000$ ohms) until the bridge is balanced, as indicated by zero galvanometer deflection.

Displace the air in the cell with another gas of known conductivity. Keep R_1 and R_2 constant. Adjust the current with R until the bridge is again balanced. Read the new value of the current through the cell on the milliammeter. Under these conditions the platinum wire is kept at constant temperature and C can then be calculated from Eq. (5).

The thermal conductivity of any gas is then obtained by noting the current necessary to balance the bridge with that gas in the cell and applying Eq. (4).

||||||||||||||||||||||||||||

EXPERIMENT 7

VISCOSITY OF A LIQUID

OBJECT. To determine the viscosity of a lubricating oil and to study the variation of viscosity with temperature.

APPARATUS. Rotating-cylinder viscosimeter. Weights. Vernier caliper. Meter stick. Thermometer. Electric heater. Stop clock.

DISCUSSION. The coefficient of viscosity (often called simply the viscosity) is defined as

$$\eta = \frac{\text{shearing stress}}{\text{rate of shear}} = \frac{f/A}{v/r} = \frac{fr}{Av} \tag{1}$$

The cgs unit of viscosity is the poise.

$$1 \text{ poise} = \frac{1 \text{ dyne} \times 1 \text{ cm}}{1 \text{ cm}^2 \times 1 \text{ cm/sec}} = 1 \text{ dyne sec/cm}^2 \tag{2}$$

A viscosity of 1 poise is one that requires a tangential force of 1 dyne for each square centimeter of surface to maintain a relative velocity of 1 cm/sec between two planes separated by a layer of fluid 1 cm thick.

In the coaxial-cylinder method of determining viscosity, a shearing takes place in which concentric cylindrical layers of liquid slip over each other. The angular velocity ω increases progressively from zero at the stationary cylinder A to ω_D at the rotating one, B in Fig. 10. The linear velocity at an intermediate surface SS' is $v = \omega r$. The velocity gradient at SS' is then

$$\frac{d}{dr}(\omega r) = \omega + r\frac{d\omega}{dr} \tag{3}$$

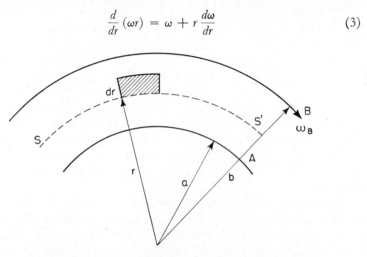

FIG. 10. Shearing stress in a liquid confined between concentric cylinders.

The first term ω on the right in Eq. (3) represents the rate of increase in v with r when all portions of the substance move with the same angular velocity. When shearing occurs, however, each cylindrical layer has an angular velocity greater than that of the one just inside it;

and the second term $r\, d\omega/dr$ represents the variation in v due to the variation in ω. In a rigid body this term would be zero. In a fluid it represents the velocity gradient due to relative movement of adjacent layers. Substituting this term for the velocity gradient v/r in Eq. (1)

$$\eta = \frac{f/A}{r(d\omega/dr)} \tag{4}$$

or

$$\eta\, d\omega = \frac{f}{A}\frac{dr}{r} \tag{5}$$

If the torque applied to the rotating cylinder is L, the tangential force at any layer SS' is L/r, and the tangential force per unit area is $L/2\pi r^2 l$ where l is the length of cylinder in contact with the fluid. Substitution in Eq. (5) gives

$$\eta\, d\omega = \frac{L}{2\pi l}\frac{dr}{r^3} \tag{6}$$

Integrating between limits $r = a$ and $r = b$ gives

$$\eta\omega_B = \frac{L}{4\pi l}\left(\frac{1}{a^2} - \frac{1}{b^2}\right) \tag{7}$$

or

$$\eta = \frac{b^2 - a^2}{4\pi a^2 b^2 l}\frac{L}{\omega_B} \tag{8}$$

The viscosity η is thus determined from the constants of the apparatus and from the experimentally determined ratio L/ω_B. In the apparatus used for this experiment, the inner cylinder A rotates inside a stationary cylinder B. However, the analysis above holds regardless of which cylinder is rotated, since it is the relative velocity that is important.

There is a torque not yet considered due to the viscous drag between the ends of the cylinders. For a given apparatus, this end effect is a constant which can be treated as a correction to be made to the length of the cylinder. Its effective length is then the immersed length l plus a factor e to be determined experimentally. Equation (8) then becomes

$$\eta = \frac{b^2 - a^2}{4\pi a^2 b^2 (l + e)}\frac{L}{\omega_B} \tag{9}$$

The torque is applied to the inner cylinder A (Fig. 11) by a fine cord that passes over a pulley and carries a mass m. The shearing torque in absolute units is $L = mgk$, where k is the radius of the drum. The angular velocity is $\omega = s/kt$, where s is the distance the mass m descends in time t.   Substituting these relations in Eq. (9)

$$\eta = \frac{(b^2 - a^2)k^2g}{4\pi a^2 b^2 s(l + e)} mt \qquad (10)$$

or

$$\eta = cmt$$

where

$$c = \frac{(b^2 - a^2)k^2g}{4\pi a^2 b^2 s(l + e)} \qquad (11)$$

is a constant all factors of which can be measured directly with the exception of the end correction e, which must be determined from an experimental curve.

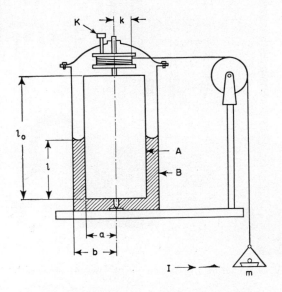

FIG. 11.   Vertical section of concentric cylinder
viscosity apparatus.

PROCEDURE.   Place oil in the viscosimeter, Fig. 12, until the level is about 1.5 cm above the lower end of the cylinder and measure the immersed length l carefully.   The depth gauge on the vernier caliper may be used, or the inner cylinder may be withdrawn and a pencil mark made on it to indicate the level of the oil.

Use a 20-gm mass.   Time its fall between index marks I a distance

s apart.   Make five determinations, increasing the effective length of
the cylinder by adding liquid, the last observation being made with
the oil level at the top of the inner cylinder.   Plot time *t vs.* length *l*.
Extrapolate the curve until it meets the *l* axis.   The *l* intercept then
gives the value of the end correction *e*, which is a positive term to be
added to the immersed length *l* to give the effective length.

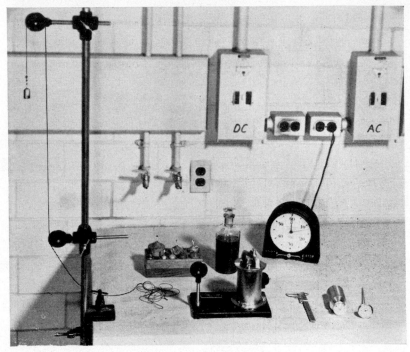

Fɪɢ. 12.   Viscosimeter for showing change of viscosity of oil with temperature
change.

With the level of the liquid at the top of the inner cylinder, take
a series of six observations varying the mass from 10 to 60 gm.   Plot
time *t vs.* reciprocal mass $1/m$.   The slope of this curve gives the average
value of the product *mt*.   Compute η from Eq. (10).

Determine η at five different temperatures (using $m = 20$ gm) up
to about 100°C.   Plot the coefficient of viscosity η *vs* temperature *t*.

Compare your experimental values with those given in a handbook
for *SAE* 20 oil.

IIIIIIIIIIIIIIIIIIIIIIIII

EXPERIMENT 8

VISCOSITY OF A GAS

OBJECT.   Determination of the viscosity of air at different temperatures by a constant-volume method.   Practice in the use of thermoregulators.

APPARATUS.   Flask.   Capillary tube.   Mercury manometer. Water bath.   Thermometer.   Heater.   Stirrer.   Thermoregulator. Cathetometer.   Timer.

DISCUSSION.   In the laminar (stream-line) flow of a fluid the force F in the direction of flow acting on an area perpendicular to the direction is proportional to the area A and to the velocity gradient dv/dr across the stream

$$F = \eta A \frac{dv}{dr} \tag{1}$$

The coefficient of viscosity η is characteristic of the fluid and depends upon temperature.   It is expressed in dyne seconds per square centimeter or poises.   Kinematic viscosity is the ratio of viscosity to density.

Poiseuille's formula for the flow of a liquid in a cylinder

$$V' = \left(\frac{\pi R^4}{8 L \eta}\right)(P_1 - P_2) \tag{2}$$

gives V', the volume of fluid passing any cross section in unit time, in terms of the radius R, the length L, the difference between the pressures at the ends $P_1 - P_2$, and the coefficient of viscosity η.   In the case of a gas the rate of flow past any section depends on the pressure there. Equation (1) may, however, be applied to an element dx of the tube and then integrated.   If this is done the relation[1] obtained is

---

[1] *See, for example,* B. L. Worsnop and H. T. Flint, *Advanced Practical Physics for Students,* New York: E. P. Dutton, 1923, pp. 174–7.

$$\eta = \frac{(\pi R^4/8LV)Pt}{\log_e\left(\dfrac{p_2 + P}{p_1 + P}\dfrac{p_1 - P}{p_2 - P}\right)} \tag{3}$$

where V is the constant volume of gas at the entrance of the tube, p_1 and p_2 are the pressures at the entrance of the capillary at the beginning and end of t seconds of observation, respectively, and P is the atmospheric pressure.

The essential apparatus is sketched in Fig. 13.[2] An adjustable

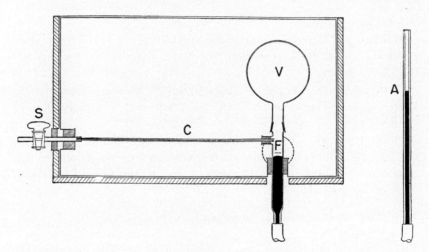

FIG. 13.   Diagram of gas viscosity apparatus.

mercury column A is connected by flexible rubber tubing and a short section of glass tube with a ground-glass joint to an inverted flask V of volume 300 ml. In an opening in the side of the glass tube is inserted one end of a capillary tube C. The other end of the capillary is fitted into a larger tube provided with a stopcock S. Air can be compressed in V by raising column A, and allowed to escape through the capillary for a time t. The volume of gas in the flask is kept constant by adjusting the column A to keep the mercury level at the fiducial mark F.

To permit measurement of the coefficient of gas viscosity at different temperatures, the flask and capillary tube are immersed in water con-

[2] R. L. Weber, American Physics Teacher 7, 163 (1939).

tained in a copper-lined wooden box. The temperature of the water bath is adjusted by a knife-type immersion heater, a bimetallic thermoregulator, and a stirring motor. Two glass windows cemented over circular openings in the sides of the tank permit observation of the fiducial mark F. A small lamp is placed behind one window to provide illumination.

PROCEDURE. The capillary tubing should be tested for uniformity of bore by measuring the length of a short (1-cm) thread of mercury at different positions in the tube. Its radius is then found indirectly by filling the tube with mercury and, from the weight and density of the mercury, calculating the volume of the capillary bore. The volume V of the flask is found by inverting it and filling it with distilled water to the reference mark F.

The following observations are needed: temperature of bath; cathetometer readings on mark F, on the mercury surface in the manometer at the beginning of a run, and on that surface at the end of the run; time of flow; and barometric pressure. These data, together with the constant of the apparatus $(\pi R^4/8LV)$, are sufficient to determine the viscosity η from Eq. (3).

By using ice for the lowest temperature, measurements can be made over the temperature range from 0 to about 60°C. Values obtained for the coefficient of viscosity may be compared with Sutherland's formula[3] expressing its dependence on temperature

$$\eta_t = \eta_0 \frac{T_0 + c}{T + c} \left(\frac{T}{T_0}\right)^{3/2} \tag{4}$$

where for air Sutherland's constant $c = 120$ and $\eta_{23} = 1822.6 \times 10^{-7}$.

---

[3] *International Critical Tables (1929)*, Vol. 5, p. 1

QUESTIONS

As shown in this experiment, the coefficient of viscosity of a gas *increases* with increase in temperature, whereas the viscosity of a liquid *decreases* with increase in temperature (Exp. 7). Can you suggest a physical mechanism which accounts for each effect?

How does the kinematic viscosity of a gas vary with temperature?

If the air in the flask of this experiment is moist, how will the experimental value of its coefficient of viscosity compare with that for dry air at the same temperature?

‖‖‖‖‖‖‖‖‖‖‖‖‖‖‖‖‖‖

EXPERIMENT 9

THERMOELECTRICITY

OBJECT. (a) Experimental demonstration of the thermocouple relations discussed in Chap. 4, Eqs. (19) to (21). (b) Calibration of a chromel-alumel thermocouple, for the range 0 to 450°C. (c) Determination of the thermoelectric power of various metals in combination with copper, for the range 0 to 450°C.

APPARATUS. A set of thermocouples made of copper in combination with each of the following: chromel, alumel, constantan, and iron. A two-range student-type potentiometer. Materials with known boiling points: water, naphthalene, benzophenone, and sulfur. Ice bath. Test tubes. Thermocouple-protecting tubes.

DISCUSSION. This experiment illustrates the method of calibrating a thermocouple by measuring its emf at each of several fixed temperatures provided by pure materials of known boiling points. The chromel-alumel thermocouple chosen for calibration is commonly used for laboratory and industrial temperature measurements. The meaning and usefulness of the concept of thermoelectric power is illustrated by calculating dE/dt for iron and constantan, each in combination with copper, from emf measurements.

When one junction of a thermocouple is held at constant temperature (usually 0°C) the variation of the thermal emf with temperature of the other junction is expressed by

$$E = a + bt + ct^2 \qquad (1)$$

Thermoelectric power is defined as the change in thermoelectromotive force for unit change in temperature and hence may be obtained by differentiating Eq. (1)

$$\frac{dE}{dt} = b + 2ct \qquad (2)$$

It will be observed that the emf-temperature relation is parabolic. The thermoelectric power vs. temperature relation is linear. The thermal emf is usually measured in millivolts, the thermoelectric power in microvolts per centigrade degree.

Boiling points may be corrected for barometric pressure p, measured in millimeters of mercury, by the formulas

Water: $t = 100.000 - 0.0367(760 - p)$
Naphthalene: $t = 217.96 \quad - 0.058 \ (760 - p)$
Benzophenone: $t = 305.9 \quad\ - 0.063 \ (760 - p)$
Sulfur: $t = 444.6 \quad\ - 0.091 \ (760 - p)$

PROCEDURE. A student-type potentiometer with variable resistance R, standard cell SC, galvanometer G, and protective resistance P connected externally is indicated in Fig. 14.   An understanding

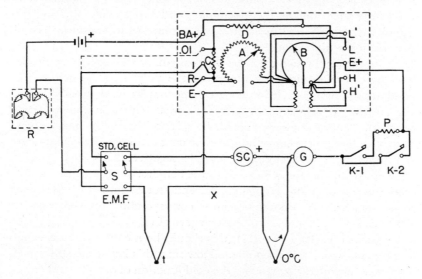

Fig. 14.   Potentiometer and thermocouple.

of this circuit and the wiring diagram of the potentiometer will aid in the intelligent use not only of this instrument but also of more specialized, self-contained potentiometers used in later experiments. (The extra terminals, end coils, and the red scale at B are to permit this instrument to be used as a Wheatstone bridge in other experiments.)

First standardize the current in the potentiometer circuit.   To do this, throw switch S (Fig. 14) to the "Std. cell" position.   Turn dial switch A and knob B until the potentiometer reading corresponds to the voltage of the standard cell being used.   The adjustable resistor R in series with the battery should then be set at about 140 ohms to limit the current through the potentiometer to approximately 0.01 amp.   Then tap key K-1 and adjust resistor R to reduce any galvanometer deflection to zero.   Make the final adjustment of R using key K-2, which gives increased galvanometer sensitivity.   The switch S is then put in the "EMF" position and the potentiometer is ready to make measurements.   However, the current should be standardized occasionally during prolonged use.   (Why?)

With the cold junction of one of the thermocouples in melting ice, measure carefully the emf when the hot junction is successively at the boiling points of water, naphthalene, benzophenone, and sulfur.   Use protecting tubes on the thermocouples, and avoid contaminating the samples by transferring protecting tubes from one to another.   Avoid overheating of the liquids.

Note the algebraic sign of the thermal emf as well as its magnitude. The sign is determined by observing the polarity at switch S and recalling the sign convention for a thermocouple: E_{ab} is positive when the positive or conventional current is from a to b at the reference junction.   For example, in Fig. 14, E_{XCu} is positive (or E_{CuX} negative). It may be found necessary to reverse the connections at S when another thermocouple is used, indicating E_{YCu} is negative.

Repeat the foregoing for each of the couples.

Using the data for chromel-copper and alumel-copper couples, plot curves of emf's as ordinates against corresponding temperatures as abscissas.   On the same sheet, plot a curve of $(E_{\text{Chromel-Cu}} - E_{\text{Alumel-Cu}})$ vs. temperature.   By Eq. (4.21), this should be a calibration curve for a chromel-alumel thermocouple.   How may this be verified?

Check Eq. (4.22) by placing the cold junction of one of the thermocouples in the steam bath (t_2) and the hot junction in boiling naphthalene (t_3).   Using previous emf readings taken with the cold junction in ice (t_1), compare $|E|_{t_1}^{t_3}$ with $|E|_{t_1}^{t_2} + |E|_{t_2}^{t_3}$.

What additional observation will permit checking the third thermocouple relation, Eq. (4.20)?   If time permits carry this out.

Using the emf-temperature data for the iron-copper and the constantan-copper couples, plot graphs of thermoelectric power vs.

temperature. These may be obtained graphically from the slopes of the emf-temperature curves. Solve for constants b and $2c$ of Eq. (2) for either one of these couples. Check your values by consulting tables which give these constants in combination with lead as a reference metal. (Note the sign convention employed in any tables you consult.)

In discussing the accuracy of this experiment, give numerical significance to your remarks by noting the least count of the potentiometer, its sensitivity (which depends upon the galvanometer), and the magnitude of random variations in measurements of a particular emf.

‖‖‖‖‖‖‖‖‖‖‖‖‖‖‖‖‖‖‖‖‖

EXPERIMENT 10

COMPARISON METHOD OF THERMOCOUPLE CALIBRATION

OBJECT. (a) Calibration of a base-metal thermocouple by comparison with a standard platinum vs. platinum-rhodium thermocouple. (b) A study of instruments used in measuring thermocouple emf's.

APPARATUS. Standard Pt–PtRh thermocouple. Uncalibrated base-metal couple (chromel-alumel, copper-constantan, or iron-constantan). Electric furnace. Rheostat or variable transformer. Potentiometer. High-resistance millivoltmeter. Low-resistance millivoltmeter. Ice bath. Mercury thermometer. Three double-pole, double-throw switches. Dry cell. Resistance dial box.

DISCUSSION. The primary standardization of a thermocouple is a calibration in terms of certain reproducible temperatures, obtained at the melting or freezing points of a series of pure metals. (See Exps. 11, 24.)

A rapid, secondary calibration of a thermocouple, sufficiently accurate for most uses, may be obtained by comparison with a standard couple.   If the two thermocouples are placed in a clean electric muffle furnace, readings of their emf's may be taken conveniently over the temperature range for which calibration is required.   To insure good thermal contact the rare-metal couple, without its protecting tube, may be pinched in a small slot cut in the hot junction of the base-metal couple; or both couples may be fused together temporarily.   Obviously neither of these methods is practical for use in routine calibration of many couples.   In this experiment good thermal contact is secured by inserting both couples in holes drilled in a small block of copper or nickel placed at the center of the furnace (Fig. 15).

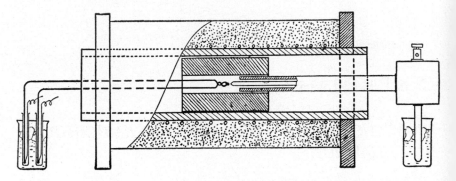

Fɪɢ. 15.   Comparison calibration of thermocouples.

It is just as important to know the temperature of the cold junction of the couple being calibrated as that of its hot junction.   The thermal emf depends upon both.   The reference junctions of each thermo-couple may be placed in melting ice.

Or, if this is not done, a reference-junction correction must be added to emf readings taken on the standard couple, and the calibra-tion of the base-metal couple must include a statement of its reference-junction temperature (measured with a mercury thermometer).

It is convenient, though not necessary, to use two potentiometers in this experiment.   The relatively low emf produced by the Pt–PtRh couple may then be read on a low-range instrument (0 to 16 mv) or on the lower scale of a multiple-range instrument.   The emf produced by the base-metal couple is measured on a higher-range potentiometer (0 to 64 mv).

Simultaneously with the calibration of the thermocouple, a study may be made of various emf-measuring instruments. A potentiometer will read the true emf of the couple, irrespective of lead resistance, since when balanced it takes no current from the couple. A millivoltmeter reading E_v, however, depends on the true emf E of the couple to which it is connected, the millivoltmeter resistance R_v, the thermocouple resistance R_c, and the line resistance R_l

$$E_v = \frac{R_v}{R_v + R_c + R_l} E \qquad (1)$$

PROCEDURE. Arrange the two thermocouples in the furnace with their hot junctions in the copper or nickel block. Close the ends of the furnace with insulating material. Provide an ice bath for the cold junction of each couple. Connect the standard couple to a potentiometer. Arrange switches to connect the base-metal couple to each of the instruments in turn.

Plan to obtain furnace temperatures from the standard thermocouple at intervals of about 100 C° up to the highest temperature safe for the particular furnace and base-metal thermocouple used. At each of the known furnace temperatures, record the emf of the base-metal thermocouple as read on each of the three indicators. It is essential that the furnace temperature be kept constant during a set of readings by adjusting the heating current.

Draw a calibration curve (emf *vs.* temperature) for the base-metal thermocouple.

Note what effect separating the thermocouples by several centimeters or removing the insulating plugs has on the emf readings. Estimate the temperature gradient encountered along the axis of the furnace. How might it be minimized?

Data taken so far will permit a qualitative check only of Eq (1). If time permits, obtain from the instructor apparatus to measure $R_l + R_c$ and R_v. Use these values to verify Eq. (1) numerically.

QUESTIONS

1. Show how to estimate the accuracy of a comparison calibration of a thermocouple, considering: (a) the least count of the measuring instrument used, (b) its sensitivity, (c) any random variation of potentiometer readings at a given temperature, and (d) any change in readings noted when the thermocouples were moved slightly in the furnace.

2. What, chiefly, distinguishes a potentiometer from other emf-measuring instruments?

3. Derive Eq. (1) by applying Ohm's law to a thermocouple circuit.

4. Explain precisely the significance of a cold-junction correction. Was it necessary in this experiment?

5. When both a Pt–PtRh and a base-metal thermocouple are used in the same furnace, need any precaution be taken to prevent the furnace atmosphere from damaging the couples? Explain.

6. Is it necessary or desirable that an electric muffle furnace used in thermocouple calibration be thermally well-insulated?

IIIIIIIIIIIIIIIIIIIIIII

EXPERIMENT 11

PRECISION CALIBRATION OF A THERMOCOUPLE

OBJECT. Graphical and analytical calibration of a thermocouple for the range from 300 to 1100°C.

APPARATUS. Thermocouple. Precision potentiometer. Timer. Electric furnace. Crucibles. Pyrex and quartz thermocouple-protecting tubes. Powdered graphite. Samples of the following, three of which should be used: tin, lead, zinc, antimony, aluminum, sodium chloride, and copper.

DISCUSSION. The emf-temperature relation for a thermocouple may be represented by

$$E = a + bt + ct^2 \tag{1}$$

where E is usually expressed in millivolts and t in degrees centigrade. The constants a, b, and c are determined by measuring the thermocouple emf at the known melting points or freezing points of each of three metals.

The application of freezing-point determinations to thermocouple standardization should be apparent from a consideration of Fig. 16. When a crucible containing pure molten metal is allowed to cool, the curve obtained by plotting temperature of the metal against time is one of decreasing temperature until the freezing point is reached. During freezing the latent heat that is associated with the transformation supplies the losses due to radiation and conduction, and the temperature of the metal remains constant until all the metal has solidified. In that region the curve is, ideally, parallel to the time axis.   Actually

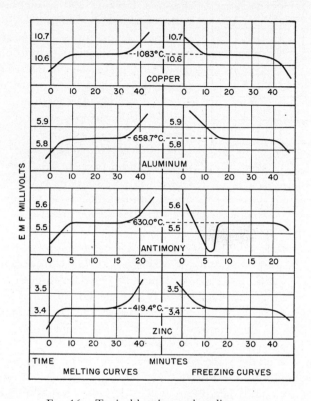

FIG. 16.   Typical heating and cooling curves.

there may be some obliquity of that part of the freezing curve and, to a greater degree, also in the corresponding melting curve.   On heating, the layer of metal near the wall of the crucible first reaches the melting point.   The temperature of that layer remains constant while heat is supplied for its fusion.   The thermocouple measures the temperature of the solid metal at the center of the crucible, and when this is surrounded by an isothermal layer, the rate at which the inside temperature increases is greatly diminished, resulting in a rounding off of the

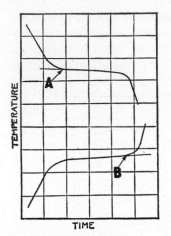

FIG. 17.   Oblique freezing and
melting curves.

temperature-time curve.   The thermocouple reads the true melting point only
for the short time the metal immediately
surrounding it is melting.   Figure 17
shows a freezing and a melting curve
with considerable obliquity.   The true
freezing temperature is obtained by
extrapolating the straight portion of the
curve and noting the temperature A at
which the straight line deviates from the
observed curve.   The melting point B is
obtained from the last part of the melting
curve in a similar way.

Undercooling in the case of most
metals seldom exceeds 0.1 C° or 0.2 C°.
In the case of antimony, however, it may
amount to as much as 30 C°, depending
on the rate of cooling.   The cooling curve for antimony in Fig. 16
illustrates undercooling.

PROCEDURE.   The electric furnace should be turned on at the
beginning of work and allowed to heat one of the samples while connections are made to the potentiometer.   Have an instructor inspect
the wiring before attempting to standardize the current through the
potentiometer.   Take a practice reading of the potentiometer with
one junction of the thermocouple at room temperature, and the
reference junction in ice.

When one of the samples has become molten, cover the surface
with powdered graphite to retard oxidation.   Insert a thermocouple-
protecting tube and then the couple.   As the metal cools, take emf
readings at intervals of 15 sec and prepare a cooling curve of emf vs.
time.   The sample may be cooled in the furnace with power off or
with the crucible in an asbestos-lined pot on the table.   A uniform rate
of cooling of about 2 C°/min from 10 C° above the melting point is
satisfactory for a freezing-point determination.   The curve should
have a flat portion corresponding to an interval of about 5 min.

With the exception of antimony, it is not advisable to stir the
molten metals because pockets of graphite are thereby formed.   If
there is doubt concerning the proper depth of immersion of the thermocouple, several determinations of its emf should be made at different

depths until a position is found from which small variations do not affect the temperature measurement. The thermocouple-protecting tube may be left in the metal for a few degrees below the freezing point without breaking. If it cannot then be removed, the metal should be remelted immediately. Time and material will be saved in obtaining freezing points if metals are not initially heated to unnecessarily high temperatures.

Submit with your report the three cooling curves and an accurate calibration for the thermocouple. Evaluate the constants a, b, and c of Eq. (1).

QUESTIONS

1. Draw a diagram of the simplest form of slide-wire potentiometer.

2. Referring to Fig. 18, list those letters which designate elements essential to a simple potentiometer such as you have diagramed above.

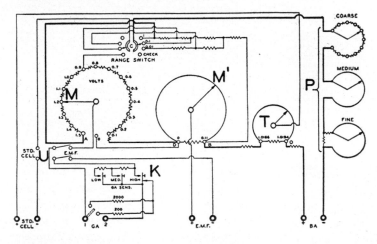

Fig. 18. Circuit diagram of a "K-2" Kohlrausch potentiometer.

3. List those parts which you have not included in (2) and explain in a phrase their function in the more elaborate instrument.

4. The current through a potentiometer has been standardized properly against a standard cell. If the following changes are made, indicate whether restandardization is necessary: (a) The galvanometer is replaced by one of higher sensitivity; (b) room temperature rises by about 10 F°; (c) the thermocouple leads are lengthened, increasing their resistance; (d) thermocouples of different metals are substituted; (e) the service cell is replaced by another; (f) the potentiometer range is changed from "1" to "0.1."

5. A potentiometer is standardized with the standard-cell dial set at 1.0183 volts. An unknown emf is then measured as $X = 0.50915$ volt. Later it is found that the correct standard-cell emf was 1.0169 volts. What then was the true value of X?

6. A millivoltmeter connected to a thermocouple reads 14.286 mv while a potentiometer connected to the same couple reads 15.000 mv. If the line and couple resistance is 2 ohms, find the resistance of the millivoltmeter.

|||||||||||||||||||||||||

EXPERIMENT 12

SURFACE TEMPERATURE MEASUREMENT

OBJECT. Comparison of various methods of measuring surface temperatures in the range 25 to 250°C.

APPARATUS. Electrically heated test plates. Current controller. Voltmeter. Ammeter. Dewar flask. Two mercury thermometers calibrated for total and partial immersion, respectively. Several types of commercial surface thermocouples. Potentiometer. Tempilstiks.

DISCUSSION. An experimental comparison of the precision obtainable with various methods of measuring surface temperatures requires a surface whose temperature can be controlled and measured accurately. This is provided by the electric heater illustrated in Fig. 19. A resistance wire R is wound in a flat spiral, insulated with asbestos paper A, and clamped between two iron plates P measuring approximately 20 cm square and 0.5 cm thick. Temperatures are indicated by iron-constantan thermocouples, the iron plate serving as one element of the couple. A leg extends from one plate, and to the bottom of it a constantan wire is welded. This serves as the reference junction and may be immersed in an ice bath.

For a given heater current, the heat loss from the plates may be calculated from

$$\frac{Q}{At} = \frac{VI}{4.18 \times 2A} \text{ (cal/cm}^2 \text{ sec)} \tag{1}$$

Here V is the voltage and I the current in amperes supplied to the heater, and A is the surface of one face in square centimeters. Using thermocouple leads 0 and 5 the temperature T_1 of the inner face of the iron plate may be measured accurately. The temperature of the

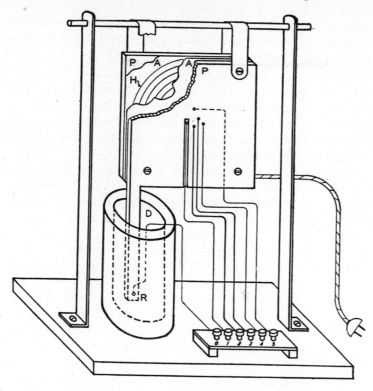

Fig. 19.   Surface-temperature test plate.

outer face is readily calculated if the thickness l and conductivity k of the iron plate are known

$$T_1 - T_2 = \frac{Ql}{kAt} = \frac{VIl}{4.18 \times 2Ak} \qquad (2)$$

The calculated difference between the temperatures of the inner and outer faces of the plate will be found to be negligibly small. Hence a thermometer or thermocouple placed in contact with the outer face of the plate might be expected to indicate a temperature equal to T_1. Actually the temperature indicated will be somewhat lower. The chief sources of this error are: (a) the presence of a gas film causing a temperature drop between plate and instrument, (b) heat conduction along the instrument, especially if it has a large cross section, and (c) radiation from the instrument, especially if it has considerable exposed area. The design of instruments for measuring surface temperatures accurately is largely concerned with the reduction of these sources of uncertainty.

PROCEDURE. Compare the temperature readings of total- and partial-immersion mercury thermometers held in contact with the plate in a manner suited to their immersion requirements. Try both upright and horizontal positions for the thermometers. Loss of heat from the thermometer bulbs may be decreased by a thin covering of paste made from asbestos and oil.

Observe the temperature indicated by several types of commercial surface thermocouples in contact with the plate; or, alternatively, construct a thermocouple of No. 28 gauge wires and one of No. 20 gauge wires, fasten to the surface of the plate with asbestos paste, and compare the temperatures indicated.

A constantan wire is spot welded to the iron plate. The wire leaves this junction in a shallow channel cut in the plate, making good thermal contact with the plate but insulated electrically from it except at the weld. Compare the temperature indicated by this thermocouple (leads 0 and 1, Fig. 19) with those indicated by the other instruments.

Make marks on the iron plate with several Tempilstiks and check the temperature data supplied for them by the manufacturer.

In reporting the results of this experiment, obtained at different plate temperatures, use graphical comparisons wherever possible.

||||||||||||||||||||||||||

EXPERIMENT 13

THE RADIATION CONSTANT, CALORIMETRIC METHOD[1]

OBJECT. Determination of the value of the constant σ in the Stefan-Boltzmann radiation law.

APPARATUS. Copper can with hemispherical bottom. Silver disk. Two copper-constantan thermocouples. Potentiometer or gal-

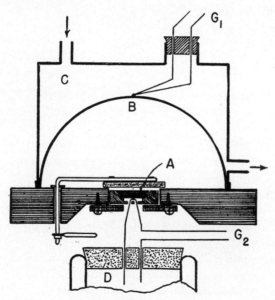

FIG. 20. Radiation constant from hemispherical radiation.

[1] A. D. Denning, *Phil. Mag.* (6) **10**, 210, (1905).

vanometer. Timer. Calipers. Dewar flask. Boiler. Bunsen burner. Camphor.

DISCUSSION.   An approximate value for the constant σ of the Stefan-Boltzmann radiation law can be obtained by a calorimetric method using simple apparatus.   A hemispherical radiator B (Fig. 20) is heated to the steam temperature, then placed over a silver disk A of known area A, mass M, and specific heat c.   Both the disk and the concave surface of the hemisphere are blackened.   From the initial rate of rise of temperature dT/dt observed for the disk, σ may be calculated from Eq. (1).

Let R_1 be the radiation absorbed by the disk per second per unit area, and R be the rate at which radiation is emitted per unit area. The energy gained by the disk per second is then $(R_1 - R)A$, where A is the exposed area of the disk.

From the general equation of calorimetry and the Stefan-Boltzmann law

$$ Mc\frac{dT}{dt} = \frac{R_1 - R}{J}A = \frac{\sigma A}{J}(T_1^4 - T^4) $$

and
$$ \sigma = \frac{JMc}{A(T_1^4 - T^4)}\frac{dT}{dt} \tag{1} $$

where T_1 is the temperature of the copper hemisphere, T the temperature of the silver disk, t the time in seconds, and J the mechanical equivalent of heat.

PROCEDURE.   After weighing and measuring the silver disk, blacken it and the hemisphere over burning camphor.   Connect a boiler to steam chamber C and pass steam through to heat hemisphere B.   The temperature of the hemisphere may be taken as that of the steam (determined from a barometer reading and steam tables) or it may be measured by a thermocouple soldered at B and connected to a galvanometer at G_1.

One junction of a thermocouple is soldered to the silver disk, the other junction placed in a Dewar of melting ice, and the leads connected to a galvanometer at G_2.   When the hemisphere has reached a steady temperature, place it over the disk.   At a noted time, remove the fiber insulation from the surface of the disk and commence a series of temperature (or emf) readings at definite time intervals for about 15 min.

Plot a temperature-time (or emf-time) graph. Evaluate dT/dt from a tangent. Using the appropriate value of T, calculate σ.

||||||||||||||||||||||||||

EXPERIMENT 14

RADIATION CONSTANT, EQUILIBRIUM METHOD

OBJECT. Determination of the constant in the Stefan-Boltzmann radiation law.

APPARATUS. Copper sphere enclosing an electric heater. Voltmeter. Ammeter. Variable resistor. Thermocouples and galvanometer. Vacuum-jacketed cylindrical vessel. Mechanical and mercury-diffusion vacuum pumps (optional). Calipers.

DISCUSSION. As an alternative to the method of Exp. 13, the radiation constant can be determined accurately from the electric power supplied to a copper sphere to maintain its temperature at a certain value when it is losing heat by radiation only.

A hollow blackened copper sphere is provided with an electric heater and a thermocouple and is suspended inside a closed Dewar flask. Power is supplied at a constant rate until the thermocouple indicates an equilibrium temperature T. The sphere is then radiating as fast as it receives heat. Hence

$$\frac{VI}{J} = 4\pi r^2 \sigma (T^4 - T_w^4) \quad \text{or} \quad \sigma = \frac{VI}{4\pi J r^2 (T^4 - T_w^4)} \quad (1)$$

The power VI is calculated from voltmeter and ammeter readings. T_w is the temperature of the walls surrounding the sphere. J is the mechanical equivalent of heat.

If vacuum pumps are available, the space between the sphere and the vacuum-jacketed container may also be evacuated. This eliminates heat loss by convection and improves the accuracy of the experiment.

|||||||||||||||||||||||

EXPERIMENT 15

THE RADIATION CONSTANT, HEATED WIRE METHOD[1]

OBJECT.   To verify the Stefan-Boltzmann law of radiation and to determine the value of the radiation constant, σ.

APPARATUS.   Cylindrical vacuum chambers (pyrex tubes). Pump. Wires of known melting temperatures. Wattmeter. Lampblack suspension. Micrometer calipers. Variac. (Optical pyrometer, optional.)

DISCUSSION.   A wire is coated with lampblack to approximate an ideal radiator.   The wire is placed between electrodes in a vacuum chamber and is connected in series with the a-c line, a wattmeter, and a Variac for the control and measurement of the power used (Fig. 21). The current in the wire is gradually increased and the power (VI) determined from the wattmeter at the instant the wire melts.   If all the electrical energy supplied were radiated from the wire

$$VI = \sigma A(T_1^4 - T_2^4) \tag{1}$$

from the Stefan-Boltzmann law, where T_1 is the absolute temperature at which the wire melts, T_2 is the absolute temperature of the surrounding space, A is the area of the radiating wire, and σ is the radiation constant.   By using wire of various elements the law can be verified for a wide range of temperature.

It is desirable to correct this experiment for (a) losses through conduction of heat from the wire to the electrodes, (b) the nonuniformity of radiation due to variation of temperature along the wire, and (c) errors in measuring the true potential difference across the

[1] P. A. Constantinides, *Am. J. Physics*, **9**, 87 (1941).

wire.   If we designate by X the correction for these errors, Eq. (1) for a wire of length L_1 and diameter d takes the form

$$V_1 I_1 = \sigma \pi d L_1 (T_1^4 - T_2^4) + X \tag{2}$$

and for a wire of diameter d and length L_2

$$V_2 I_2 = \sigma \pi d L_2 (T_1^4 - T_2^4) + X \tag{3}$$

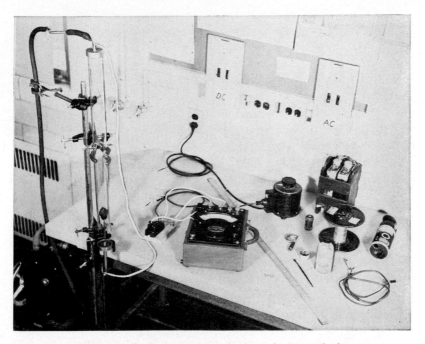

Fig. 21.   Radiation constant by heated-wire method.

where X is the same for both equations, since the end effects are identical.   Subtracting Eq. (3) from Eq. (2), we have

$$V_1 I_1 - V_2 I_2 = \sigma \pi d (L_1 - L_2)(T_1^4 - T_2^4) \tag{4}$$

or if T_2^4 is small with respect to T_1^4

$$V_1 I_1 - V_2 I_2 = \sigma \pi d (L_1 - L_2) T_1^4 \tag{5}$$

PROCEDURE.   Determine the value of the radiation constant σ by the method outlined and Eq. (5).   Optional: Use an optical pyrometer to check the validity of the assumption that the wire radiates as a blackbody.

||||||||!|||||||||||||||

EXPERIMENT 16

RADIATION PYROMETER

OBJECT.   Study of the theory, calibration, and use of a total-radiation pyrometer.

APPARATUS.   Féry total-radiation pyrometer with galvanometer temperature indicator.   Calibrated thermocouple.   Portable potentiometer.   Low-range precision potentiometer.   Electric furnace with current controller.

DISCUSSION.   Previous study of radiation laws has shown that it is possible to measure the temperature of a body in terms of either the energy radiated in a narrow band of wavelengths or the total energy radiated.   Instruments employing the first method are called optical pyrometers.   They use Wien's law.   Instruments for the second method are called total-radiation pyrometers.   Their operation is described by the Stefan-Boltzmann law.

In the Féry radiation pyrometer (Fig. 7.1) a concave mirror surfaced with gold, silver, or aluminum concentrates radiation from the hot body upon one junction of a small thermocouple.   The reference junction of the thermocouple is shielded from radiation and remains approximately at room temperature.

The galvanometer indicator connected to a radiation pyrometer may be calibrated to read temperatures directly, assuming a blackbody source of radiation.   The relation between the deflection of the indicator and the absolute temperature of the source may be predicted on the following assumptions:

(a) The galvanometer deflection D is proportional to the applied emf.

(b) The emf-temperature relation for the thermocouple is linear.

(c) Newton's law of cooling is applicable to the equilibrium temperature of the thermocouple.

(d) The net rate of receiving heat is proportional to the difference of the fourth powers of the temperatures of source and surroundings $T^4 - T_0^4$, which is the Stefan-Boltzmann law.

These relations may be expressed algebraically

$$D = a \text{ (emf)} = b(T_2 - T_1) = c(T^4 - T_0^4) \tag{1}$$

or
$$D = AT^4 + B \tag{2}$$

If T_0 is small compared to T, then B may be neglected. Equation (2) can be put in the form

$$\log D = 4 \log T = \text{constant} \tag{3}$$

Of course the assumptions made above represent only approximately the physical phenomena. The optical system in a total-radiation pyrometer has a transmission (or reflection) coefficient which varies appreciably with the radiation, and hence with the temperature T of the source. The temperature T_0 of the receiver varies with T. As a result the emf is not given by a law in T^4. Experiment shows that it may be represented as a function of T by a relation of the form

$$E = m(T^n - T_0^n) \tag{4}$$

where n is an exponent, constant for a given instrument, whose value varies considerably from the ideal exponent 4.

For measuring high temperatures a diaphragm is placed in front of the pyrometer to suppress part of the incident radiation. The diaphragm is a sectored disk so that the central and marginal rays of the objective lens (or mirror) are diaphragmed in the same ratio. If a curve of $\log T$ vs. $\log$ emf is plotted for an instrument thus diaphragmed, it will not generally have the same slope as the corresponding curve obtained for the instrument without the diaphragm. This is explained by the fact that the temperature of the reference junction of the thermocouple, for a given source temperature, is lower than in the absence of a diaphragm.

PROCEDURE. Put the hot junction of a calibrated thermocouple in a small hole drilled in a block of graphite or nickel and place near the center of the electric furnace. Sight the radiation pyrometer on the furnace opening, using, if necessary, small diaphragms to approximate blackbody conditions in the furnace.

Connect the thermocouple to a portable potentiometer. Use a double-pole double-throw switch to connect the radiation pyrometer in turn to a galvanometer indicator and to a low-range potentiometer.

Plan to take readings at intervals of about 100 C° over the range available with the furnace used. Prepare a table showing (a) emf of standard thermocouple, (b) temperature corresponding to that emf, read from tables, (c) radiation pyrometer emf, (d) temperature read from pyrometer indicator, (e) temperature calculated from the pyrometer calibration made as described in the next paragraph.

Determine the calibration constants m and n from a graph of log E vs. log T.

For one particular furnace temperature, observe the effect of placing a clear glass plate between the pyrometer and the furnace. Explain.

For a constant furnace temperature, take readings at successively increased distances from the furnace. Explain the effect of distance on the pyrometer readings with the aid of a diagram.

||||||||||||||||||||||||||

EXPERIMENT 17

OPTICAL PYROMETER

OBJECT. Study of the principles of optical pyrometry. (a) Calibration of an optical pyrometer. (b) Extension of the range of an optical pyrometer. (c) Determination of the emissivity of a metal.

APPARATUS. Disappearing-filament-type optical pyrometer to be calibrated. Standard optical pyrometer. Broad-filament tungsten lamp with current controller and ammeter. Sectored disk with motor. Colored glass filters. Calipers. Electric furnace. Calibrated thermocouple and indicator. Crucible with metal sample.

DISCUSSION. Temperature measurement with an optical pyrometer consists in matching monochromatic radiation from the source being measured against that from the filament of a standard lamp. Comparison is made in some instruments by varying the filament current, in others by varying a wedge filter in the viewing telescope.

The calibrations of optical pyrometers are compared readily by the use of a special accessory lamp. This is the method used in comparing the standards maintained by the various national standardizing laboratories. The comparison lamp has a broad filament. The ribbon may be wedge-shaped to provide approximately blackbody radiation. Using one pyrometer, a curve of current *vs.* temperature is prepared for the comparison lamp. This lamp is then used to check the calibration of a second pyrometer when sighted upon it.

Fig. 22.   Optical pyrometer calibration.

The range of an optical pyrometer is extended by decreasing the radiation from the source by a known factor. If a filter of thickness t having absorption coefficient k is placed before the pyrometer, its scale reading T_a is related to the true temperature of a blackbody source by

$$\frac{1}{T} - \frac{1}{T_a} = -\frac{k\lambda t}{c_2} = \text{constant} \qquad (1)$$

Alternatively a rotating sectored disk may be used to reduce the incident radiation. If the fractional part of the open sector is A, the relation between true and indicated temperatures becomes

$$\frac{c_2}{\lambda}\left(\frac{1}{T} - \frac{1}{T_a}\right) = \log_e A \qquad (2)$$

If an optical pyrometer calibrated for blackbody conditions is used for measurements on a surface of emissivity ϵ_λ the observed temperature is related to the true temperature by

$$\frac{\lambda}{c_2} \log_e \epsilon_\lambda = \frac{1}{T} - \frac{1}{T_a} \qquad (3)$$

PROCEDURE. Calibrate the Morse-type optical pyrometer by comparison with the standard optical pyrometer (Fig. 22). Construct a calibration graph from your data.

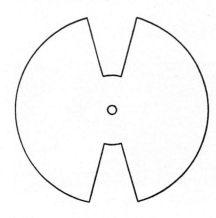

FIG. 23.   Sectored disk.

From paper or thin sheet aluminum prepare a disk similar to Fig. 23. The total angular opening should be about 30°. Sight one of the pyrometers through the open sector of the stationary disk and read the temperature of the incandescent filament of the comparison lamp. Repeat the reading when the disk is spinning, keeping the current in the comparison lamp constant. Compare the second pyrometer reading with that calculated from Eq. (2).

Determine the emissivity of a molten metal by obtaining its true temperature from a calibrated thermocouple and reading its apparent temperature on an optical pyrometer. The emissivity is given by Eq. (3). Compare results obtained when the optical pyrometer is sighted on the bright surface of the metal and then on the surface covered with oxide or with powdered graphite. If all measurements are made at the solidifying temperature of the metal, they may be readily reproduced and checked.

||||||||||||||||||||||||||||

EXPERIMENT 18

SPECIFIC HEAT OF A LIQUID BY RADIATION METHOD

OBJECT.   To determine the specific heat of a liquid by comparing its rate of cooling with the rate of cooling of water.

APPARATUS.   Radiation calorimeter.   Two 50°C thermometers, graduated in 0.1 C° divisions.   One 100°C thermometer. Beaker.   Boiler and stand.   Bunsen burner.   Timer.   Balance.

DISCUSSION.   The radiation calorimeter (Fig. 24) contains two tubes A and B having the same size, shape, and surface characteristics. The tubes are surrounded by air spaces and a water jacket whose temperature is practically constant.   When A and B are at the same temperature, heat is lost at the same rate from each.   The rates of cooling, however, will be inversely proportional to the thermal capacities of the tubes and their contents.   The difference in the rates of cooling may be used to compare the thermal capacities.

Sample cooling curves for tubes containing equal volumes of different liquids are shown in Fig. 25.   The average rate at which tube A loses heat in the temperature interval ΔT is

$$R_A = (c_A + c_w m_w) \frac{\Delta T}{\Delta t_A} \tag{1}$$

where c_A is the thermal capacity of the tube and thermometer, m_w the mass of liquid (water) in the tube, and c_w the specific heat of the liquid. For tube B the corresponding rate is

$$R_B = (c_B + c_x m_x) \frac{\Delta T}{\Delta t_B} \tag{2}$$

Since the surfaces of the tubes are alike, and since they have passed through the same temperature range, $R_A = R_B$ and

$$\frac{c_A + c_w m_w}{\Delta t_A} = \frac{c_B + c_x m_x}{\Delta t_B} \tag{3}$$

Equation (3) may be used to determine the specific heat c_x of the liquid in tube B in terms of the known specific heat c_w of water in tube A. It should be noted that in deriving Eq. (3) Newton's law of cooling was not assumed and that the validity of the equation is not affected by approximations in this law.

PROCEDURE.   Place the supporting strip S and the jackets C and D in position as shown in Fig. 24.   Fill the outer vessel V with water at room temperature.

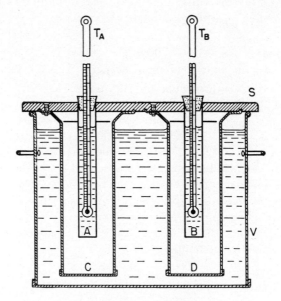

FIG. 24.   Radiation calorimeter.

Weigh the cup A when empty and again when almost full of water. In like manner weigh cup B when empty and again when almost full of the liquid whose specific heat is to be determined.   Put thermometers T_A and T_B, supported by cork stoppers, in the tubes and place the tubes in a beaker of hot water at about 60°C.   When both thermometers read the same temperature, remove the tubes from the hot water and, after drying their outside surfaces, place them in the calorimeter as shown in Fig. 24.

Read each thermometer every 2 min until the temperature has fallen at least 15 C°. One thermometer may be read on the odd minutes, the other on the even. Since one tube cools more slowly than the other, its temperatures must be noted for a longer period of time. Record the temperature of the large vessel V.

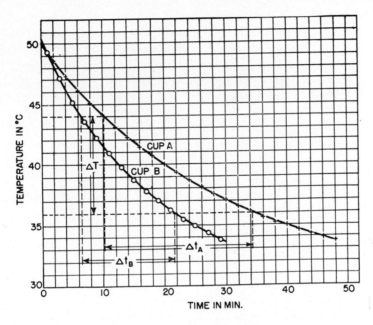

Fig. 25.   Cooling curves of the two liquids.

Determine the thermal capacity of each tube and thermometer. The specific heat of the brass from which these tubes are made is 0.090 cal/(gm C°). Only that portion of the thermometer which is immersed need be considered in computing its thermal capacity. Why? Equal volumes of mercury and glass have the same thermal capacities, 0.46 cal/(cm³ C°). A measurement of the volume of the submerged part of the thermometer is needed in order to calculate its thermal capacity. The submerged volume is easily determined by a displacement method.

Use a graduated cylinder of 50-cm³ size containing about 35 cm³ of water. Immerse the thermometer in this water to the same depth to which the thermometer was immersed in the experiment. Note the submerged volume from the rise of the water level in the graduated cylinder.

Plot cooling curves for both tubes. Choose a convenient temperature interval ΔT and determine from the graph the times Δt_A and Δt_B. Use Eq. (3) to calculate the specific heat c_x. Repeat for another temperature range.

Use the data plotted in the manner of Fig. 25 to check Newton's law of cooling. For five different temperatures of tube A, determine dT_A/dt from the slope of curve A. Plot a graph showing the relationship between rate of cooling dT_A/dt and the difference in temperature $(T_A - T_V)$ between tube and its surroundings. Do the same for tube B. Interpret these curves.

IIIIIIIIIIIIIIIIIIIIIIIIII

EXPERIMENT 19

RESISTANCE THERMOMETER

OBJECT. Calibration of a platinum or a nickel resistance thermometer. Measurement of an unknown temperature with the resistance thermometer.

APPARATUS. Platinum or nickel resistance thermometer. Mueller temperature bridge. Galvanometer. Battery. Barometer. Ice, steam, naphthalene, benzophenone, and sulfur baths. (See Fig. 26.)

DISCUSSION. A second-degree (parabolic) equation is necessary to express accurately the resistance R_t of a resistance thermometer coil as a function of its temperature t and its resistance R_0 at 0°C

$$R_t = R_0(1 + at + bt^2) \qquad (1)$$

Equation (1) represents the calibration of a platinum resistance thermometer throughout the range from −50 to 1100°C.

A nickel thermometer is used to measure temperatures which do not exceed 300°C. This upper limit to its range is due to the change

FIG. 26. Apparatus for calibrating resistance thermometer.

in the resistance-temperature relation as the transition temperature of nickel is approached. (See Exp. 28.) In the range 0 to 300°C a two-constant equation holds approximately

$$\log R_t = m + nt \qquad (2)$$

Simplified wiring diagrams of a Mueller temperature bridge are shown in Fig. 8.4, p. 135, and Fig. 27. When used with a three-lead resistance thermometer the connections are made directly at C', tc, and T'. When, however, a four-lead thermometer is used, a commutator is added as in Fig. 27. It permits interchange of the T and C leads and substitution of lead t for lead c at tc.

PROCEDURE. If a platinum resistance thermometer is used, measure its resistance at the ice, steam, and sulfur points, and at an

additional temperature to be checked. The boiling temperatures
may be corrected for barometric pressure by the formulas on p. 301.
If a nickel thermometer is used, two standardization points are needed,
of which the boiling temperature of benzophenone may be the higher.

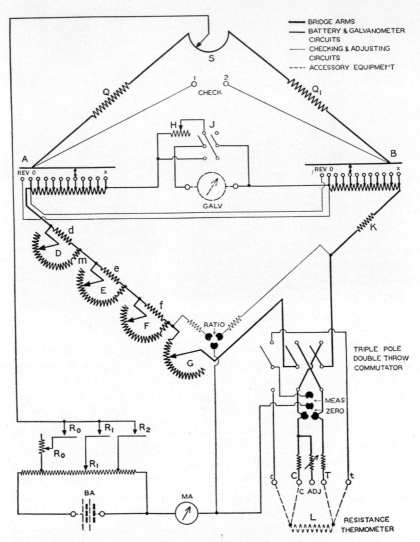

FIG. 27. Diagram of a modified Mueller temperature bridge.

The resistance at a third temperature should be recorded for checking.

Calculate and indicate clearly in your report the values of the constants that appear in the calibration equation for the thermometer used. Plot a curve of resistance vs. temperature. If data were obtained for a platinum thermometer, include with the calibration curve a graph of resistance vs. platinum temperature.

🔢🔢🔢🔢🔢🔢🔢🔢🔢🔢🔢🔢🔢🔢🔢🔢🔢

EXPERIMENT 20

A CONTINUOUS-FLOW CALORIMETER

OBJECT. Measurement of the mechanical equivalent of heat using a Callendar and Barnes continuous-flow calorimeter.

APPARATUS. Continuous-flow calorimeter. Constant-level water tank. Two 0 to 50°C thermometers. Batteries (or 110/6-volt transformer). Ammeter. Voltmeter. Switch. Pan balance with weights. Timer. Two beakers. 1-liter graduated cylinder.

DISCUSSION. The discovery that heat is a form of energy was the basis for a fundamental law of physics: Energy can be neither created nor destroyed, only transformed. This is the principle of the conservation of energy.

The mechanical equivalent of heat is numerically the number of units of mechanical energy equivalent to one unit of heat. Thus if mechanical energy W is converted into an amount of heat Q

$$W = JQ \tag{1}$$

where the numerical value of the mechanical equivalent of heat J depends upon the units in which W and Q are expressed. Thus J may be stated in ergs per calorie, in joules per calorie, or in foot-pounds per Btu.

When electrical energy is converted into heat

$$W = VIt = JQ \tag{2}$$

where the product of potential difference V (volts), current I (amp), and time t (sec) represents the electrical energy (joules).

The energy Q may be determined from the rise in temperature, $T_2 - T_1$, which it produces in a known mass m of water

$$Q = mc(T_2 - T_1) \qquad (3)$$

where c is its specific heat, 1 cal/(gm C°).

Although J could thus be determined from a static calorimeter, a flow calorimeter has advantages: (1) Since the temperatures T_1 and T_2 are held constant, the thermal capacities of the calorimeter, heating element, and thermometers are not involved in the computations. (2) A correction can readily be made for heat lost from the calorimeter to its surroundings.

An electric current is maintained in the resistance wire in a glass tube through which water is flowing. The temperature of the water is measured where it enters and where it leaves the tube. From the mass of water flowing through the tube in a known time and from the rise in temperature the amount of heat generated by the current in that time can be calculated. Combining Eqs. (2) and (3)

$$J = \frac{VIt}{mc(T_2 - T_1)} \qquad (4)$$

PROCEDURE. Arrange the apparatus as shown in Fig. 28. Do not close the switch until water is flowing through the calorimeter. Have the connections inspected by the instructor before closing the switch.

Insert thermometers into stoppers and place these in the thermometer wells, making sure that the thermometer bulbs do not strike the bottoms of the wells.

Regulate the flow of water between 200 and 350 cm^3/min through the calorimeter. Determine this rate by collecting the water from the outlet in a graduate for 1 min.

When a steady flow of water has been established, close the switch and adjust the electric power input to about 25 watts. Observe temperatures T_1 and T_2 and when they become steady record the values. Also record current, voltage. mass of water collected. and the time interval.

Increase the power by about 25 watts and again allow the temperatures to become steady. Record all values as before. Continue in this way up to a maximum power input of about 125 watts. With each determination check the rate of flow. It is important that this rate be kept constant.

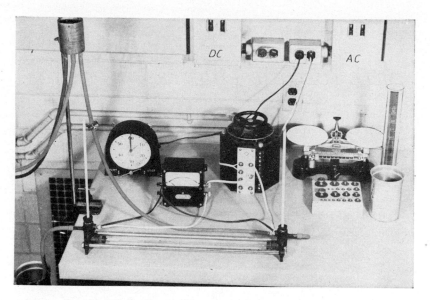

FIG. 28.   Callendar and Barnes continuous-flow calorimeter.

Plot a curve of power input VI against temperature difference $T_2 - T_1$. Determine the slope k of this curve. Compute the value of J from

$$\text{Power } P = VI = \frac{mc}{t} J(T_2 - T_1) \tag{5}$$

or

$$P = k(T_2 - T_1) \tag{6}$$

where slope

$$k = \frac{mcJ}{t} \quad \text{or} \quad J = \frac{kt}{mc} \tag{7}$$

Notice what information the initial values of inlet and outlet temperatures (power off) give about heat exchange between calorimeter and room. What does the curve of P vs. $(T_2 - T_1)$ indicate about heat losses?

|||||||||||||||||||||||||||

EXPERIMENT 21

SIMPLE FUEL CALORIMETER

OBJECT. To obtain the heating value of coal and fuel-oil samples.

APPARATUS. Cussons' fuel calorimeter. Oxygen cylinder with reducing valve. Woulff bottle. Thermometer. Balance. Samples of coal and fuel. Sulfur.

DISCUSSION. Figure 29 represents an elementary form of fuel calorimeter. It consists of a copper tube around which is wound a

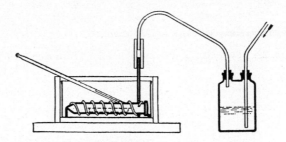

Fig. 29. Simple fuel calorimeter.

spiral of small-bore copper tubing, the whole being immersed horizontally in a water bath. The bath is surrounded and supported on heat-insulating material.

Combustion is carried out in the horizontal tube. The fuel is measured into a porcelain, quartz, or nickel boat that is introduced into the tube at the open end into which a copper plug is afterward inserted. The products of combustion are expelled through small holes in the coil and bubble through the water. A continuous stream of oxygen at low pressure is introduced through the inlet tube to secure steady and complete burning.   With the exception of the combustion boat the whole apparatus is made of copper, so that the water equivalent may be determined readily.

From the rise in temperature $t_1 - t_2$ produced in the calorimeter by the combustion of mass m of fuel the heat of combustion may be calculated

$$H = \frac{(m_w + m_c)(t_1 - t_2)}{m} c_w \qquad (1)$$

where m_w is the weight of water in the bath, m_c is the water equivalent of the apparatus, and c_w is the specific heat of water.

PROCEDURE.   Spread the fuel sample evenly along the combustion boat.   If a liquid is used, introduce a little kaolin to absorb it. Insert the boat for most of its length in the tube.   Place a bit of sulfur on the fuel and ignite it.   Immediately push the boat to the center of the tube, cap the tube, and immerse it.   Read the thermometer. Adjust the oxygen supply to give a slow, steady bubbling of the exhaust gases.   Take temperature readings at intervals of about 1 min.   From the initial and maximum temperatures observed, calculate the heat of combustion for the sample.

EXPERIMENT 22

OXYGEN BOMB CALORIMETER

OBJECT.   Determination of the heat of combustion of a fuel with an oxygen bomb calorimeter.

APPARATUS.   Parr oxygen bomb calorimeter with accessories. Thermometer.   Tank of compressed oxygen.   Electric timer.   Analytical balance.   Pan scales.   Graduate.   Three beakers.   Burette. Wash bottle.   Methyl orange.   Sodium carbonate.   Benzoic acid. Coal sample.

   DISCUSSION.   One of the most important tests of material used
primarily for fuel is the determination of the amount of heat generated
by the complete combustion of unit mass of the material.   This
quantity, called the heat of combustion, is commonly expressed in
calories per gram, large calories per kilogram, or Btu per pound.

   Instruments employed for this type of measurement are known as
calorimeters.   They are of two distinct types, depending upon whether
they are designed for testing solid and liquid samples or for testing
gases.   The calorimeter used in this experiment is of the first type.
Gas calorimetery is discussed in the next experiment.   In all commonly
used calorimeters a known weight of the sample is burned completely
in an apparatus which permits the heat developed by the combustion
to be absorbed by a definite mass of water.   From the rise in temperature of the water it is possible to calculate the number of heat units
liberated.   In calorimeters for solid and liquid samples, complete

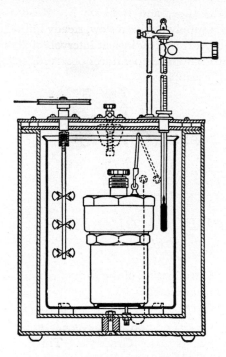

FIG. 30.   Section of oxygen-bomb
          calorimeter.

combustion is insured by use of oxygen gas under pressure or the use of sodium peroxide as the oxidizing agent.

An oxygen bomb calorimeter consists of three essential parts: (a) the bomb or container in which the sample is burned, (b) the calorimeter vessel or bucket, containing a measured quantity of water in which the bomb, stirring device, and thermometer are immersed, and (c) the jacket, for minimizing heat transfer between the calorimeter and its surroundings. These parts are illustrated in Fig. 30.

FIG. 31. Oxygen-bomb calorimeter and accessories.

The bomb and its mechanically sealed cover must withstand normal working pressures of 100 to 150 atm and maximum pressures up to about 600 atm (8820 lb/in.^{2}). Nitrogen of the air and any sulfur present in the sample burned are converted into acids which, with the excess oxygen at high temperature, form a corrosive atmosphere which will etch ordinary metals. In early forms of bombs a lining of platinum, gold, enamel, or nickel was used to retard corrosion. In the Parr instrument the bomb is made of a proprietary alloy, illium.

The accuracy of calorimetric measurements is largely dependent upon the accuracy with which calorimeter temperatures are read. Either a Beckmann or a solid-stem mercurial thermometer is commonly used. The small range of a Beckmann thermometer (5 C°), together with the need for applying several corrections for each test, usually offset the advantage of finer graduations in that type of thermometer. For general calorimetric use a solid-stem thermometer is preferable. This may be about 24 in. long and cover the range from

65 to 90°F in units of 0.05 F°.   When readings are taken with a lens, temperatures can be estimated to the nearest 0.005 F°.   Each thermometer is generally supplied with an individual certificate showing in chart or tabular form the corrections to be applied to its scale readings.

When a calorimeter is at a higher temperature than its surroundings it loses heat, and when at a lower temperature it gains heat from the surroundings.   In making precise calorimetric measurements it is essential to minimize this source of error.

The general method of correcting the temperature rise for thermal leakage has been discussed in Chap. 10 (see Fig. 10.3, p. 175).   For routine calculations, Dickinson has demonstrated the validity of the following shorter method of calculation.

Temperature readings are taken during a fore interval of about 5 min to give the slope of line ab.   The fuel sample is ignited and temperature-time readings continued to locate the maximum temperature. Readings are continued during the after interval of about 5 min to establish the slope of line de.   The vertical sf is then drawn at the position on the time axis where the calorimeter has undergone 0.6 of its observed temperature rise.   Lines ab and ed are extrapolated to intersect the vertical line, at s and at f.   The temperature interval represented by sf is then used as the corrected value of ΔT in the calorimeter equation.   While it is instructive to make the correction for thermal leakage graphically, for repeated calculations it is usually made numerically, following Dickinson's 60-per cent method, as illustrated in the sample calculation at the end of this discussion.

PROCEDURE.   For a detailed discussion of the method of sampling coal the student is referred to the recommendation of the American Society for Testing Materials, published in the ASTM Volume of Standards for 1933.   Assuming that a coal sample has been obtained and pulverized, the procedure for determining its heat of combustion may be given conveniently in outline form.

1. Weigh accurately about 1 gm of coal in the fuel capsule.

2. Attach the fuse wire (10 cm) and set the fuel capsule in place in the loop electrode.

3. Wet the rim of the bomb cylinder with moist finger tips, set the cover in place, taking care not to upset the sample.   Place the bomb in the bench socket and tighten the cap with a wrench.   Fill the

bomb with oxygen, slowly, to a gauge pressure of 20 atm. Screw the protective nut over the bomb check valve.

4. Add 2000 gm of water to the calorimeter bucket. The temperature of the water is to be adjusted so that the final temperature, after combustion, will not be more than 1 F° above room temperature. This means that the initial temperature should usually be approximately 3 F° below room temperature.

5. Place the bucket of water in the calorimeter, set the bomb in the bucket, attach the clip terminal of the firing circuit to the bomb, close the cover, insert the thermometer, attach the pulley and drive belt, and start the stirring motor.

6. Allow the stirrer to run for at least 2 min, then record thermometer readings at 1-min intervals for a period of 5 min.

7. On the fifth minute, fire the charge by closing the ignition switch. Open the switch immediately after the pilot lamp ceases to glow. (Why?)

8. Record the thermometer readings at 15-sec intervals for 2 min after firing the charge. Then continue readings at 1-min intervals until 5 min after a maximum temperature is reached.

9. Dismantle the calorimeter, release the residual pressure, and open the bomb.

10. Remove carefully the pieces of the 10-cm fuse wire that remain and measure the combined length of the pieces.

11. Rinse all inner surfaces of the bomb with distilled water and collect the washings in a clean beaker. Titrate the washings with a standard sodium carbonate solution using methyl orange indicator, to determine the amount of acid formed.

An outline of the calculations required to give the heat of combustion from these data is given in the following paragraphs.

(a) Apply the proper scale and radiation corrections to the initial and final temperatures.

(b) Determine the total heat liberated by multiplying the net temperature rise by the total water equivalent of the calorimeter.

(c) Subtract from the total thermal units a correction of 2.8 cal for each centimeter of fuse wire burned.

(d) Subtract the correction for acids formed, based upon the titration. If a solution containing 3.658 gm of Na_2CO_3 per liter is used, the correction will be 1 cal for each milliliter of solution used in titrating.

If the sample were free of sulfur, the correction here considered would be for nitrogen, each gram of which liberates 1035 cal when oxidized in the bomb and absorbed in water to form HNO_3. The amount of HNO_3 formed is measured by titration with Na_2CO_3 according to the reaction

$$2HNO_3 + Na_2CO_3 \rightarrow 2NaNO_3 + H_2CO_3$$

Most fuels contain sulfur which is oxidized and converted to H_2SO_4 in the bomb. When S in a fuel burns to SO_2 in ordinary combustion, it liberates 2162 cal per gram of S. But when it burns to SO_3 in the oxygen bomb and is absorbed in water to form H_2SO_4, it liberates 4389 cal/gm. Therefore, the combustion of S in the bomb liberates $4389 - 2162 = 2227$ cal/gm more than is liberated in normal burning, and correction must be made for that amount. In addition to the reaction above, when H_2SO_4 is present in the bomb washings, the following reaction occurs during titration:

$$H_2SO_4 + Na_2CO_3 \rightarrow Na_2SO_4 + H_2CO_3$$

Rather than attempt to separate the HNO_3 and the H_2SO_4 to determine the amount of each, it is convenient to compute the acid correction based on the assumption that only HNO_3 is present. However, the heat liberated by the formation of H_2SO_4 is greater than that liberated when an equivalent amount of HNO_3 is formed. It is necessary to apply an extra correction for the heat generated by the H_2SO_4 in addition to that which is accounted for in the titration (i.e., 906 cal per gram of S). This additional correction is $2227 - 906 = 1321$ cal per gram of S. Subtract this correction together with that described in the first paragraph of (d).

(e) Having subtracted the foregoing corrections for fuse, acids, and sulfur from the total thermal units, divide the remainder by the weight of the coal sample to determine its heat of combustion.

A convenient form for data and calculations is given on p. 339. When many determinations are to be made, calculations may be facilitated by the use of nomographs.[1]

The use of a calorimeter to determine the heat of combustion of a fuel requires knowledge of the total heat capacity of the calorimeter. This may be expressed conveniently in terms of the "water equivalent"

---

[1] Parr Instrument Company, *Parr Oxygen Bomb Calorimeters* . . . , Moline Ill., 1938.

of the calorimeter, which includes that of the container, the water, the bomb and its contents, and parts of the thermometer, stirring device, and supports for the container. Rather than calculate or measure these individually, it is convenient to determine the total water equivalent of the calorimeter from the combustion of a known amount of a standard material whose heat of combustion is accurately known.

Three materials are commonly used for standard combustion samples.[2] In order of their suitability they are:

Benzoic acid. Heat of combustion is about 6320 cal/gm. This material is not very hygroscopic, burns easily and completely, and may be compressed readily into pellets for ease in handling.

Naphthalene. Heat of combustion is about 9614 cal/gm. This material is rather volatile but not hygroscopic. Some care is necessary to avoid errors due to sublimation.

Sucrose or cane sugar. Heat of combustion is about 3949 cal/gm. This material is neither volatile nor strongly hygroscopic, but it is difficult to ignite and occasionally does not burn completely.

SAMPLE DATA AND CALCULATIONS

	Time, Min.	Temperature, °F		Time, Min.	Temperature, °F
	0	74.825		6.50	80.610
	1	74.830		6.75	81.220
	2	74.835		7.75	82.290
	3	74.840		8.75	82.510
	4	74.845		9.75	82.605
(a)	5	74.850	(c)	10.75	82.610
	5.25	74.920		11.75	82.605
	5.50	75.280		12.75	82.600
	5.75	77.100		13.75	82.590
	6.0	78.530		14.75	82.585
(b)	*6.191*	*79.506*		15.75	82.565
	6.25	79.810			

Thermometer corrections

Initial reading:	74.850 °F	Final reading:	82.610 °F
Scale correction:	0.001	Scale correction:	0.000
Initial temperature:	74.851	Final temperature:	82.610

Observed temperature rise: 7.759 F°
0.6 of rise in temperature: 4.655
Temperature when 0.6 rise is attained: 79.507

---

[2] Obtainable from the National Bureau of Standards.

Time when 0.6 rise is attained: 6.191 min
$$(79.810 - 78.530)/15 = 0.0853 F°/sec$$
$$(79.507 - 78.530)/0.0853 = 11.45 \text{ sec} = 0.191 \text{ min}$$

Radiation correction for initial period
  Duration of preliminary period $(b - a)$:
$$6.191 - 5 = 1.191 \text{ min}$$
  Rate of rise:
$$r_1 = (74.850 - 74.825)/5 = 0.005 \text{ F°/min}$$
  Correction to initial temperature:
$$r_1(b - a) = (.005)(1.191) = 0.0059 \text{ F°}$$
  Corrected initial temperature: 74.856°F

Radiation correction for final period
  Duration of final period $(c - b)$:
$$10.75 - 6.191 = 4.559 \text{ min}$$
  Rate of fall:
$$r_2 = (82.610 - 82.565)/5 = 0.009 \text{ F°/min}$$
  Correction to final temperature:
$$r_2(c - b) = (4.559)(0.009) = 0.041 \text{ F°}$$
  Corrected final temperature: 82.651°F
  Net corrected temperature rise: 7.795 F° = 4.331 C°
  Total water equivalent for calorimeter: 2511 gm

Total heat liberated: (2511)(4.331)   = 10,875 cal

Corrections: fuse wire: (10 − 1)(2.8)   =   25.2 cal
  Volume Na_2CO_3 used in titrating: 32 ml   32.
  Sulfur: (1.4447)(0.015)(1321) =   28.7
                                                                     ――――
Total correction: 85.9 cal

Net heating value of coal sample: $(10{,}875 - 86)/1.4447 =$ 7468 cal/gm
                                                          = 13,442 Btu/lb

‖‖‖‖‖‖‖‖‖‖‖‖‖‖‖‖‖‖‖‖‖

EXPERIMENT 23

GAS CALORIMETER

OBJECT. Measurement of the heating value of gas in a water-flow-type gas calorimeter.

APPARATUS. Sargent-type calorimeter. Gas meter. Pressure regulator. Pan balance with weights. Two beakers. Four thermometers. Gas burner. Psychrometer. Gas Calorimeter Tables.[1]

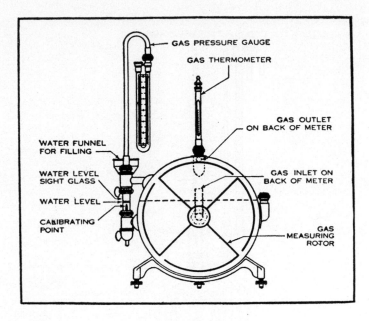

GAS PRESSURE GAUGE

GAS THERMOMETER

GAS OUTLET
ON BACK OF METER

WATER FUNNEL
FOR FILLING

WATER LEVEL
SIGHT GLASS

GAS INLET ON
BACK OF METER

WATER LEVEL

CALIBRATING
POINT

GAS
MEASURING
ROTOR

FIG. 32. Wet-test gas meter.

DISCUSSION. The total heating value of a gas refers to the number of heat units generated by the combustion of a unit volume of the gas. The volume is usually reduced to standard conditions: the volume the gas would occupy when saturated with water vapor at 60°F and under a pressure equivalent to that of 30 in. of mercury at 32°F. Recently there has been a tendency to express the heating value under conditions actually existing at the time of measurement of the gas.

The net heating value of the gas is defined as the total heating value less the heat of vaporization—at the initial temperature of the gas and air—of the water formed in the combustion of the gas.

Gas is passed through a meter (Fig. 32) and pressure regulator and

---

[1] *Nat. Bur. Standards Circular C417.*

is burned in the calorimeter (Fig. 33). The temperatures of the gas as it enters the burner and the products of combustion as they leave the calorimeter are read on thermometers. A stream of water flows

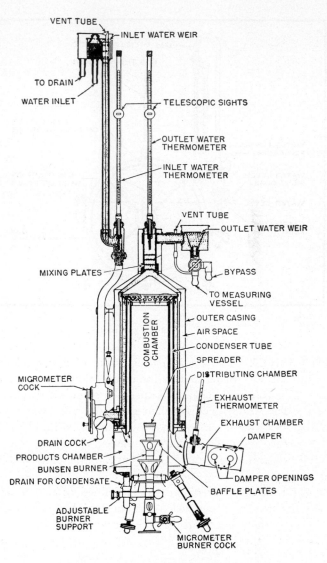

VENT TUBE
INLET WATER WEIR
TO DRAIN
WATER INLET
TELESCOPIC SIGHTS
OUTLET WATER THERMOMETER
INLET WATER THERMOMETER
VENT TUBE
OUTLET WATER WEIR
MIXING PLATES
BYPASS
TO MEASURING VESSEL
OUTER CASING
AIR SPACE
CONDENSER TUBE
SPREADER
COMBUSTION CHAMBER
DISTRIBUTING CHAMBER
MICROMETER COCK
EXHAUST THERMOMETER
EXHAUST CHAMBER
DAMPER
DRAIN COCK
PRODUCTS CHAMBER
BUNSEN BURNER
DRAIN FOR CONDENSATE
DAMPER OPENINGS
BAFFLE PLATES
ADJUSTABLE BURNER SUPPORT
MICROMETER BURNER COCK

FIG. 33. Sargent-type gas calorimeter.

through the calorimeter jacket, its rate being controlled by a valve and a constant-level reservoir, and is collected in a measuring vessel. Thermometers are placed to read the temperature of the water as it enters and leaves the calorimeter. Water vapor formed by combustion of the gas condenses and is collected in a separate beaker.

The heating value H of the gas is given by the equation

$$H = \frac{m_w c_w(t - t') - m_s L_v - m_s c_w(t_s - t_c)}{V} \tag{1}$$

where V is the volume (reduced to normal standard conditions) of gas burned in a given time; m_w is the weight of water passing through the calorimeter in that time; t' and t are temperatures of water entering and leaving the calorimeter; m_s is the weight of steam condensed; t_s and t_c are the temperatures at which it condenses and that at which the condensate leaves the calorimeter; c_w is the mean specific heat of water and L_v its latent heat of vaporization.

The gas is assumed to be saturated with water after passing through the water in the meter and pressure regulator. The observed volume is multiplied by a factor to reduce it to standard conditions. The magnitude of this correction factor may be obtained (to 0.01 per cent) from Table III in the Gas Calorimeter Tables. Or it may be calculated from the ideal gas laws

$$\text{Correction factor} = \frac{(p_g - p_w)(60 + 459.7)}{(t + 459.7)(30 - 0.5217)} \tag{2}$$

where p_g is the total gas pressure and p_w the vapor pressure of water at $t°F$.

In a precise measurement of the heating value of a gas, the observed value must be corrected for humidity, heat loss, the effect of buoyancy of the air on the observed weight of water, and the difference between inlet-water temperature and room temperature. A discussion of these corrections and tables for evaluating some of them can be found in the Gas Calorimeter Tables. All tables in that publication have been computed for gas rates corresponding to 3000 Btu/hr and 40 per cent of excess air. A well-fitted damper with two half-inch holes, when in the "closed" position, will allow about 40 per cent of excess air to pass through the calorimeter when gas is burned at 3000 Btu/hr.

Gas distributors are accustomed to base their rates on measurement of the heating value of the gas under the conditions in the meter. This gross heating value is given by

$$H = \frac{W(t_2 - t_1)}{V\left[\dfrac{17.64(B - p_w)}{460 + t_3}\right]} \tag{3}$$

where H is the heating value in Btu per cubic foot of gas, W the weight of water in pounds, V the volume of gas in cubic feet as shown by the meter, B the height of barometer in inches of mercury, t_1 the temperature of inlet water in degrees Fahrenheit, t_2 the temperature of outlet water in degrees Fahrenheit, t_3 the temperature of gas at meter in degrees Fahrenheit, and p_w the pressure of water vapor in inches of mercury at t_3.

PROCEDURE. With the gas valve at the burner closed, connect the gas supply through the meter and regulator. Notice whether the index of the meter moves. If it does, find the leak and remedy it. Start the flow of water through the calorimeter and then light the burner. Adjust the flow of water so the temperature change inside the calorimeter is about 15 F°. Adjust the damper as mentioned above.

While waiting for the establishment of a steady thermal condition, prepare a data sheet[2] and record the preliminary observations: room temperature, barometric pressure, pressure and temperature of the gas in the meter, wet- and dry-bulb readings on the psychrometer, and temperature of the combustion products.

When all thermometers indicate nearly steady conditions, note simultaneously the meter reading and the inlet and outlet water temperatures. Immediately place beakers to receive the outlet water and condensate. Record thermometer readings every 30 sec until about 2 l of water have been collected. Then take a meter reading and remove the beakers. Determine m_w and m_s by weighing. Data are then available for calculating the heating value of the gas and for making the necessary corrections.

---

[2] Pads of data sheets similar to the form recommended by the Bureau of Standards can be purchased from calorimeter supply companies.

|||||||||||||||||||||||||||||

EXPERIMENT 24

THERMAL ANAYLSIS

OBJECT. Verification of the essential features of the phase diagram for the Pb-Sn system. Thermal analysis of a Pb-Sn sample of unknown composition. Practice in the use of a recording potentiometer.

APPARATUS. Electric furnace. Variable transformer. Gas furnace. Crucibles containing lead; tin; Pb-Sn eutectic mixture, 62 per cent Sn; alloy of 10 per cent Sn; alloy of 20 per cent Sn; and

FIG. 34. Apparatus for thermal analysis, showing a laboratory precision potentiometer and a recording potentiometer.

alloy of unknown composition. Labeled rack for crucibles. Thermocouples with pyrex protectors. Precision potentiometer. Recording potentiometer. Two batteries. Standard cell. Two electric timers. Asbestos-lined iron pot. Crucible tongs. Ice-filled Dewar flask. (See Fig. 34.)

DISCUSSION. An equilibrium diagram of the Pb-Sn system is given in Fig. 11.7. From the cooling curves obtained in the laboratory it is desired to verify the following: (a) the melting point of Pb, (b) the melting point of Sn, (c) the composition of the eutectic mixture and the eutectic temperature, (d) existence of a solid solution, region II of Fig. 11.7, (e) the limit of solubility of Sn in Pb.

Tin has three allotropic forms: γ, stable from 232 to 161°C; β, stable from 161 to 18°; and α, stable below 18°. The influence of these transformations does not appear to justify including additional horizontal lines indicating phase changes in the Pb-Sn diagram. Cooling curves of alloys containing 18 to 62 per cent Sn may show an exothermic halt about 155°C. This was formerly included as a phase transformation. Now the change is attributed to supersaturation followed by sudden precipitation.

Temperatures at which changes of state occur are determined by any of the methods discussed in Chap. 11, i.e., (a) ordinary cooling-curve method, (b) inverse-rate method, (c) differential method, or (d) derived differential method.

PROCEDURE. The recording potentiometer is used to obtain cooling curves for pure Sn and for pure Pb. Make the necessary external connections of battery and thermocouple to the potentiometer recorder. Standardize the potentiometer current and make any necessary internal adjustments only under supervision of the instructor. Heat one of the samples in the gas furnace. When molten, insert a thermocouple protected by a pyrex tube. Turn off the gas and obtain a cooling curve, leaving the specimen in the furnace.

With the recording potentiometer in operation and requiring little attention, obtain cooling data for each of the remaining samples.

Finally, determine the composition of the unknown sample by comparing its phase-change temperatures with the Pb-Sn phase diagram. To find on which side of the eutectic composition it lies, consult the instructor or make a rough determination of the density of the alloy.

1. On a Pb-Sn phase diagram, indicate (with colored lines) those features which you verified in the laboratory.

2. At the side of your Pb-Sn phase diagram, draw qualitative examples of cooling curves (temperature *vs.* time) that would be obtained in cooling alloys of the following compositions: (a) 100 per cent Pb, (b) 100 per cent Sn, (c) 62 per cent Sn, and (d) 85 per cent Sn.

3. A Pb-Sn alloy of 10 per cent Sn is cooled from 350 to 0°C. Indicate all transitions that occur and the temperatures at which they occur.

4. For each of the areas that have been numbered (I–VI) in Fig. 11.7 state the number of phases present, the number of components, and identify the phases.

IIIIIIIIIIIIIIIIIIIIIIIIII

EXPERIMENT 25

RATIO OF THE SPECIFIC HEATS OF AIR

OBJECT. To measure the ratio γ of tne specific heats of air c_p/c_v by the method of Clément and Desormes.

APPARATUS. Five-liter pyrex flask with metal cover plate. Oil manometer. Pump or pressure bulb. Pinch clamp. Stopcock grease. Drierite. Barometer.

DISCUSSION. A mass of dry air, slightly compressed, is enclosed in a large flask sealed by a sliding valve. The valve is opened for an instant, permitting the pressure inside the flask to become equal to atmospheric pressure. A fall in temperature accompanies the expansion. After the valve is closed, the gas warms to room temperature and its pressure increases slightly. The ratio γ of the specific heats c_p/c_v is obtained from measurements of initial and final pressures.

The initial pressure p_1 is measured by the difference in heights h_1 of the two columns of a manometer (Fig. 35) containing oil of density d (gm/cm³) so that the pressure, in dynes per square centimeter, is

$$p_1 = p_0 + h_1 dg \tag{1}$$

where p_0 is the barometric pressure. When the valve is opened momentarily, the rapid expansion of the gas is adiabatic. The compressed gas does work in forcing some of the gas out of the flask, and hence its temperature falls. If the gas is now allowed to warm to room temperature, the pressure increases to some value p_2 given by

$$p_2 = p_0 + h_2 dg \tag{2}$$

where h_2 is the new difference in the heights of the manometer columns.

Let V_1, V_0, and V_2 denote the initial, intermediate, and final volumes of unit mass of the gas in the flask, so that in each case the same mass of gas is considered. For an adiabatic expansion of the gas from the initial state, pressure p_1, volume V_1, to the intermediate

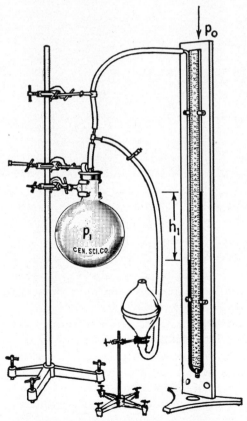

FIG. 35. Specific heats of air by Clément and
Desormes apparatus.

state, pressure p_2, volume V_2, the pressures and volumes are related by the equation

$$p_1 V_1^\gamma = p_0 V_0^\gamma \tag{3}$$

where γ is the ratio of the specific heats. Since in the final state the temperature of the gas is the same as the original temperature, the relation between pressures and volumes is given by Boyle's law

$$p_1 V_1 = p_2 V_2 \tag{4}$$

There is the same mass of gas in the vessel in the intermediate and final states, so $V_2 = V_0$. We may eliminate the various volumes in Eqs. (3) and (4) to find the relationships between the pressures.

By raising both sides of Eq. (4) to the γ power

$$\left(\frac{V_1}{V_2}\right)^\gamma = \left(\frac{p_2}{p_1}\right)^\gamma \tag{5}$$

From Eq. (3) and the fact that $V_2 = V_0$

$$\left(\frac{V_1}{V_2}\right)^\gamma = \frac{p_0}{p_1} \tag{6}$$

Thus

$$\left(\frac{p_2}{p_1}\right)^\gamma = \frac{p_0}{p_1} \tag{7}$$

or

$$\gamma = \frac{\log\,(p_0/p_1)}{\log\,(p_2/p_1)} \tag{8}$$

If the pressures used do not differ greatly from atmospheric pressure, one may use the relation, $\log_e (1 + p) = p - p^2/2 \ldots$, to obtain the simple approximate relation

$$\gamma = \frac{h_1}{h_1 - h_2} \tag{9}$$

PROCEDURE. Place a small amount of drying agent, anhydrous $CaSO_4$ (Drierite), in the flask. Grease the ground edge of the flask and test the cover for a gas-tight fit.

Force air into the bulb until the difference in the manometer levels is about 30 cm. Clamp the inlet tube, wait for the manometer reading to become steady, and record it. Remove the cover from the flask, replace it without excessive haste but without noticeable delay, and record the final manometer reading.

Repeat this procedure at successively lower manometer differences, making about 10 trials. In each case try to remove and replace the cover plate in the same way.

Take a set of about 10 similar readings, but start with the gas in the flask *below* atmospheric pressure.

Take a set of five readings in which the original pressure is, as nearly as possible, the same amount above atmospheric pressure, but vary the |time during which the flask is opened. Start with the shortest interval easily attainable and increase this by about one-second increments (by counting "1001, 1002, etc.").

Draw up a table showing values of γ with corresponding values of h_1, in order of size of h_1, for pressures above atmospheric. Make a similar table for pressures below atmospheric.

Prepare a table of values of γ in order of increasing time during which the flask was opened.

Discuss any trends noted in the tables. Give the average value of γ from the first two tables, with a statement of percentage uncertainty.

QUESTIONS

1. Why is it necessary for the flask to be opened only momentarily?

2. Which graph is steeper, a p-V diagram for a gas compressed (a) isothermally, or (b) adiabatically? Why?

3. In this experiment, have you determined γ strictly for *air*?

4. If some gas other than air were being used, should values of pressure less than atmospheric be used?

5. If the flask contained water vapor, would the value of γ for this moist air be greater or less than the value of γ for dry air?

IIIIIIIIIIIIIIIIIIIIIIIIIII

EXPERIMENT 26

VAPOR PRESSURE OF WATER; RELATIVE HUMIDITY

OBJECT. (a) To study the relationship between temperature and the pressure of saturated water vapor. (b) To determine the relative and absolute humidity of the atmosphere, and to compare several types of hygrometers.

DISCUSSION. (a) At ordinary room temperatures the pressure exerted by saturated water vapor is small, between 1 and 2 cm of mercury. As the temperature rises the vapor pressure rises at an increasing rate. The water boils when the pressure of its vapor equals the applied pressure. For a given pressure the temperature of the boiling water remains constant as long as there is any liquid to vaporize.

The apparatus (Fig. 36) is similar to that designed by Regnault (1843) for determining the pressure-temperature relation for saturated

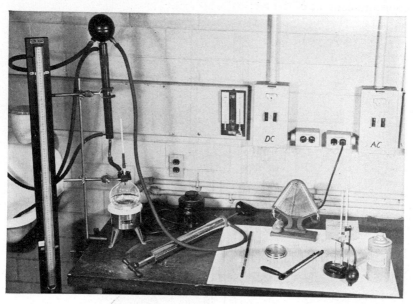

Fig. 36. Vapor pressure apparatus (left), and several types of hygrometers (right).

water vapor by the dynamic method. Water is boiled and the vapor condensed in a closed system in which the pressure may be varied. As water is boiled in the pyrex flask, the vapor passes upward into a cooling jacket where it condenses and returns to the boiler.

The temperature of the boiling liquid is read from a thermometer placed in the vapor that is in equilibrium with the liquid. The vapor pressure p is determined by adding to the barometric pressure B the manometer reading h (open-tube minus closed-tube levels)

$$p = B + h \tag{1}$$

A spherical reservoir between the condenser and the mercury manometer serves to equalize any sudden changes of pressure due to irregularities in boiling.

(b) Human comfort, many scientific measurements, and various industrial processes are dependent on the maintenance of suitable climatic conditions. The condition of the atmosphere, aside from contamination, is determined by the temperature and the amount of moisture which it contains. There are several ways of stating the moisture content of the air:

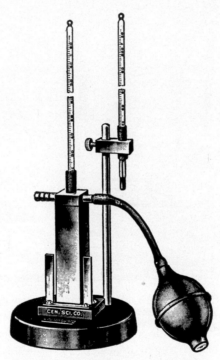

FIG. 37.   Alluard-type dew-point
hygrometer.

Absolute humidity (vapor density) is the mass of water vapor per unit volume of air.   It is commonly expressed in grains per cubic foot or in grams per cubic meter.

Specific humidity is the mass of water vapor per unit mass of air, and is expressed in grams per kilogram, grains per pound, etc.

Relative humidity is defined as the ratio of actual vapor pressure to the saturated vapor pressure at that temperature.

The *dew point* is the temperature to which the air must be cooled, at constant pressure, to produce saturation.

Absolute humidity is measured by absorbing physically or chemically the water present as vapor in a given volume of air. The equipment needed is somewhat elaborate and the method requires time and very exact observations.

A common empirical method, frequently employed in household instruments, is to measure the change in length of a hygroscopic material such as hair. Instruments of this type must be calibrated by an absolute method, and frequent recalibration is desirable.

An accurate method for determining the moisture content of air is a determination of the dew point, the highest temperature at which the water vapor present in the air is sufficient to saturate it. From a vapor pressure table (Appendix) or from your experimental curve of part (a), the relative humidity can be calculated from the observed dew point.

The dew point hygrometer (Fig. 37) consists of a highly polished metal container that can be cooled by evaporating a volatile liquid (Vapofreeze) in it until moisture appears on the surface. The temperature of the cooling liquid is varied between appearance and disappearance of the film and the average of the observed temperatures gives the dew point with high accuracy.

A more common device for humidity measurements is the wet- and dry-bulb hygrometer. The wet bulb is surrounded by a wick saturated with water. Evaporation of water from the wick absorbs heat from the wet bulb and lowers its temperature. The lower the relative humidity, the greater will be the evaporation and the lower the wet-bulb temperature. Empirical formulas are used to determine relative humidity from the wet-bulb temperature t_W and the atmospheric temperature t_R for either (a) no forced ventilation, or (b) ventilation of wet bulb in an air stream of specified speed. If the air speed at the wet bulb exceeds 3 m/sec, it is found that the vapor pressure p is given by the equation

$$p = p_W - 0.00066B(t_R - t_W) \qquad (2)$$

where p_W is the pressure of saturated water vapor at the temperature t_W and B is the barometric pressure (p and B in same units).

PROCEDURE.   (a) Connect the reservoir of the vapor pressure apparatus to the vacuum side of the vacuum-pressure pump.   At the lowest pressure you can attain, close the pinch clamp.   Test for leaks by noting whether the reading of the manometer remains constant.

Heat the water in the boiler and observe the thermometer as its readings increase until they become constant.   Record this temperature and the emergent stem correction Δt that must be added to the observed temperature t

$$\Delta t = 0.00016n(t - t_s) \tag{3}$$

where t_s is the temperature of the midpoint of the exposed thread of

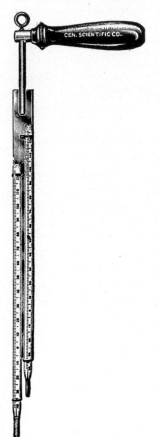

mercury and n is the length of the exposed column expressed in degrees.   Record the readings of the manometer and barometer. Calculate the pressure corresponding to the observed boiling point.

Change the pressure by allowing a little air to enter the system.   Note and record manometer and thermometer readings when the steady state has been reached.   Continue these observations at about five different pressures until atmospheric pressure is reached.

Connect the system to the pressure side of the pump and cautiously increase pressure until the mercury in the closed tube is about 10 cm from the bottom of the manometer.   Bring the water to boiling temperature.   Make sure that the manometer level does not go below 10 cm. Continue readings at successively lower pressures, by admitting air, until atmospheric pressure is reached.

Plot the observed boiling point vs. pressure curve.   On the same sheet, plot a curve representing the data for saturated water vapor pressure found in the Appendix.

(b) Make a quick, approximate determination of the dew point.   Next make

FIG. 38.   Sling psychrometer.

three sets of observations of the temperatures at which the film appears and disappears, allowing the temperatures to change slowly in the neighborhood of the point previously determined. Record temperature of the room and barometric pressure.

Determine the relative humidity by means of each of the instruments available: wet- and dry-bulb hygrometer, sling hygrometer (Fig. 38), hair hygrometer, hygrodeik. Follow the manufacturer's directions as to ventilation and reading. Repeat the readings in still air.

Calculate the relative humidity and the absolute humidity of the laboratory as indicated by each of the instruments. Present data in tabular form for comparison. Compare the instruments used as to accuracy and convenience.

Make an approximate computation of the total amount of water present in the air of the room.

QUESTIONS

1. What is the purpose of the condenser in the vapor pressure apparatus?

2. Which is the more useful term, specific humidity or relative humidity?

3. What does the factor 0.00016 in Eq. (3) represent?

4. Why is it desirable to observe a dew point hygrometer through a reading telescope when making accurate determinations?

5. Show that the density of saturated vapor at the dew point is $d_A(t_R + 273)/(t_D + 273)$.

6. When a sling hygrometer is used in bright sunlight, should the dry bulb be shielded? Why?

7. Is it correct to say that a furnace *dries* the air in a home in the sense of lowering (appreciably) the absolute humidity? Does it lower the relative humidity?

8. Explain why cold surfaces are more likely to "sweat" (show condensation) in the summer than in winter.

9. When the relative humidity is 0.47 at 21°C, what is the dew point?

10. How much water would have to be evaporated to raise the relative humidity of a house whose temperature is 70°F and whose interior is 12,000 ft³ from 20 to 35 per cent?

|||||||||||||||||||||||||

EXPERIMENT 27

PYROMETRIC CONES

OBJECT. Investigation of the response of pyrometric cones to heat treatment.

APPARATUS. Furnace.   Thermocouple pyrometer.   Optical pyrometer.   Pyrometric cones.   (Fig. 39.)

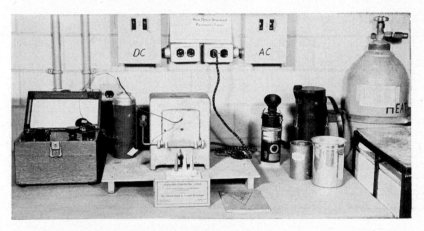

FIG. 39. Apparatus for investigating response of pyrometric cones to heat treatment.

PROCEDURE. Outline an experimental procedure for investigating the following characteristics of a series of pyrometric cones:

1. Accuracy of the softening-temperature calibration when heated at the specified rate.

2. Uniformity of cones bearing the same number.

3. Effect of rapid and slow heating rates on the softening temperature.

4. Response of cones to oxidizing and reducing atmospheres.

After the outline of the proposed procedure has been approved by the instructor, carry out the experiment. Use graphs in your report, where possible, to indicate the significance of the observations.

ꜰꜰꜰꜰꜰꜰꜰꜰꜰꜰꜰꜰꜰꜰꜰꜰꜰ

EXPERIMENT 28

THE CURIE TEMPERATURE OF NICKEL

OBJECT. A qualitative investigation of variation of ferromagnetic susceptibility with temperature. Determination of the Curie point for nickel.

APPARATUS. Nickel sample N (Fig. 40). Furnace F. Thermocouple TC. Portable potentiometer P. Transformer T. Two

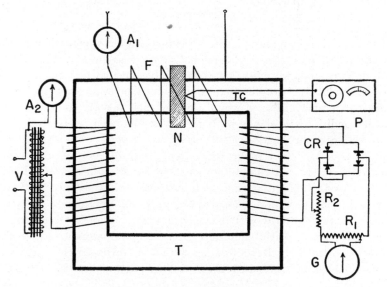

FIG. 40. Curie point apparatus.

variable transformers V. Copper-oxide rectifier CR. Ammeter A_1. Milliammeter A_2. Galvanometer G. Two 10,000-ohm dial decade resistance boxes R_1 and R_2. Mercury thermometer. Timer.

DISCUSSION. It is the purpose of this experiment to investigate the variation of ferromagnetic susceptibility with temperature. Without necessarily adopting a particular theory of the mechanism of

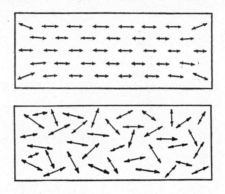

FIG. 41. Magnetic dipoles aligned (top), magnetic dipoles in random orientation (bottom).

ferromagnetism,[1] we may picture a magnetized ferromagnetic material as composed of magnetic "carriers" aligned as in Fig. 41. If the sample is heated, we might expect that the thermal motion imparted to the molecules would affect the molecular alignment and with sufficient temperature rise would destroy their orderly state, resulting in the condition also shown by Fig. 41. If there is a definite relationship between the energy of the magnetized state and the thermal energy necessary to remove the magnetism, this loss of magnetism should occur at a definite temperature for each material. Pierre Curie found (1895) that each ferromagnetic substance lost its ferromagnetism at a certain temperature, and that thereafter the small remaining susceptibility was inversely proportional to the temperature. That is, ferromagnetic materials become paramagnetic above the Curie temperature. Recent values for some Curie temperatures are: iron, 770°C $\pm$ 5 C°; cobalt, 1120°C $\pm$ 20 C°; and nickel 358°C $\pm$ 2 C°.

---

[1] See, for example, C. E. Stoner, *Magnetism and Matter*, London: Methuen, 1934.

PROCEDURE.   If the sample of nickel is included as part of the magnetic circuit of a transformer, a simple method suggests itself for finding the Curie temperature of the nickel.   As the nickel is heated a constant alternating current is maintained in the transformer primary. Any change in the secondary current is then an indication of a change in the characteristics of the magnetic circuit.   When the nickel loses its ferromagnetism there will be a marked decrease in the secondary current.

Connect the apparatus according to Fig. 40.   The alternating current from the transformer secondary is changed to direct current by a copper-oxide rectifier *CR* and measured with a galvanometer *G*. The temperature of the nickel sample *N* is obtained with a calibrated thermocouple connected to a potentiometer *P*.

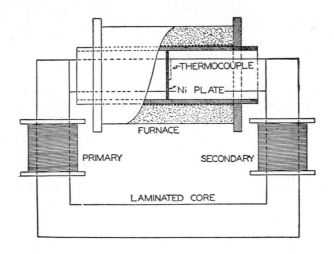

Fig. 42.   Curie point apparatus: details of furnace and
transformer.

Connect the electric furnace through an ammeter and variable transformer to the a-c line.   Connect the primary of the transformer through a milliammeter and variable transformer to an a-c source. When connections have been completed, set the galvanometer resistance R_2 to 10,000 ohms, then turn on the primary current and adjust it to 0.5 amp.   It is important that the current be kept constant throughout the experiment.

Check the zero reading of the galvanometer by setting the shunt resistance R_1 to zero. Then by adjusting R_1 bring the galvanometer to approximately half-scale reading. Turn on the furnace heating current. Notice and explain any immediate change in galvanometer reading.

Galvanometer readings will increase gradually as the furnace temperature rises to about 320 to 340°C, then decrease over the range 330 to 370°C, and finally begin to increase again for still higher temperatures. Potentiometer and galvanometer readings should be taken at intervals of about 25 C° up to 320°C and then at 5 C° intervals. It will be well to turn off the furnace current momentarily while taking readings. (Why?)

After the furnace has reached a temperature of about 380°C the heating current should be turned off and readings continued as the furnace cools. Plot a graph of galvanometer deflection vs. temperature for both increasing and decreasing temperatures. Indicate clearly the Curie point (or region) on each curve. Discuss any displacement of one curve with respect to the other.

On what basis would you explain the hysteresis or lag in the return of ferromagnetism to the nickel as the temperature decreases?

Changes in what other physical properties could be used to locate the Curie point of a metal?

A Jackson-Russell alloy of Fe-Ni-Cr-Si can be made with its Curie point at any temperature by varying its composition. Suggest how such an alloy could be used to protect generators from overheating, for automatic fire alarms, for air-conditioning control, and for controlling the temperature of a small laboratory furnace.

IIIIIIIIIIIIIIIIIIIIIIIIII

EXPERIMENT 29

MEASUREMENT OF FLAME TEMPERATURE

OBJECT. Measurement of the temperature of a flame by a spectroscopic line-reversal method and by a thermocouple extrapolation method.

APPARATUS. Burner with sodium (yellow) and strontium (red) coloring attachments. Prism spectroscope. Tungsten lamp and Variac. Optical pyrometer. Thermocouple set. Potentiometer. Micrometer.

DISCUSSION. Whenever light from an incandescent source (arc or tungsten filament) passes through a flame emitting a bright-line spectrum, the flame absorbs from the light passing through it just those radiations which appear in its own spectrum. If one focuses this light on the slit of a spectrometer and views it after dispersion by the prism, one will see, depending on the relative temperatures of incandescent source and flame, either (a) bright lines characteristic of the flame, (b) a continuous spectrum of the incandescent source crossed by dark absorption lines of the (cooler) flame, or (c) a continuous spectrum in which the line spectrum is blended.

This last condition of balance occurs when incandescent source and flame have the same temperature. Measurement of the temperature of the tungsten filament with an optical pyrometer then yields the temperature of the flame. This method is particularly advantageous for determining the temperatures of nonluminous flames. Addition of metallic vapor in the form of NaCl or SrCl, whose resonance radiation is in the visible region, provides a flame which is practically transparent to visible radiation except at the wavelength of the resonance radiation of the metallic vapor in the flame.

As an alternative method, one might try to measure the temperature of a flame by inserting a thermocouple in it. The cooling effect of thermal conduction along the wires inevitably leads to too low an indicated temperature. If, however, thermocouples of successively finer wires are used, successively higher temperatures will be indicated. One can then plot indicated temperature against wire diameter and by extrapolating to zero diameter get a good estimate of the flame temperature uninfluenced by conduction effects.

FIG. 43.   Flame temperature measurement.

PROCEDURE. Arranging the apparatus as suggested by Fig. 43, adjust the current in the lamp until reversal of the Na or Sr line is obtained. Readjust the lamp until this line blends with the continuous spectrum. Read the temperature of the lamp (equal to that of the flame) with the optical pyrometer.

Use the set of thermocouples provided to get an extrapolated result for the flame temperature. Compare the results obtained.

APPENDIX

IIIIIIIIIIIIIIIIIIIIIIIIIII

HOW TO SOLVE PHYSICAL PROBLEMS

The ability to solve problems is a mark of an effective and efficient scientist or engineer. Through practice in the solution of problems commensurate with one's knowledge, one attains ability and confidence in independent thinking.

In problem solving the following systematic approach is highly recommended. First, read the statement of the problem carefully and decide exactly what is required. Then:

1. Draw a suitable diagram and list the data given.

2. Identify the type of problem and write physical principles which seem relevant to its solution. These may be expressed concisely as algebraic equations.

3. Determine if the data given are adequate. If not, decide what is missing and how to get it. This may involve consulting a table, making a reasonable assumption, or drawing upon your general knowledge for such information as the value of c_w, the specific heat of water, 1 cal/(gm C°).

4. Decide whether in the particular problem it is easier to substitute numerical values immediately or first to carry out an algebraic solution. Some quantities may cancel in the latter case.

5. Substitute numerical data in the equations obtained from physical principles. Include the units for each quantity, making sure that they are all in the same system in any one problem.

6. Compute the numerical value of the unknown, preferably with the aid of a slide rule. Determine the units in which the answer is expressed. Examine the reasonableness of the answer. Can it be obtained by an alternative method to check the result?

The numerous solved examples in the text demonstrate the form of solution recommended for physics problems.

An orderly procedure aids clear thinking, helps to avoid errors, and usually saves time. Most important, it enables one to analyze and eventually to solve those more complex problems whose solutions are not immediately or intuitively apparent.

GENERAL LABORATORY PROCEDURE

The chief purpose of the laboratory exercises is to illustrate and clarify physical principles. Other important benefits may be derived from laboratory work carried out with discriminating effort. One, obviously, is the ability to *plan* experiments and to *draw valid conclusions* from experimental data. Another is the ability to estimate critically the best *accuracy* obtainable with the apparatus available and to attain that accuracy with economy of time. Report writing should lead to facility in the clear *expression* of ideas and develop the ability to read scientific work critically.

Each student should bring to the laboratory the textbook, a slide rule, data forms, carbon paper, and several sheets of graph paper (twentieth inch or millimeter divisions). It is recommended that all paper work for this course be done on 8½ by 11 in. sheets and that these be filed in a loose-leaf notebook.

In recording experimental data, one member of the group may make copies for all, using carbon paper. This secretarial duty should be rotated. While the data should be, and the calculations may be, the same for all members of the group, the conclusions are expected to be the product of individual thought and writing.

The word *accuracy* has various shades of meaning depending on the circumstances in which it is used. Accuracy commonly denotes the reliability of the indications of a measuring instrument. As applied to the final result of an experiment, accuracy is expressed by stating the *uncertainty* of the numerical result, that is, the estimated maximum amount by which the result may differ from the "true" or accepted value.

The *error* in a numerical result is the experimental value minus the true value. Since in physical measurements one never knows the "true" value, strictly, the error is usually stated as the experimental value minus the accepted value.

In reporting an experiment one should always state the estimated uncertainty in a numerical result. The error should also be stated when one has available an accepted value in standard tables or from work with more precise apparatus. If the error is larger than the uncertainty claimed, one should examine the experimental procedure for hidden sources of *systematic* errors.

The following factors are important in arriving at an estimate of the uncertainty of an experimental result in terms of the individual measurements made.

The *least count* of an instrument is the value of the smallest division on its scale. One should estimate readings to a fraction (usually a tenth) of the least count.

The *scale error* of an instrument is the observed value minus the correct value. The appropriate *scale correction* (negative of the scale error) should be applied to readings when known, as from a thermometer certificate.

In recording the result of a measurement or a calculation, one and only one doubtful digit is retained.

In addition and subtraction, do not carry the operations beyond the first column that contains a doubtful figure.

In multiplication and division, carry the result to the same number of significant figures that there are in the quantity entering into the calculation which has the *least* number of significant figures.

In dropping figures that are not significant, the last figure retained should be unchanged if the first figure dropped is less than 5. It should be increased by 1 if the first figure dropped is greater than 5. If the first figure dropped is 5, the preceding digit should be unchanged if it is an even number but increased by 1 if it is an odd number. Examples: 3.4$\overline{5}$5 becomes 3.46, 3.3$\overline{7}$5 becomes 3.38, 4.79$\overline{0}$1 becomes 4.790, 3.5$\overline{4}$5 becomes 3.54.

A systematic use of the rules given above relating to significant figures results in two advantages: (1) Time is saved by carrying out calculations only to that number of figures which the data justify, and (2) intelligent recording of data is encouraged by noting always the least accurate of a number of measurements needed for a given determination. Attention can then be concentrated on improving the least accurate measurement or, if this is not possible, other measurements need be taken only to an accuracy commensurate with it.

It is desirable when possible to repeat a measurement or an entire experiment as an insurance against blunders and accident. Duplication also reduces the *accidental error* to $\sqrt{2}$ or 0.7 of its value for a single determination. But the repetitions become less effective as their number is increased. And, of course, a single measurement made carefully is preferable to several made casually or carelessly.

When the object of an experiment is to determine the value of a quantity from measurements of other quantities connected with it by a formula, it is possible to calculate the uncertainty of the final result from the uncertainties recorded for the measured quantities that are substituted in the formula. Assume that two quantities whose *true* values are x and y have been measured with the result that x is found to be $a + e_1$ and y is found to be $b + e_2$, where e_1 and e_2 are the uncertainties in a and b. Comparing the product of the measurements, $(a + e_1)(b + e_2)$, with the product ab, we have for the difference

$$(a + e_1)(b + e_2) - ab = ae_2 + be_1 + e_1e_2 \tag{1}$$

But e_1e_2 is so small a quantity numerically that it may be neglected in comparison with the first two quantities. Thus when the uncertainty of a is e_1 and that of b is e_2, the uncertainty of ab is $ae_2 + be_1$. Writing e for the uncertainty in ab, we have

$$e = ae_2 + be_1 \tag{2}$$

or
$$\frac{e}{ab} = \frac{e_1}{a} + \frac{e_2}{b} \tag{3}$$

where e/ab, expressed in hundredths, is the percentage uncertainty of ab, e_1/a is similarly the percentage uncertainty of a, etc. Consequently, *the percentage uncertainty of a product is the sum of the percentage uncertainties of the factors.* The rule can obviously be extended to any number of factors and applies also to division.

Consider next the addition of two quantities whose measured values are found to be $a + e_1$ and $b + e_2$. Comparing the sum of the measurements, $a + b$, with $(a + e_1) + (b + e_2)$, it is evident that the uncertainty e in the sum is $(e_1 + e_2)$.

$$e = e_1 + e_2 \tag{4}$$

The uncertainty of a sum is the sum of the uncertainties of the individual terms. The rule can be extended to any number of terms and applies also to subtraction.

If the sums of certain products enter an equation, the uncertainty of each product must be calculated separately. Their sum gives the uncertainty of the calculated quantity.

If in the formula used with the experimental data a factor appears to the nth power, the percentage uncertainty of this factor introduces in the product a percentage uncertainty n times as great as if it entered to the first power only, because the percentage uncertainties are added. Therefore a quantity which appears in the formula as squared or cubed should be measured with much greater care than a quantity which appears in the same product only to the first power.

EXAMPLE: The data below were obtained with the copper conductometer (Exp. 3). Calculate the thermal conductivity k and the percentage uncertainty in k.

Bar temperatures: $T_1 = 81.0°C \pm 0.5\ C°$
$T_2 = 59.8°C \pm 0.5\ C°$

Bar length: $L = 10.1 \pm 0.1$ cm
Bar diameter: $d = 3.79 \pm 0.05$ cm
Cooling water temperatures: $T_4 = 32.3°C \pm 0.2\ C°$
$T_3 = 18.3°C \pm 0.2\ C°$

Time of collecting water: $t = 5$ min ± 2 sec
Mass of water collected: $m = 442 \pm 3$ gm

$$k = \frac{m\, c_w (T_4 - T_3) L}{t\, A (T_1 - T_2)} = \frac{442\text{ gm }(1.00\text{ cal/gm C°}) \times 14\ C° \times 10.1\text{ cm}}{300\text{ sec} \times \pi/4 \times 3.79^2\text{ cm}^2 \times 21.2\ C°}$$

$$k = 0.870\text{ cal/(sec cm}^2\text{ C°/cm)}$$

Uncertainties:			
m	442 $\pm$ 3 gm	or	0.68 per cent
c_w	1 cal/(gm C°)		(negligible)
$(T_4 - T_3)$	14.0 C° $\pm$ 0.4 C°	or	2.86 per cent
L	10.1 $\pm$ 0.1 cm		1.0
t	300 $\pm$ 2 sec		.67
d	1.32 per cent		
A	$\pi d^2/4$		2.64
$(T_1 - T_2)$	21.1 C° $\pm$ 1.0 C°		4.72

Uncertainty in k: $\pm$ 12.57 per cent

The *error* in the value of k determined in this experiment would likely be less than 12.57 per cent, for some of the errors in individual measurements would be positive, others negative, the compensations tending to reduce the overall error. But in reporting the *uncertainty* in k we recognize the unfortunate case when all errors are cumulative in the same sense.

In view of the uncertainties, we are justified in retaining only two significant figures for k, and the experimental value for the thermal conductivity is

$$k = 0.87\text{ cal/(sec cm}^2\text{ C°/cm)} \pm 13\text{ per cent}$$

||||||||||||||||||||||||||||||

LABORATORY REPORTS

Reports on heat laboratory experiments should be submitted on the printed laboratory record forms ($8\frac{1}{2}$ by 11 in.). Particular attention should be given to *conclusions*. Brevity is desirable. Discriminate between the essential and the less important. The following report form is suggested for completeness and order:

1. *Title*.
2. *Object*. Give a statement of the purpose of the experiment in your own words.
3. *Apparatus*. List the essential apparatus only. Give the range of calibration and the least count of each instrument.
4. *Analysis*. Give a brief statement of the theory used and a derivation of the working equation. Mention any points of experimental procedure not covered in the printed directions. Sketch a diagram of the apparatus when appropriate. (Optional.)
5. *Data*. Present your original data. Arrange it in tabular form, with proper column headings, units, significant figures, and percentage uncertainties indicated. Always include the original data sheet with your report even though it may have been rewritten for neatness in the report.
6. *Calculations*. Give a sample calculation of each type in full.
7. *Conclusions*. (a) State the significance of the experiment. What principles were verified or illustrated by the experiment? (b) List *final numerical results*, with proper units and uncertainties indicated. Give each graph an informative *title* and indicate the *units* used. (c) Discuss the accuracy of your results, giving the sources of error (in order of importance) and any special precautions taken to reduce them. (d) Compare the method or instruments used in the experiment with others known to you, as to accuracy, convenience, etc. (Optional.)

|||||||||||||||||||||||||||||

VISUAL AIDS

The following motion picture films are useful in illustrating or supplementing the material discussed in this book. Unless otherwise indicated, all are 16 mm black-and-white sound films. For additional information and titles consult Educational Film Guide (H. W. Wilson Co., 950 University Avenue, New York 52, N. Y.) and Index of Training Films (Business Screen Magazine, 157 E. Erie Street, Chicago, Ill.).*

Basic principles of lubrication. 25 min (1945). General Motors.

Electric heat in industry. General Electric.

Energy and its transformations. 10 min (1933). Encyclopaedia Britannica Films, Inc. (EBF).

Excursions in science, No. 3 (electron theory of magnetism, Curie temperature). 11 min. General Electric.

Fuels and heat. 11 min (1938). EBF.

Heat and its control. 40 min (1934). Johns Manville.

Heat and light from electricity. 15 min, silent (1930). EBF.

Jet propulsion. 15 min, color (1946). General Electric.

Principles of lubrication. 16 min. U. S. Office of Education (Castle Films, distributor).

Principles of refrigeration. 20 min (1945). USOE, Castle.

Properties of water. 11 min (1941). Coronet.

Radio frequency heating. 40 min, color (1944). Westinghouse Electric.

The slide rule (multiplication and division). 24 min (1944). USOE, Castle.

The slide rule (percentage, proportion, squares, and square roots). 21 min (1944). USOE, Castle.

Steam locomotive. 22 min (1944). New York Central.

Steam power. 15 min (1930). EBF.

Steam turbines, no. S-2110. 13 min. General Electric.

Thermodynamics. 11 min (1938). EBF.

Tornado in a box (the gas turbine). 28 min (1946). Allis-Chalmers.

---

* For other instructional films in physics see Weber, R. L., "Films Selected for First-Year College Physics," *Am. J. Physics,* **17**, 408 (1949).

SYMBOLS AND QUANTITIES

IIIIIIIIIIIIIIIIIIIIIIIIII

[References are to the page on which a symbol is introduced or a particular meaning defined.]

A, angstrom (92)
A, area
A, B, C, constants
A, B, C, $\cdots$, temperature-dependent coefficients in gas law (26)
a, b, Van der Waals' constants (227)
a, b, c, d, thermoelectric coefficients (55)
a_0, mean temperature coefficient of resistance (137)
a_1, a_2, a_3, expansion constants (14)
B, barometric pressure
B, luminous intensity (119)
B_λ, spectral brightness (119)
b, Wien's displacement constant (104)
b_1, b_2, b_3, volume expansion coefficients (17)
c, a constant, or calibration constant (100, 115)
c, concentration (99)
c, specific heat (172)
c, speed of light (211)
c_p, specific heat at constant pressure (211)
c_v, specific heat at constant volume (211)
c_1, first radiation constant (103)
c_2, second radiation constant (103)
C, number of compounds (190)
C_p, molar heat capacity at constant pressure (213)
C_v, molar heat capacity at constant volume (213)
D, deflection (100, 115)
D, diffusivity (40, 43)
d, density
E, efficiency (217)
E, emf, electromotive force
E, illuminance (95)
E', Peltier emf (51)

$\mathcal{E}$, Thomson emf (52)
dE/dt, thermoelectric power (55)
e, electronic charge (372)
e, uncertainty (368)
F, degree of freedom (190)
$^\circ F$, degrees Fahrenheit, a temperature (6)
F°, Fahrenheit degrees, a temperature interval (6)
f, force
f, frequency (41)
g, gravitational acceleration (372)
H, heating value of a fuel (333)
H, irradiance (93)
H, magnetizing field (237)
h, film coefficient (44)
h, height (349)
h, Planck's constant (103)
$h\nu$, quantum (103)
I, current
I, luminous intensity (94)
J, mechanical equivalent of heat (372)
J, radiant intensity (93)
K, differential expansivity (19)
$^\circ K$, degrees Kelvin, a temperature (6)
K°, Kelvin degrees, a temperature interval (6)
k, a constant of proportionality
k, Boltzmann constant (103)
k, coefficient of absorption (99)
k, thermal conductivity (33)
L, length
L_t, length, at temperature t (13)
l, length (294)
M, mass
M, mole number (26)
m, mass

370

m, n, calibration constants (327)
$m\mu$, millimicron (92)
N, radiance (93)
n, index of refraction
n, number of degrees of emergent stem (19)
n, thermal resistivity (33)
P, number of phases (190)
P, pressure (25)
P, radiant flux (93)
P_t, pressure, at temperature t (25)
p_c, critical pressure (215)
Q, quantity of heat (33)
q, charge, quantity of electricity
$°R$, degrees Rankine (6)
R, ideal gas constant (26, 212)
R, radiancy (93)
R, resistance
r, radius
r, resistance
S_λ, brightness temperature (122)
T, temperature (absolute); or temperature, $°C$ or $°F$, when t is used for time in the same equation
$\Delta T/\Delta L$, temperature gradient (33)
T_c, critical temperature (215)
T_i, inversion temperature, gas (231)
T_0, ice point
t, centigrade temperature
t, path length (99)
t, time
t_i, inversion temperature, thermocouple (57)
t_n, neutral temperature (57)
t_{pt}, platinum temperature (138)
U, internal energy (210)
U, radiant energy (93)
u, radiant density (93)
V, potential difference
V, volume
V_t, volume, at temperature t (17)
v, speed
v_c, critical volume (228)
W, energy, external work

W, radiant flux density (93)
X, unknown
XU, X-unit (92)
x, y, z, rectangular coordinates

α, (alpha) linear expansivity
α, total absorptance (93)
β, (beta) specific absorptivity (99)
β, volume expansivity (17)
β_p, volume expansivity of a gas (25)
β_v, coefficient of gas pressure change at constant volume (25)
γ, (gamma) ratio of specific heats (211)
Δ, (delta) increment, i.e., ΔL change in length
∇, (del) mathematical operator (40)
$\Delta T/\Delta L$, temperature gradient (33)
∂, (delta) variation, i.e., ∂x variation in x
δ, (delta) Callendar constant (139)
ϵ, (epsilon) total emittance (93)
η, (eta) coefficient of viscosity (293)
θ, (theta) angle
λ, (lambda) lag coefficient (20)
μ, (mu) micron (92)
$\mu\mu$, micromicron (92)
ν, (nu) frequency
π, (pi) the number $3.14159+$
ρ, (rho) density
ρ, total reflectance (93)
ω, (omega) angular speed, $2\pi f$ (41)
ω, solid angle (93)
σ, (sigma) Thomson coefficient (52)
σ, Stefan-Boltzmann constant (372)
τ, (tau) total transmittance (93)
χ, (chi) magnetic susceptibility (238)
$\propto$, varies directly as
$<$, is less than
$>$, is greater than
$\doteq$, is approximately equal to
$'$, prime, denotes different values of a variable or different variables
$^-$, vinculum, indicates first doubtful digit in a measured quantity

TABLE 1[1]

PHYSICAL CONSTANTS[2]

Symbol	Quantity	Numerical value	Unit	Log_{10}
g	Gravity, standard	980.665	cm/sec^2	2.991521
ρ_{Hg}	Density of mercury (STP)	13.5950	gm/cm^3	1.133380
atm	Standard atmosphere	760.00	mm of mercury	2.880814
		1,013,246	bars	6.005716
		1.0333	kg/cm^2	0.014227
gm v	Gram-molecular volume	2.24146×10^4	$cm^3/mole$	4.350530
AMU	Atomic mass unit ($\frac{1}{16}$ mass of $_8O^{16}$ atom)	1.66035×10^{-24}	gm	6.220200 − 30
m_0	Mass of electron at rest	9.1066×10^{-28}	gm	2.959357 − 30
$_1M^1$	Mass of hydrogen atom	1.67339×10^{-24}	gm	0.22360 − 24
N_0	Avogadro number	6.023×10^{23}	molecules/mole	23.779812
n_0	Loschmidt number	2.687×10^{19}	molecules/cm^3	19.429268
R_m	Ideal gas constant, molar	8.31436×10^7	ergs/mole K°	7.919828
		1.98646	cal/mole K°	0.298080
k	Boltzmann constant	1.3805×10^{-16}	erg/K° particle	4.140037 − 20
	Density of water, maximum	0.999972	gm/cm^3	9.999988 − 10
l	Liter (1 kg water)	1000.028	cm^3	3.000012
J	Mechanical equivalent of heat	4.1855×10^7	ergs/cal	7.621748
T_0	Ice point	273.16	°K	2.436417
e	Electronic charge	4.8025×10^{-10}	statcoulomb	0.681467 − 10
		1.60203×10^{-19}	abcoulomb	1.204671 − 20
F	Faraday constant	96,501	int. coulomb/mole	4.984532
c	Speed of light (vacuum)	2.99776×10^{10}	cm/sec	10.476796
σ	Stefan-Boltzmann constant	5.672×10^{-5}	$\dfrac{erg}{cm^2\ sec\ °K^4}$	5.753737 − 10
$b = \lambda T_m$	Wien displacement constant	0.28971	cm K°	9.461950 − 10
h	Planck constant	6.624×10^{-27}	erg sec	3.821121 − 30
$c_2 = \dfrac{hc}{k}$	Second radiation constant	1.4385	cm K°	0.15791

[1] Unless otherwise indicated, these tables are taken by permission from *Temperature—Its Measurement and Control in Science and Industry*. Reinhold Publishing Corp., 1941.

[2] R. T. Birge, "The General Physical Constants," *Reports on Progress in Physics*, **8**, 90 (1942), London, The Physical Society; *Rev. Mod. Phys.*, **13**, 233 (1941).

TABLE 2

TEMPERATURE CONVERSION TABLE: DEGREES CENTIGRADE TO DEGREES FAHRENHEIT[1]

°C	0	10	20	30	40	50	60	70	80	90
	F	F	F	F	F	F	F	F	F	F
−200	−328	−346	−364	−382	−400	−418	−436	−454	.....	.....
−100	−148	−166	−184	−202	−220	−238	−256	−274	−292	−310
−0	+32	+14	−4	−22	−40	−58	−76	−94	−112	−130
0	32	50	68	86	104	122	140·	158	176	194
100	212	230	248	266	284	302	320	338	356	374
200	392	410	428	446	464	482	500	518	536	554
300	572	590	608	626	644	662	680	698	716	734
400	752	770	788	806	824	842	860	878	896	914
500	932	950	968	986	1004	1022	1040	1058	1076	1094
600	1112	1130	1148	1166	1184	1202	1220	1238	1256	1274
700	1292	1310	1328	1346	1364	1382	1400	1418	1436	1454
800	1472	1490	1508	1526	1544	1562	1580	1598	1616	1634
900	1652	1670	1688	1706	1724	1742	1760	1778	1796	1814
1000	1832	1850	1868	1886	1904	1922	1940	1958	1976	1994
1100	2012	2030	2048	2066	2084	2102	2120	2138	2156	2174
1200	2192	2210	2228	2246	2264	2282	2300	2318	2336	2354
1300	2372	2390	2408	2426	2444	2462	2480	2498	2516	2534
1400	2552	2570	2588	2606	2624	2642	2660	2678	2696	2714
1500	2732	2750	2768	2786	2804	2822	2840	2858	2876	2894
1600	2912	2930	2948	2966	2984	3002	3020	3038	3056	3074
1700	3092	3110	3128	3146	3164	3182	3200	3218	3236	3254
1800	3272	3290	3308	3326	3344	3362	3380	3398	3416	3434
1900	3452	3470	3488	3506	3524	3542	3560	3578	3596	3614
2000	3632	3650	3668	3686	3704	3722	3740	3758	3776	3794
2100	3812	3830	3848	3866	3884	3902	3920	3938	3956	3974
2200	3992	4010	4028	4046	4064	4082	4100	4118	4136	4154
2300	4172	4190	4208	4226	4244	4262	4280	4298	4316	4334
2400	4352	4370	4388	4406	4424	4442	4460	4478	4496	4514
2500	4532	4550	4568	4586	4604	4622	4640	4658	4676	4694
2600	4712	4730	4748	4766	4784	4802	4820	4838	4856	4874
2700	4892	4910	4928	4946	4964	4982	5000	5018	5036	5054
2800	5072	5090	5108	5126	5144	5162	5180	5198	5216	5234
2900	5252	5270	5288	5306	5324	5342	5360	5378	5396	5414
3000	5432	5450	5468	5486	5504	5522	5540	5558	5576	5594
3100	5612	5630	5648	5666	5684	5702	5720	5738	6756	5774
3200	5792	5810	5828	5846	5864	5882	5900	5918	5936	5954
3300	5972	5990	6008	6026	6044	6062	6080	6098	6116	6134
3400	6152	6170	6188	6206	6224	6242	6260	6278	6296	6314
3500	6332	6350	6368	6386	6404	6422	6440	6458	6476	6494
3600	6512	6530	6548	6566	6584	6602	6620	6638	6656	6674
3700	6692	6710	6728	6746	6764	6782	6800	6818	6836	6854
3800	6872	6890	6908	6926	6944	6962	6980	6998	7016	7034
3900	7052	7070	7088	7106	7124	7142	7160	7178	7196	7214
°C	0	10	20	30	40	50	60	70	80	90

°C	°F
1	1.8
2	3.6
3	5.4
4	7.2
5	9.0
6	10.8
7	12.6
8	14.4
9	16.2
10	18.0

°F	°C
1	0.56
2	1.11
3	1.67
4	2.22
5	2.78
6	3.33
7	3.89
8	4.44
9	5.00
10	5.56
11	6.11
12	6.67
13	7.22
14	7.78
15	8.33
16	8.89
17	9.44
18	100.00

Examples: 1347°C = 2444°F + 12.6 F° = 2456.6°F. 3367°F = 1850°C+2.78 C° = 1852.78°C.

[1] Nat. Bur. Standards misc. pub. M126 (1937).

TABLE 2 (Continued)

TEMPERATURE CONVERSION TABLE: DEGREES FAHRENHEIT TO DEGREES CENTIGRADE

(Single boldface figures indicate recurring decimals)

°F	0	10	20	30	40	50	60	70	80	90
	C	C	C	C	C	C	C	C	C	C
−400	−240.0	−245.5	−251.1	−256.6	−262.2	−267.7	...	...	...	...
−300	−184.4	−190.0	−195.5	−201.1	−206.6	−212.2	−217.7	−223.3	−228.8	−234.4
−200	−128.8	−134.4	−140.0	−145.5	−151.1	−156.6	−162.2	−167.7	−173.3	−178.8
−100	−73.3	−78.8	−84.4	−90.0	−95.5	−101.1	−106.6	−112.2	−117.7	−123.3
−0	−17.7	−23.3	−28.8	−34.4	−40.0	−45.5	−51.1	−56.6	−62.2	−67.7
0	−17.7	−12.2	−6.6	−1.1	+4.4	+10.0	+15.5	+21.1	+26.6	+32.2
100	37.7	43.3	48.8	54.4	60.0	65.5	71.1	76.6	82.2	87.7
200	93.3	98.8	104.4	110.0	115.5	121.1	126.6	137.2	137.7	143.3
300	148.8	154.4	160.0	165.5	171.1	176.6	182.2	187.7	193.3	198.8
400	204.4	210.0	215.5	221.1	226.6	232.2	237.7	243.3	248.8	254.4
500	260.0	265.5	271.1	276.6	282.2	287.7	293.3	298.8	304.4	310.0
600	315.5	321.1	326.6	332.2	337.7	343.3	348.8	354.4	360.0	365.5
700	371.1	376.6	382.2	387.7	393.3	398.8	404.4	410.0	415.5	421.1
800	426.6	432.2	437.7	443.3	448.8	454.4	460.0	465.5	471.1	476.6
900	482.2	487.7	493.3	498.8	504.4	510.0	515.5	521.1	526.6	532.2
1000	537.7	543.3	548.8	554.4	560.0	565.5	571.1	576.6	582.2	587.7
1100	593.3	598.8	604.4	610.0	615.5	621.1	626.6	632.2	637.7	643.3
1200	648.8	654.4	660.0	665.5	671.1	676.6	682.2	687.7	693.3	698.8
1300	704.4	710.0	715.5	721.1	726.6	732.2	737.7	743.3	748.8	754.4
1400	760.0	765.5	771.1	776.6	782.2	787.7	793.3	798.8	804.4	810.0
1500	815.5	821.1	826.6	832.2	837.7	843.3	848.8	854.4	860.0	865.5
1600	871.1	876.6	882.2	887.7	893.3	898.8	904.4	910.0	915.5	921.1
1700	926.6	932.2	937.7	943.3	948.8	954.4	960.0	965.5	971.1	976.6
1800	982.2	987.7	993.3	998.8	1004.4	1010.0	1015.5	1021.1	1026.6	1032.2
1900	1037.2	1043.3	1048.8	1054.4	1060.0	1065.5	1071.1	1076.6	1082.2	1087.7
2000	1093.3	1098.8	1104.4	1110.0	1115.5	1121.1	1126.6	1132.2	1137.7	1143.3
2100	1148.8	1154.4	1160.0	1165.5	1171.1	1176.6	1182.2	1187.7	1193.3	1198.8
2200	1204.4	1210.0	1215.5	1221.1	1226.6	1232.2	1237.7	1243.3	1248.8	1254.4
2300	1260.0	1265.5	1271.1	1276.6	1282.2	1287.7	1293.3	1298.8	1304.4	1310.0
2400	1315.5	1321.1	1326.6	1332.2	1337.7	1343.3	1348.8	1354.4	1360.0	1365.5
2500	1371.1	1376.6	1382.2	1387.7	1393.3	1398.8	1404.4	1410.0	1415.5	1421.1
2600	1426.6	1432.2	1437.7	1443.3	1448.8	1454.4	1460.0	1465.5	1471.1	1476.6
2700	1482.2	1487.7	1493.3	1498.8	1504.4	1510.0	1515.5	1521.1	1526.6	1532.2
2800	1537.7	1543.3	1548.8	1554.4	1560.0	1565.5	1571.1	1576.6	1582.2	1587.7
2900	1593.3	1598.8	1604.4	1610.0	1615.5	1621.1	1626.6	1632.2	1637.7	1643.3
3000	1648.8	1654.4	1660.0	1665.5	1671.1	1676.6	1682.2	1687.7	1693.3	1698.8
3100	1704.4	1710.0	1715.5	1721.1	1726.6	1732.2	1737.7	1743.3	1748.8	1754.4
3200	1760.0	1765.5	1771.1	1776.6	1782.2	1787.7	1793.3	1798.8	1804.4	1810.0
3300	1815.5	1821.1	1826.6	1832.2	1837.7	1843.3	1848.8	1854.4	1860.0	1865.5
3400	1871.1	1876.6	1882.2	1887.7	1893.3	1898.8	1904.4	1910.0	1915.5	1921.1
3500	1926.6	1932.2	1937.7	1943.3	1948.8	1954.4	1960.0	1965.5	1971.1	1976.6
3600	1982.2	1987.7	1993.3	1998.8	2004.4	2010.0	2015.5	2021.1	2026.6	2032.2
°F	0	10	20	30	40	50	60	70	80	90

°F	°C
1	0.5
2	1.1
3	1.6
4	2.2
5	2.7
6	3.3
7	3.8
8	4.4
9	5.0

Examples: $-246.0°F = -1511°C - 3.33\ C° = -154.44°C$

$3762°F = 2071.1°C + 1.1\ C° = 2072.2°C$

$2423.5°F = 1326.66°C + 1.66\ C°\ 0.27\ C° = 1328.61°C$

TABLE 2 (Continued)
°F to °C

°F	0	10	20	30	40	50	60	70	80	90
	C	C	C	C	C	C	C	C	C	C
3700	2037.7	2043.3	2048.8	2054.4	2060.0	2065.5	2071.1	2076.6	2082.2	2087.7
3800	2093.3	2098.8	2104.4	2110.0	2115.5	2121.1	2126.6	2132.2	2137.7	2143.3
3900	2148.8	2154.4	2160.0	2165.5	2171.1	2176.6	2182.2	2187.7	2193.3	2198.8
4000	2204.4	2210.0	2215.5	2221.1	2226.6	2232.2	2237.7	2243.3	2248.8	2254.4
4100	2260.0	2265.5	2171.1	2276.6	2282.2	2287.7	2293.3	2298.8	2304.4	2310.0
4200	2315.5	2321.1	2326.6	2332.2	2337.7	2343.3	2348.8	2354.4	2360.0	2365.5
4300	2371.1	2376.6	2382.2	2387.7	2393.3	2398.8	2404.4	2410.0	2415.5	2421.1
4400	2426.6	2432.2	2437.7	2443.3	2448.8	2454.4	2460.0	2465.5	2471.1	2476.6
4500	2482.2	2487.7	2493.3	2498.8	2504.4	2510.0	2515.5	2521.1	2526.6	2532.2
4600	2537.7	2543.3	2548.8	2554.4	2560.0	2566.5	2571.1	2576.6	2582.2	2587.7
4700	2593.3	2598.8	2604.4	2610.0	2615.5	2621.1	2626.6	2632.2	2637.7	2643.3
4800	2648.8	2654.4	2660.0	2665.5	2671.1	2676.6	2682.2	2687.7	2693.3	2698.8
4900	2704.4	2710.0	2715.5	2721.1	2726.6	2732.2	2737.7	2743.3	2748.8	2754.4
5000	2760.0	2765.5	2771.1	2776.6	2782.2	2787.7	2793.3	2798.8	2804.4	2810.0
5100	2815.5	2821.1	2826.6	2832.2	2837.7	2843.3	2848.8	2854.4	2860.0	2865.5
5200	2871.1	2876.6	2882.2	2887.7	2893.3	2898.8	2904.4	2910.0	2915.5	2921.1
5300	2926.6	2932.2	2937.7	2943.3	2948.8	2954.4	2960.0	2965.5	2971.1	2976.6
5400	2982.2	2987.7	2993.3	2998.8	3004.4	3010.0	3015.5	3021.1	3026.6	3032.2
5500	3037.7	3043.3	4048.8	3054.4	3060.0	3065.5	3071.1	3076.6	3082.2	3087.7
5600	3093.3	3098.8	3104.4	3110.0	3115.5	3121.1	3126.6	3132.2	3137.7	3143.3
5700	3148.8	3154.4	3160.0	3165.5	3171.1	3176.6	3182.2	3187.7	3193.3	3198.8
5800	3204.4	3210.0	3215.5	3221.1	3226.6	3232.2	3237.7	3243.3	3248.8	3254.4
5900	3260.0	3265.5	3271.1	3276.6	3282.2	3287.7	3293.3	3298.8	3304.4	3310.0
6000	3315.5	3321.1	3326.6	3332.2	3337.7	3343.3	3348.8	3354.4	3360.0	3365.5
6100	3371.1	3376.6	3382.2	3387.7	3393.3	3398.8	3404.4	3410.0	3415.5	3421.1
6200	3426.6	3432.2	3437.7	3443.3	3448.8	3454.4	3460.0	3465.5	3471.1	3476.6
6300	3482.2	3487.7	3493.3	3498.8	3504.4	3510.0	3515.5	3521.1	3526.6	3532.2
6400	3537.7	3543.3	3548.8	3554.4	3560.0	3565.5	3571.1	3576.6	3582.2	3587.7
6500	3593.3	3598.8	3604.4	3610.0	3615.5	3621.1	3626.6	3632.2	3637.7	3643.3
6600	3648.8	3654.4	3660.0	3665.5	3671.1	3676.6	3682.2	3687.7	3693.3	3698.8
6700	3704.4	3710.0	3715.5	3721.1	3726.6	3732.2	3737.7	3743.3	3748.8	3754.4
6800	3760.0	3765.5	3771.1	3776.6	3782.2	3787.7	3793.3	3798.8	3804.4	3810.0
6900	3815.5	3821.1	3826.6	3832.2	3837.7	3843.3	3848.8	3854.4	3860.0	3865.5
7000	3871.1	3876.6	3882.2	3887.7	3893.3	3898.8	3904.4	3910.0	3915.5	3921.1
7100	3926.6	3932.2	3937.7	3943.3	3948.8	3954.4	3960.0	3965.5	3971.1	3976.6
7200	3982.2	3987.7	3993.3	3998.8	4004.4	4010.0	4015.5	4021.1	4026.6	4032.2
7300	4037.7	4043.3	4048.8	4054.4	4060.0	4065.5	4071.1	4076.6	4082.2	4087.7
7400	4093.3	4098.8	4104.4	4110.0	4115.5	4121.1	4126.6	4132.2	4137.7	4143.3
7500	4148.8	4154.4	4160.0	4165.5	4171.1	4176.6	4182.2	4187.7	4193.3	4198.8
7600	4204.4	4210.0	4215.5	4221.1	4226.6	4232.2	4237.7	4243.3	4248.8	4254.4
7700	4260.0	4265.5	4271.1	4276.6	4282.2	4287.7	4293.3	4298.8	4304.4	4310.0
7800	4315.5	4321.1	4236.6	4332.2	4337.7	4343.3	4348.8	4354.4	4360.0	4365.5
7900	4371.1	4376.6	4382.2	4387.7	4393.3	4398.8	4404.4	4410.0	4415.5	4421.1
°F	0	10	20	30	40	50	60	70	80	90

°F	°C
1	0.5
2	1.1
3	1.6
4	2.2
5	2.7
6	3.3
7	3.8
8	4.4
9	5.0

TABLE 3

The Chemical Elements: Their Atomic Numbers, Symbols, and Weights, and Their Melting Points on the International Temperature Scale[1]

(Temperatures below $-190°C$ are on the Centigrade Thermodynamic Scale.)

The atomic weights given constitute the complete list of the International Weights of 1936, as approved and reported by the Committee on Atomic Weights of the International Union of Chemistry. There is reason to believe that the following (unofficial) values may prove more nearly correct: aluminum, 26,974; carbon, 12.009; gallium, 69.74.

Atomic number	Atomic symbol	Name of element	Melting point, °C	Atomic weight
89	Ac	Actinium..............................	*1600	
13	Al	Aluminum.............................	660.0 ± 0.1	26.97
51	Sb	Antimony.............................	630.5 ± 0.1	121.76
18	A	Argon................................	−189.3 ± 0.5	39.944
33	As	Arsenic.......	*814	74.91
56	Ba	Barium...............................	704 ± 20	137.36
4	Be	Beryllium............................	1280 ± 40	9.02
83	Bi	Bismuth..............................	271.3 ± 0.1	209.00
5	B	Boron................................	2300 ± 300	10.82
35	Br	Bromine..............................	−7.2 ± 0.2	79.916
48	Cd	Cadmium.............................	320.9 ± 0.1	112.41
20	Ca	Calcium..............................	850 ± 20	40.08
6	C	Carbon...............................	3700 ± 100	12.00
58	Ce	Cerium...............................	600 ± 50	140.13
55	Cs	Cesium...............................	28 ± 2	132.91
17	Cl	Chlorine..............................	−101 ± 2	35.457
24	Cr	Chromium............................	1800 ± 50	52.01
27	Co	Cobalt...............................	1490 ± 20	58.94
41	Cb	Columbium...........................	2000 ± 50	92.91
29	Cu	Copper...............................	1083.0 ± 0.1	63.57
66	Dy	Dysprosium...........................	....	162.46
68	Er	Erbium...............................	....	167.64
63	Eu	Europium.............................	....	152.0
9	F	Fluorine.......................	−223 ± 10	19.00
64	Gd	Gadolinium...........................	....	157.3
31	Ga	Gallium..............................	29.78 ± 0.02	69.72
32	Ge	Germanium...........................	958 ± 10	72.60
79	Au	Gold.................................	1063.0 ± 0.0	197.2
72	Hf	Hafnium..............................	*1700	178.6
2	He	Helium...............................	*−271.4 ± 0.2	4.002
67	Ho	Holmium.............................	....	163.5
1	H	Hydrogen.............................	−259.2 ± 0.1	1.0078
		H₂ (normal).........................	−259.2 ± 0.1	
		HD................................	−256.5 ± 0.2	
		D₂ (normal).........................	−254.5 ± 0.2	
61	Il	Illinium...............................		
49	In	Indium...............................	156.4 ± 0.1	114.76
53	I	Iodine...............................	114 ± 1	126.92
77	Ir	Iridium...............................	2454 ± 3	193.1
26	Fe	Iron.................................	1535 ± 3	55.84
36	Kr	Krypton..............................	−157 ± 0.5	83.7

[1] Nat. Bur. Standards misc. pub. M126 (1937).

TABLE 3 *(Continued)*

THE CHEMICAL ELEMENTS

Atomic number	Atomic symbol	Name of element	Melting point, °C	Atomic weight
57	La	Lanthanum................................	826 ± 5	138.92
82	Pb	Lead.....................................	327.4 ± 0.1	207.22
3	Li	Lithium..................................	186 ± 5	6.940
71	Lu	Lutecium.................................	....	175.0
12	Mg	Magnesium...............................	650 ± 2	24.32
25	Mn	Manganese................................	1260 ± 20	54.93
43	Ma	Masurium.................................	ª2700	
80	Hg	Mercury..................................	−38.87 ± 0.02	200.61
42	Mo	Molybdenum..............................	2625 ± 50	96.0
60	Nd	Neodymium...............................	840 ± 40	144.27
10	Ne	Neon.....................................	−248.6 ± 0.3	20.183
28	Ni	Nickel...................................	1455 ± 1	58.69
7	N	Nitrogen.................................	−210.0 ± 0.3	14.008
76	Os	Osmium..................................	2700 ± 200	191.5
8	O	Oxygen..................................	−218.8 ± 0.3	16.0000
46	Pd	Palladium................................	1554 ± 1	106.7
15	P	Phosphorus, Y............................	44.1 ± 0.1	31.02
		Phosphorus, R............................	ᵈ590	
78	Pt	Platinum.................................	1773.5 ± 1	195.23
84	Po	Polonium.................................	ª600	
19	K	Potassium................................	63 ± 1	39.096
59	Pr	Praseodymium............................	940 ± 50	140.92
91	Pa	Protactinium.............................	ª3000	231
88	Ra	Radium..................................	700	226.05
86	Rn	Radon...................................	−71	222
75	Re	Rhenium.................................	ª3000	186.31
45	Rh	Rhodium.................................	1966 ± 3	102.91
37	Rb	Rubidium................................	39 ± 1	85.44
44	Ru	Ruthenium...............................	2500 ± 100	101.7
62	Sm	Samarium................................	>1300	150.43
21	Sc	Scandium................................	1200	45.10
34	Se	Selenium.................................	220 ± 5	78.96
14	Si	Silicon...................................	1430 ± 20	28.06
47	Ag	Silver....................................	960.5 ± 0.0	107.880
11	Na	Sodium..................................	97.7 ± 0.2	22.997
38	Sr	Strontium................................	770 ± 10	87.63
16	S	Sulfur:		32.06
		Monoclinic............................	119.2 ± 0.2	
		Rhombic..............................	112.8 ± 0.2	
73	Ta	Tantalum................................	3000 ± 100	180.88
52	Te	Tellurium................................	450 ± 10	127.61
65	Tb	Terbium.................................	327 ± 5	159.2
81	Tl	Thallium.................................	300 ± 3	204.39
90	Th	Thorium.................................	1800 ± 150	232.12
69	Tm	Thulium.................................	....	169.4
50	Sn	Tin......................................	231.9 ± 0.1	118.70
22	Ti	Titanium.................................	1820 ± 100	47.90
74	W	Tungsten................................	3410 ± 20	184.0
92	U	Uranium.................................	ª3600	238.14
23	V	Vanadium................................	1735 ± 50	50.95
54	Xe	Xenon...................................	−112 ± 1	131.3
70	Yb	Ytterbium................................	....	173.04
39	Y	Yttrium..................................	1490 ± 200	88.92
30	Zn	Zinc.....................................	419.5 ± 0.1	65.38
40	Zr	Zirconium................................	1750 ± 700	91.22
85	....	Element 85...............................	ª250	
87	....	Element 87...............................	ª23	

ª Computed.   ᵇ At 36 atm.   ᶜ At 30 atm.   ᵈ At 43 atm.

TABLE 4

PROPERTIES OF MATERIALS

Many values are approximate only. For properties that vary with temperature, the values given are for room temperature or average values over the range 0 to 100°C. Data compiled chiefly from *Handbook of Chemistry and Physics*, 30th ed., Chemical Rubber Publishing Co., 1947, and *International Critical Tables*, McGraw-Hill Book Co., Inc., 1926.

PART A. SOLIDS

Substance	Molecular or atomic weight gm/mole	Density gm/cm³	Softening or melting point, °C	Boiling point °C	Heat of Fusion cal/gm	Heat of vaporization cal/gm	Specific Heat cal/gm C°	Thermal conductivity cal/sec cm² C°/cm	Linear expansion 10^{-6}/C°
Aluminum	26.97	8.40	669.7	800	76.8	2000	0.214	0.504	25.5
Antimony	121.76	6.691	630.5	1380			0.050	0.042	12.
Bismuth	209.00	9.78	271.3	1450	12.64		0.0294	0.0194	13.5
Brass, yellow		8.40	900				0.092	0.023	18.9
Cadmium	112.41	8.65	320.9	767	13.7	230	0.055	0.222	28.8
Carbon, amorphous	12.01	1.88		4200		7200	0.204	0.091	5.4
Carbon, graphite	12.01	2.25	>3500				0.12	0.34	7.86
Cobalt	58.94	8.71	1480	3000	60.3	1500	0.100	0.17	12.4
Copper	162.46	8.94	1083	2300	42	860	0.092	0.918	16.8
Cork		0.24						0.00013	
Gold	197.2	19.32	1063	2600	15.8	330	0.0312	0.700	14.3
Glass, crown		2.6	450				0.161	0.0025	8.97
Glass, pyrex		2.25	815				0.20		3.2
Ice	18.02	0.917	0.000	100.00	79.71	539.55	0.53	0.0022	41.7
Iron	55.84	7.86	1535	3000	478	1600	0.107	0.161	12.1
Magnesium	24.32	1.74	651	1320	29.9	1110	0.25	0.376	26.1
Mica		2.9					0.206	0.0018	
Molybdenum	99.5	10.2	2620	3700		830	0.065	0.346	4.9
Lead	207.21	11.35	327.4	1620	5.86	230	0.0306	0.083	29.4
Nickel	58.69	8.90	1455	2900	73.8	1010	0.105	0.142	12.8
Palladium	106.7	12.16	1545	2200	36.3	610	0.054	0.168	11.0
Platinum	195.23	21.37	1773.5	4300	27.2	320	0.0324	0.166	8.99
Silver	107.88	10.50	960.5	1950	21.1	490	0.0558	0.990	18.8
Steel		7.83	1430				0.11	0.11	13.2
Sulfur, mono	32.06	1.96	119.0	444.6	13.2	67	0.181	0.00050	
Sulfur, rh	32.06	2.07	112.8	444.6		67	0.176	0.00070	64
Tin, gray	118.70	5.75	231.9	2260	14.0	480	0.0542	0.155	26.9
Tungsten	183.92	19.3	3370	5900		500	0.034	0.41	4.44
Uranium	238.07	18.7	<1850			350	0.028		
White oak, ⊥		0.77					0.33	0.048	54.4
Zinc	65.58	7.14	419.5	907	28.1	430	0.0925	0.265	26.3

TABLE 4 (*Continued*)
Properties of Materials

Part B. Liquids

Substance	Molecular or atomic weight gm/mole	Density gm/cm³	Boiling point °C	Freezing point °C	Heat of vaporization cal/gm	Heat of Fusion cal/gm	Specific heat cal/gm C°	Volume expansion $10^{-3}/C°$	Thermal conductivity cal/sec cm² C°/cm	Viscosity centipoise
Alcohol, ethyl C_2H_5OH	46.07	0.789	78.3	−117	204	24.8	0.581	1.12	0.00043	1.72
Alcohol, methyl CH_3OH	32.04	0.796	64.7	−97.8	262.8	22.0	0.600	1.20	0.00050	0.596
Acetone $(CH_3)_2CO$	53.08	0.792	57.0	−95	124.5	23.4	0.528	1.49	0.00042	0.303
Carbon tetrachloride CCl_4	153.84	1.595	76	−22.8	46.5	4.15	0.201	1.24	0.00026	0.975
Carbon disulfide CS_2	76.13	1.263	46.3	−108.6	84.1			1.22	0.00038	0.376
Castor oil		0.969		−12					0.00043	9.86
Ethyl ether $(C_2H_5)_2O$	74.12	0.714	34.6	−117.6	83.8		0.540	1.66	0.00033	0.223
Gasoline		0.67	80	−130						0.40
Kerosene		0.82			60				0.00037	2.0
Mercury	200.61	13.6	356.9	−38.87	65	2.78	0.0333	0.181	0.0192	1.55
Water	18.02	1.00	100.00	0.000	539.55	79.8	1.00		0.00014	1.01
Toluene $C_6H_5CH_3$	92.13	0.866	110.8	−95	86.3		0.428		0.00038	0.590

Part C. Gases

Substance	Molecular or atomic weight gm/mole	Density gm/l	c_p cal/gm C°	c_p/c_v	Thermal conductivity 10^{-5} cal/sec cm² C°/cm	Molecular diameter 10^{-8} cm	Viscosity 10^{-6} poise	Critical temperature °C	Critical pressure atm
Air	29	1.292	0.238	1.403	5.3		181	−140.7	37.2
Ammonia	17.03	0.771	0.523	1.310	4.6	2.97	110	132.4	111.5
Argon	39.944	1.784	0.125	1.67	3.8	2.88	221	−122	48
Carbon dioxide	44.00	1.977	0.199	1.304	3.4	3.34	148	31.1	73.0
Carbon monoxide	28.00	1.250	0.248	1.404	5.3	3.19	172	−139	35
Chlorine	35.457	3.214	0.115	1.355	1.7		130	144.0	76.1
Helium	4.003	0 178	1.31	1.66	33.6	1.90	109	−267.9	2.26
Hydrogen	1.9080	0.0899	3.389	1.410	38.0	2.40	88.7	−239.9	12.8
Neon	20.183	0.900		1.64	10.6		312	−228.7	25.9
Nitrogen	14.008	1.251	0.248	1.404	5.5	3.15	176	−147.1	33.5
Oxygen	16.000	1.429	0.218	1.401	5.57	2.98	196	−118.8	49.7
Sulfur dioxide	64.07	2.923	1.52	1.29	1.84		124	157.2	77.7
Water vapor	18.02				5.19		98	374.0	217.72

TABLE 5
Plat. vs. Plat. + 10% Rhodium Thermocouple[1]
(Degrees Centigrade, Reference Junction 0°C)

Deg. C	0°	100°	200°	300°	400°	500°	600°	700°	800°
					Millivolts				
0°	0	.643	1.436	2.316	3.251	4.219	5.222	6.260	7.330
2°	.011	.658	1 453	2.334	3.270	4.239	5.243	6.281	7.352
4°	.023	.672	1.470	2.352	3.289	4.258	5.263	6.302	7.374
6°	.034	.687	1.487	2.370	3.308	4.278	5.284	6.323	7.396
8°	.046	.702	1.504	2.388	3.327	4.298	5.304	6.344	7.417
10°	.057	.717	1.521	2.406	3.346	4.518	5.325	6.365	7.439
12°	.068	.732	1.538	2.425	3.365	4.337	5.345	6.387	7.461
14°	.080	.747	1.555	2.443	3.384	4.357	5.366	6.408	7.483
16°	.091	.762	1.572	2.462	3.403	4.377	5.386	6.429	7.505
18°	.103	.777	1.589	2.480	3.422	4.397	5.407	6.450	7.527
20°	.114	.792	1.606	2.498	3.441	4.417	5.427	6.471	7.548
22°	.126	.807	1.623	2.517	3.461	4.436	5.448	6.493	7.570
24°	.138	.822	1.641	2.536	3.480	4.456	5.469	6.514	7.592
26°	.150	.838	1.658	2.554	3.499	4.476	5.489	6.535	7.614
28°	.162	.853	1.675	2.573	3.519	4.496	5.510	6.556	7.636
30°	.174	.869	1.692	2.591	3.538	4.516	5.530	6.578	7.658
32°	.186	.884	1.710	2.610	3.557	4.536	5.551	6.599	7.680
34°	.198	.899	1.727	2.628	3.577	4.556	5.571	6.620	7.702
36°	.211	.915	1.744	2.647	3.596	4.576	5.592	6.642	7.724
38°	.223	.931	1.762	2.665	3.615	4.596	5.613	6.663	7.746
40°	.235	.946	1.779	2.684	3.634	4.616	5.633	6.684	7.768
42°	.248	.962	1.797	2.703	3.653	4.636	5.654	6.706	7.790
44°	.260	.977	1.814	2.721	3.673	4.656	5.675	6.727	7.812
46°	.273	.993	1.832	2.740	3.692	4.676	5.696	6.748	7.834
48°	.286	1.009	1.850	2.759	3.711	4.696	5.717	6.769	7.856
50°	.299	1.025	1.867	2.778	3.731	4.716	5.737	6.790	7.878
52°	.312	1.041	1.885	2.796	3.750	4.736	5.758	6.812	7.900
54°	.325	1.057	1.902	2.815	3.770	4.756	5.779	6.834	7.922
56°	.338	1.073	1.920	2.834	3.789	4.776	5.800	6.855	7.944
58°	.351	1.089	1.938	2.852	3.808	4.796	5.821	6.877	7.966
60°	.365	1.105	1.956	2.871	3.828	4.817	5.841	6.898	7.989
62°	.378	1.121	1.973	2.890	3.847	4.837	5.862	6.920	8.011
64°	.391	1.137	1.991	2.909	3.867	4.857	5.883	6.941	8.033
66°	.405	1.154	2.009	2.928	3.886	4.877	5.904	6.963	8.055
68°	.418	1.170	2.027	2.947	3.906	4.897	5.925	6.984	8.077
70°	.432	1.186	2.045	2.965	3.925	4.918	5.945	7.005	8.100
72°	.445	1.203	2.063	2.984	3.945	4.938	5.966	7.027	8.122
74°	.459	1.219	2.081	3.003	3.964	4.958	5.987	7.049	8.144
76°	.473	1.236	2.099	3.022	3.984	4.978	6.008	7.070	8.166
78°	.487	1.252	2.117	3.041	4.003	4.998	6.029	7.092	8.188
80°	.500	1.269	2.134	3.060	4.023	5.019	6.050	7.113	8.211
82°	.514	1.285	2.152	3.079	4.042	5.039	6.071	7.135	8.233
84°	.528	1.302	2.170	3.098	4.062	5.059	6.092	7.157	8.255
86°	.542	1.318	2.189	3.117	4.081	5.080	6.113	7.179	8.277
88°	.557	1.335	2.207	3.136	4.101	5.100	6.134	7.200	8.300
90°	.571	1.352	2.225	3.155	4.121	5.120	6.155	7.222	8.322
92°	.585	1.368	2.243	3.174	4.140	5.141	6.176	7.244	8.344
94°	.600	1.385	2.261	3.193	4.160	5.161	6.197	7.265	8.367
96°	.614	1.402	2.279	3 212	4.180	5.182	6.218	7.287	8.389
98°	.629	1.419	2.297	3.232	4.200	5.202	6.239	7.309	8.411
100°	.643	1.436	2.316	3.251	4.219	5.222	6.260	7.330	8.434
M V per °C	.00643	.00793	.00880	.00935	.00968	.0100	.0104	.0107	.0110

[1] Leeds & Northrup Std. 21031.

See also W. F. Roeser and H. T. Wensel, *Bur. Standards J. Research*, **10**, 275 (1933).

TABLE 5 (*Continued*)

PLAT. VS. PLAT. + 10% RHODIUM THERMOCOUPLE

Deg. C	900°	1000°	1100°	1200°	1300°	1400°	1500°	1600°	1700°
					Millivolts				
0°	8.434	9.569	10.736	11.924	13.120	14.312	15.498	16.674	17.841
2°	8.456	9.592	10.759	11.948	13.144	14.336	15.521	16.698	17.864
4°	8.479	9.615	10.783	11.972	13.168	14.360	15.545	16.721	17.887
6°	8.501	9.638	10.807	11.995	13.192	14.383	15.569	16.744	17.910
8°	8.523	9.661	10.830	12.019	13.216	14.407	15.592	16.768	17.934
10°	8.546	9.685	10.854	12.043	13.239	14.431	15.615	16.792	17.957
12°	8.568	9.708	10.878	12.067	13.263	14.455	15.639	16.815	17.980
14°	8.591	9.731	10.901	12.091	13.287	14.479	15.663	16.838	18.004
16°	8.613	9.754	10.925	12.115	13.311	14.502	15.687	16.861	18.027
18°	8.636	9.777	10.949	12.139	13.335	14.526	15.710	16.885	18.050
20°	8.658	9.800	10.973	12.163	13.358	14.550	15.733	16.908	18.073
22°	8.681	9.823	10.996	12.187	13.382	14.574	15.757	16.932	—
24°	8.703	9.846	11.020	12.211	13.406	14.597	15.781	16.955	—
26°	8.726	9.869	11.044	12.235	13.430	14.621	15.805	16.978	—
28°	8.748	9.893	11.067	12.259	13.454	14.645	15.828	17.002	—
30°	8.771	9.916	11.091	12.283	13.478	14.668	15.852	17.026	—
32°	8.794	9.939	11.115	12.307	13.502	14.692	15.875	17.049	—
34°	8.816	9.962	11.139	12.330	13.526	14.716	15.899	17.072	—
36°	8.839	9.985	11.162	12.354	13.550	14.740	15.923	17.095	—
38°	8.861	10.009	11.186	12.378	13.574	14.764	15.946	17.119	—
40°	8.884	10.033	11.209	12.402	13.598	14.787	15.969	17.142	—
42°	8.907	10.056	11.233	12.426	13.621	14.811	15.993	17.165	—
44°	8.929	10.079	11.257	12.450	13.645	14.835	16.017	17.189	—
46°	8.952	10.102	11.281	12.474	13.669	14.859	16.040	17.212	—
48°	8.975	10.125	11.305	12.498	13.693	14.882	16.064	17.235	—
50°	8.998	10.149	11.329	12.522	13.717	14.906	16.087	17.259	—
52°	9.020	10.172	11.352	12.546	13.741	14.930	16.111	17.282	—
54°	9.043	10.195	11.376	12.570	13.765	14.953	16.135	17.305	—
56°	9.066	10.219	11.400	12.594	13.788	14.977	16.158	17.329	—
58°	9.088	10.242	11.424	12.618	13.812	15.001	16.182	17.352	—
60°	9.111	10.266	11.448	12.642	13.836	15.024	16.205	17.376	—
62°	9.134	10.289	11.471	12.666	13.860	15.048	16.229	17.399	—
64°	9.157	10.313	11.495	12.690	13.884	15.072	16.252	17.422	—
66°	9.180	10.336	11.519	12.714	13.907	15.096	16.276	17.445	—
68°	9.202	10.359	11.543	12.738	13.931	15.119	16.299	17.468	—
70°	9.225	10.383	11.567	12.762	13.955	15.143	16.322	17.492	—
72°	9.248	10.406	11.590	12.785	13.979	15.167	16.346	17.515	—
74°	9.271	10.430	11.614	12.809	14.003	15.190	16.369	17.538	—
76°	9.294	10.453	11.638	12.833	14.026	15.214	16.393	17.562	—
78°	9.317	10.476	11.662	12.857	14.050	15.237	16.416	17.585	—
80°	9.340	10.500	11.686	12.881	14.074	15.261	16.440	17.608	—
82°	9.362	10.524	11.709	12.905	14.098	15.285	16.463	17.631	—
84°	9.385	10.547	11.733	12.929	14.122	15.308	16.487	17.655	—
86°	9.408	10.571	11.757	12.953	14.145	15.332	16.510	17.678	—
88°	9.431	10.594	11.781	12.977	14.169	15.356	16.533	17.701	—
90°	9.454	10.618	11.805	13.000	14.193	15.379	16.557	17.724	—
92°	9.477	10.641	11.828	13.024	14.217	15.403	16.580	17.748	—
94°	9.500	10.665	11.852	13.048	14.241	15.427	16.604	17.771	—
96°	9.523	10.689	11.876	13.072	14.264	15.450	16.627	17.794	—
98°	9.546	10.712	11.900	13.096	14.288	15.474	16.651	17.817	—
100°	9.569	10.736	11.924	13.120	14.312	15.498	16.674	17.841	—
M V per °C	.0114	.0117	.0119	.0120	.0119	.0119	.0118	.0117	.0116

TABLE 6
PLAT. VS. PLAT. + 10% RHODIUM THERMOCOUPLE[1]
(Degrees Fahrenheit, Reference Junction 32°F)

Deg. F	0°	100°	200°	300°	400°	500°	600°	700°
				Millivolts				
0°	−.0920	.221	.595	1.016	1.473	1.956	2.457	2.975
5°	−.0778	.239	.615	1.038	1.497	1.980	2.482	3.001
10°	−.0636	.257	.635	1.060	1.521	2.005	2.508	3.028
15°	−.0494	.274	.655	1.082	1.544	2.030	2.534	3.054
20°	−.0351	.292	.676	1.105	1.568	2.055	2.560	3.081
25°	−.0207	.310	.696	1.127	1.592	2.080	2.585	3.107
30°	−.0060	.328	.717	1.150	1.616	2.105	2.611	3.133
35°	+.0090	.346	.737	1.173	1.640	2.130	2.637	3.159
40°	.0243	.365	.758	1.196	1.664	2.155	2.663	3.186
45°	.0398	.383	.779	1.218	1.688	2.180	2.689	3.212
50°	.0555	.401	.800	1.241	1.712	2.205	2.715	3.239
55°	.0714	.420	.821	1.264	1.736	2.230	2.741	3.266
60°	.0875	.439	.843	1.287	1.760	2.255	2.767	3.293
65°	.104	.458	.864	1.310	1.784	2.280	2.793	3.319
70°	.120	.477	.886	1.333	1.808	2.305	2.819	3.346
75°	.137	.496	.907	1.356	1.832	2.330	2.845	3.372
80°	.153	.516	.929	1.380	1.857	2.356	2.871	3.399
85°	.170	.535	.950	1.403	1.881	2.381	2.897	3.425
90°	.187	.555	.972	1.426	1.906	2.406	2.923	3.452
95°	.204	.575	.994	1.449	1.931	2.431	2.949	3.478
100°	.221	.595	1.016	1.473	1.956	2.457	2.975	3.505
M V per °F	.00313	.00374	.00421	.00457	.00483	.00501	.00518	.00530

Deg. F	800°	900°	1000°	1100°	1200°	1300°	1400°	1500°
				Millivolts				
0°	3.505	4.044	4.594	5.155	5.725	6.307	6.898	7.500
5°	3.532	4.071	4.621	5.183	5.754	6.336	6.928	7.530
10°	3.559	4.098	4.649	5.211	5.783	6.366	6.958	7.561
15°	3.585	4.125	4.677	5.239	5.812	6.395	6.987	7.591
20°	3.612	4.153	4.705	5.268	5.841	6.424	7.017	7.621
25°	3.639	4.180	4.733	5.296	5.869	6.453	7.047	7.651
30°	3.667	4.208	4.761	5.324	5.898	6.483	7.077	7.682
35°	3.694	4.235	4.789	5.352	5.927	6.512	7.107	7.713
40°	3.720	4.263	4.817	5.381	5.956	6.542	7.137	7.744
45°	3.747	4.290	4.845	5.409	5.985	6.571	7.167	7.774
50°	3.774	4.318	4.873	5.438	6.015	6.601	7.198	7.805
55°	3.801	4.345	4.901	5.466	6.044	6.630	7.228	7.835
60°	3.828	4.373	4.929	5.495	6.073	6.660	7.258	7.866
65°	3.855	4.400	4.957	5.524	6.102	6.690	7.288	7.897
70°	3.882	4.428	4.985	5.553	6.132	6.720	7.318	7.928
75°	3.909	4.455	5.013	5.581	6.161	6.749	7.348	7.958
80°	3.936	4.483	5.042	5.610	6.190	6.779	7.379	7.989
85°	3.963	4.511	5.070	5.638	6.219	6.808	7.409	8.020
90°	3.990	4.539	5.098	5.667	6.249	6.838	7.439	8.051
95°	4.017	4.566	5.126	5.696	6.278	6.868	7.469	8.081
100°	4.044	4.594	5.155	5.725	6.307	6.898	7.500	8.112
M V per °F	.00539	.00550	.00561	.00570	.00582	.00591	.00602	.00612

[1] Leeds & Northrup Std. 21031.

See also W. F. Roeser and H. T. Wensel, *Bur. Standards J. Research*, **10**, 275 (1933).

TABLE 6 (*Continued*)
PLAT. vs. PLAT. + 10% RHODIUM THERMOCOUPLE

Deg. F	1600°	1700°	1800°	1900°	2000°	2100°	2200°	2300°
					Millivolts			
0°	8.112	8.734	9.365	10.007	10.657	11.316	11.977	12.642
5°	8.143	8.765	9.397	10.039	10.690	11.349	12.010	12.675
10°	8.174	8.796	9.429	10.071	10.723	11.382	12.043	12.708
15°	8.205	8.827	9.461	10.103	10.756	11.415	12.076	12.741
20°	8.236	8.859	9.493	10.136	10.789	11.448	12.110	12.775
25°	8.267	8.890	9.525	10.168	10.822	11.481	12.143	12.808
30°	8.298	8.922	9.557	10.201	10.855	11.514	12.177	12.841
35°	8.329	8.953	9.589	10.233	10.887	11.547	12.210	12.874
40°	8.360	8.985	9.621	10.266	10.920	11.580	12.243	12.907
45°	8.391	9.016	9.653	10.298	10.953	11.613	12.276	12.941
50°	8.422	9.048	9.685	10.331	10.986	11.646	12.310	12.974
55°	8.453	9.079	9.717	10.363	11.019	11.679	12.343	13.007
60°	8.484	9.111	9.749	10.396	11.052	11.712	12.376	13.040
65°	8.515	9.143	9.781	10.428	11.085	11.745	12.409	13.074
70°	8.546	9.175	9.813	10.461	11.118	11.778	12.442	13.107
75°	8.577	9.206	9.845	10.493	11.151	11.811	12.475	13.140
80°	8.609	9.238	9.877	10.526	11.184	11.844	12.509	13.173
85°	8.640	9.270	9.909	10.558	11.217	11.877	12.542	13.206
90°	8.671	9.302	9.942	10.591	11.250	11.911	12.575	13.239
95°	8.702	9.333	9.974	10.624	11.283	11.944	12.608	13.272
100°	8.734	9.365	10.007	10.657	11.316	11.977	12.642	13.305
M V per °F	.00622	.00631	.00642	.00650	.00659	.00661	.00665	.00663

Deg. F	2400°	2500°	2600°	2700°	2800°	2900°	3000°	3100°
					Millivolts			
0°	13.305	13.968	14.629	15.288	15.943	16.596	17.247	17.892
5°	13.339	14.001	14.662	15.321	15.976	16.629	17.279	17.925
10°	13.372	14.034	14.695	15.353	16.009	16.661	17.311	17.957
15°	13.405	14.067	14.728	15.386	16.042	16.694	17.344	17.989
20°	13.438	14.100	14.761	15.418	16.074	16.726	17.376	18.021
25°	13.472	14.133	14.794	15.451	16.107	16.759	17.408	—
30°	13.505	14.166	14.826	15.484	16.139	16.791	17.440	—
35°	13.538	14.200	14.859	15.517	16.172	16.824	17.473	—
40°	13.571	14.233	14.892	15.550	16.205	16.856	17.505	—
45°	13.604	14.266	14.925	15.583	16.238	16.889	17.538	—
50°	13.637	14.299	14.958	15.615	16.270	16.922	17.570	—
55°	13.670	14.332	14.991	15.648	16.303	16.955	17.602	—
60°	13.703	14.365	15.024	15.680	16.335	16.987	17.634	—
65°	13.737	14.398	15.057	15.713	16.368	17.020	17.667	—
70°	13.770	14.431	15.090	15.746	16.401	17.052	17.699	—
75°	13.803	14.464	15.123	15.779	16.434	17.085	17.731	—
80°	13.836	14.497	15.156	15.812	16.466	17.117	17.763	—
85°	13.869	14.530	15.189	15.845	16.499	17.150	17.796	—
90°	13.902	14.563	15.222	15.878	16.531	17.182	17.828	—
95	13.935	14.596	15.255	15.911	16.564	17.215	17.860	—
100°	13.968	14.629	15.288	15.943	16.596	17.247	17.892	—
M V per °F	.00663	.00661	.00659	.00655	.00653	.00651	.00645	.00645

TABLE 7

PLAT. vs. PLAT. + 13% RHODIUM THERMOCOUPLE[1]
(Degrees Centigrade, Reference Junction 0°C)

Deg. C	0°	100°	200°	300°	400°	500°	600°	700°	800°
					Millivolts				
0	0.000	.646	1.464	2.394	3.398	4.454	5.561	6.720	7.927
2	.011	.661	1.482	2.414	3.419	4.476	5.583	6.743	7.951
4	.022	.676	1.500	2.433	3.439	4.497	5.606	6.767	7.976
6	.033	.691	1.518	2.453	3.460	4.519	5.629	6.791	8.000
8	.044	.706	1.536	2.472	3.480	4.540	5.652	6.815	8.025
10	.056	.721	1.553	2.492	3.501	4.562	5.675	6.839	8.049
12	.067	.736	1.570	2.512	3.521	4.583	5.698	6.862	8.073
14	.079	.752	1.588	2.531	3.542	4.605	5.721	6.886	8.098
16	.090	.767	1.606	2.551	3.563	4.627	5.744	6.910	8.123
18	.102	.783	1.624	2.570	3.584	4.649	5.767	6.934	8.148
20	.113	.798	1.642	2.590	3.605	4.671	5.790	6.958	8.173
22	.125	.813	1.660	2.609	3.626	4.693	5.813	6.981	8.198
24	.137	.829	1.678	2.629	3.647	4.715	5.836	7.005	8.222
26	.149	.845	1.696	2.649	3.668	4.737	5.859	7.029	8.247
28	.161	.861	1.714	2.669	3.689	4.759	5.882	7.053	8.271
30	.173	.877	1.733	2.689	3.711	4.781	5.905	7.077	8.296
32	.185	.893	1.751	2.709	3.732	4.803	5.928	7.100	8.321
34	.197	.909	1.770	2.729	3.753	4.825	5.951	7.124	8.346
36	.209	.925	1.788	2.749	3.774	4.847	5.974	7.148	8.371
38	.221	.941	1.807	2.769	3.795	4.869	5.997	7.172	8.396
40	.234	.957	1.825	2.789	3.816	4.891	6.020	7.196	8.421
42	.247	.973	1.844	2.809	3.837	4.913	6.043	7.220	8.446
44	.259	.990	1.862	2.829	3.858	4.935	6.066	7.244	8.471
46	.272	1.006	1.881	2.849	3.879	4.957	6.089	7.268	8.496
48	.284	1.023	1.899	2.869	3.900	4.979	6.112	7.292	8.521
50	.297	1.039	1.918	2.889	3.921	5.002	6.135	7.317	8.546
52	.310	1.055	1.937	2.909	3.942	5.024	6.158	7.341	8.571
54	.324	1.072	1.955	2.929	3.963	5.046	6.181	7.365	8.596
56	.337	1.088	1.974	2.949	3.984	5.068	6.204	7.389	8.621
58	.351	1.105	1.992	2.969	4.005	5.090	6.227	7.413	8.646
60	.364	1.121	2.011	2.990	4.027	5.113	6.251	7.438	8.671
62	.377	1.138	2.030	3.010	4.048	5.135	6.274	7.462	8.696
64	.391	1.154	2.049	3.030	4.069	5.157	6.298	7.487	8.721
66	.404	1.171	2.068	3.050	4.090	5.179	6.321	7.511	8.746
68	.418	1.187	2.087	3.070	4.111	5.201	6.345	7.536	8.771
70	.431	1.204	2.106	3.091	4.133	5.224	6.368	7.560	8.796
72	.444	1.221	2.125	3.111	4.154	5.246	6.391	7.584	8.821
74	.458	1.238	2.144	3.132	4.175	5.269	6.415	7.609	8.847
76	.472	1.255	2.163	3.152	4.196	5.291	6.438	7.633	8.872
78	.486	1.272	2.182	3.173	4.217	5.314	6.462	7.658	8.898
80	.500	1.290	2.201	3.193	4.239	5.336	6.485	7.682	8.923
82	.514	1.307	2.220	3.213	4.260	5.358	6.508	7.706	8.948
84	.529	1.324	2.239	3.234	4.282	5.381	6.532	7.731	8.973
86	.543	1.341	2.258	3.254	4.303	5.403	6.555	7.755	8.998
88	.558	1.358	2.277	3.275	4.325	5.426	6.579	7.780	9.023
90	.572	1.376	2.297	3.295	4.346	5.448	6.602	7.804	9.049
92	.587	1.394	2.316	3.316	4.368	5.471	6.626	7.829	9.075
94	.602	1.411	2.336	3.336	4.389	5.493	6.649	7.853	9.100
96	.617	1.429	2.355	3.357	4.411	5.516	6.673	7.878	9.126
98	.632	1.446	2.375	3.377	4.432	5.538	6.696	7.902	9.151
100	.646	1.464	2.394	3.398	4.454	5.561	6.720	7.927	9.177
M V per °C	.00646	.00818	.00930	.01004	.01056	.01107	.01159	.01207	.01250

[1] Leeds & Northrup Std. 21031.
See also W. F. Roeser and H. T. Wensel, *Bur. Standards J. Research*, **10**, 275 (1933).

TABLE 7 (*Continued*)

PLAT. VS. PLAT. + 13% RHODIUM THERMOCOUPLE

Deg. C	900°	1000°	1100°	1200°	1300°	1400°	1500°	1600°	
					Millivolts				
0	9.177	10.470	11.811	13.181	14.563	15.940	17.316	18.680	—
2	9.202	10.496	11.838	13.208	14.591	15.968	17.343	18.707	—
4	9.228	10.522	11.865	13.236	14.618	15.995	17.371	18.734	—
6	9.253	10.548	11.892	13.263	14.646	16.023	17.398	18.761	—
8	9.279	10.574	11.919	13.291	14.673	16.050	17.426	18.788	—
10	9.304	10.601	11.947	13.318	14.701	16.078	17.453	18.815	—
12	9.330	10.627	11.974	13.346	14.728	16.105	17.480	18.842	—
14	9.355	10.654	12.002	13.373	14.756	16.133	17.508	18.869	—
16	9.381	10.680	12.029	13.401	14.783	16.160	17.535	18.896	—
18	9.406	10.707	12.057	13.428	14.811	16.188	17.563	18.923	—
20	9.432	10.733	12.084	13.456	14.838	16.215	17.590	18.951	—
22	9.458	10.759	12.111	13.483	14.865	16.242	17.617	18.978	—
24	9.483	10.786	12.138	13.511	14.893	16.270	17.645	19.005	—
26	9.509	10.813	12.165	13.539	14.920	16.298	17.672	19.032	—
28	9.534	10.840	12.192	13.567	14.948	16.326	17.700	19.059	—
30	9.560	10.867	12.219	13.595	14.975	16.354	17.727	19.087	—
32	9.585	10.894	12.246	13.623	15.002	16.381	17.754	19.114	—
34	9.611	10.920	12.274	13.650	15.030	16.409	17.782	19.141	—
36	9.637	10.947	12.301	13.678	15.038	16.437	17.809	19.168	—
38	9.663	10.973	12.329	13.705	15.086	16.465	17.837	19.195	—
40	9.689	11.000	12.356	13.733	15.114	16.493	17.864	19.222	—
42	9.715	11.027	12.383	13.761	15.142	16.521	17.891	19.249	—
44	9.740	11.054	12.411	13.788	15.169	16.548	17.918	19.276	—
46	9.766	11.081	12.438	13.816	15.197	16.576	17.945	19.303	—
48	9.791	11.108	12.466	13.843	15.224	16.603	17.972	19.330	—
50	9.817	11.135	12.493	13.871	15.252	16.631	18.000	19.357	—
52	9.843	11.161	12.520	13.898	15.279	16.659	18.027	19.384	—
54	9.869	11.188	12.548	13.926	15.307	16.686	18.054	19.411	—
56	9.895	11.215	12.575	13.954	15.334	16.714	18.081	19.438	—
58	9.921	11.242	12.603	13.982	15.362	16.741	18.108	19.465	—
60	9.947	11.269	12.630	14.010	15.389	16.769	18.135	19.492	—
62	9.973	11.296	12.658	14.037	15.417	16.796	18.162	19.519	—
64	9.999	11.323	12.685	14.065	15.444	16.824	18.189	19.546	—
66	10.025	11.350	12.713	14.092	15.472	16.851	18.216	19.573	—
68	10.051	11.377	12.740	14.120	15.499	16.879	18.243	19.600	—
70	10.078	11.404	12.768	14.147	15.527	16.906	18.271	19.627	—
72	10.104	11.431	12.796	14.175	15.554	16.933	18.298	19.654	—
74	10.130	11.458	12.823	14.202	15.582	16.961	18.325	19.681	—
76	10.156	11.485	12.851	14.230	15.609	16.988	18.352	19.708	—
78	10.182	11.512	12.878	14.257	15.637	17.016	18.379	19.735	—
80	10.208	11.540	12.906	14.285	15.664	17.043	18.407	19.762	—
82	10.234	11.567	12.933	14.312	15.691	17.070	18.434	19.789	—
84	10.260	11.594	12.961	14.340	15.719	17.098	18.461	19.816	—
86	10.286	11.621	12.988	14.368	15.747	17.125	18.488	19.843	—
88	10.312	11.648	13.016	14.396	15.775	17.153	18.515	19.870	—
90	10.339	11.676	13.043	14.424	15.803	17.180	18.543	19.897	—
92	10.365	11.703	13.071	14.451	15.830	17.207	18.570	19.924	—
94	10.391	11.730	13.098	14.479	15.858	17.234	18.598	19.951	—
96	10.417	11.757	13.126	14.507	15.885	17.261	18.625	19.978	—
98	10.443	11.784	13.153	14.535	15.913	17.288	18.653	20.005	—
100	10.470	11.811	13.181	14.563	15.940	17.316	18.680	20.032	—
M V per °C	.01293	.01341	.01370	.01382	.01377	.01376	.01364	.01352	—

TABLE 8

PLAT. VS. PLAT. + 13% RHODIUM THERMOCOUPLE[1]
(Degrees Fahrenheit, Reference Junction 32°F)

Deg. F	0°	100°	200°	300°	400°	500°	600°	700°
					Millivolts			
0	−.0890	.220	.596	1.030	1.504	2.012	2.546	3.102
5	−.0756	.237	.617	1.052	1.528	2.038	2.574	3.131
10	−.0621	.255	.637	1.075	1.553	2.064	2.601	3.159
15	−.0484	.272	.658	1.098	1.578	2.090	2.629	3.187
20	−.0346	.290	.679	1.121	1.603	2.117	2.656	3.216
25	−.0205	.308	.700	1.144	1.628	2.143	2.684	3.244
30	−.0060	.326	.721	1.168	1.653	2.169	2.711	3.272
35	+.0090	.344	.742	1.191	1.678	2.196	2.739	3.301
40	.0244	.363	.764	1.214	1.703	2.223	2.766	3.329
45	.0399	.381	.785	1.238	1.728	2.249	2.794	3.358
50	.0555	.400	.807	1.262	1.754	2.276	2.822	3.387
55	.0712	.419	.829	1.285	1.779	2.303	2.850	3.415
60	.0871	.438	.851	1.309	1.805	2.330	2.878	3.444
65	.103	.457	.873	1.333	1.830	2.357	2.906	3.473
70	.119	.477	.895	1.357	1.856	2.384	2.934	3.501
75	.136	.496	.917	1.381	1.882	2.411	2.962	3.530
80	.152	.516	.939	1.406	1.908	2.438	2.990	3.559
85	.169	.536	.962	1.430	1.933	2.465	3.018	3.588
90	.186	.556	.984	1.454	1.959	2.492	3.046	3.617
95	.203	.576	1.007	1.479	1.985	2.519	3.074	3.646
100	.220	.596	1.030	1.504	2.012	2.546	3.102	3.675
M V per °F	.00131	.00376	.00434	.00474	.00508	.00534	.00556	.00573

Deg. F	800°	900°	1000°	1100°	1200°	1300°	1400°	1500°
					Millivolts			
0	3.675	4.263	4.867	5.486	6.122	6.773	7.438	8.118
5	3.704	4.293	4.898	5.517	6.155	6.806	7.471	8.152
10	3.733	4.323	4.928	5.548	6.187	6.839	7.505	8.187
15	3.763	4.353	4.959	5.580	6.219	6.872	7.539	8.221
20	3.792	4.382	4.990	5.611	6.251	6.905	7.573	8.255
25	3.821	4.412	5.021	5.643	6.284	6.938	7.606	8.290
30	3.850	4.442	5.051	5.675	6.316	6.971	7.640	8.324
35	3.880	4.472	5.082	5.706	6.348	7.004	7.674	8.359
40	3.909	4.502	5.113	5.738	6.381	7.037	7.708	8.393
45	3.938	4.532	5.144	5.770	6.413	7.071	7.742	8.428
50	3.968	4.562	5.175	5.802	6.446	7.104	7.776	8.463
55	3.997	4.593	5.206	5.834	6.478	7.137	7.810	8.497
60	4.027	4.625	5.237	5.866	6.511	7.170	7.844	8.532
65	4.056	4.653	5.268	5.898	6.544	7.204	7.878	8.567
70	4.086	4.684	5.299	5.930	6.576	7.237	7.912	8.601
75	4.115	4.714	5.330	5.962	6.609	7.270	7.947	8.636
80	4.145	4.745	5.361	5.994	6.642	7.304	7.981	8.671
85	4.174	4.775	5.392	6.026	6.675	7.337	8.015	8.706
90	4.204	4.806	5.432	6.058	6.707	7.371	8.049	8.741
95	4.234	4.836	5.454	6.090	6.740	7.404	8.084	8.776
100	4.263	4.867	5.486	6.122	6.773	7.438	8.118	8.811
M V per °F	.00588	.00604	.00619	.00636	.00651	.00665	.00680	.00693

[1] Leeds & Northrup Std. 21031.
See also W. F. Roeser and H. T. Wensel, *Bur. Standards J. Research*, **10**, 275 (1933).

TABLE 8 (Continued)
PLAT. VS. PLAT. + 13% RHODIUM THERMOCOUPLE

Deg. F	1600°	1700°	1800°	1900°	2000°	2100°	·2200°	2300°
					Millivolts			
0	8.811	9.518	10.237	10.970	11.720	12.478	13.242	14.010
5	8.846	9.553	10.274	11.008	11.758	12.516	13.280	14.048
10	8.881	9.589	10.310	11.045	11.796	12.554	13.319	14.087
15	8.916	9.625	10.346	11.082	11.834	12.592	13.357	14.125
20	8.951	9.661	10.383	11.119	11.871	12.630	13.396	14.164
25	8.986	9.696	10.419	11.157	11.909	12.668	13.434	14.202
30	9.021	9.732	10.455	11.194	11.947	12.707	13.472	14.240
35	9.056	9.768	10.492	11.231	11.985	12.745	13.511	14.279
40	9.092	9.804	10.528	11.269	12.023	12.783	13.549	14.317
45	9.127	9.840	10.565	11.306	12.061	12.821	13.588	14.355
50	9.162	9.876	10.602	11.344	12.098	12.859	13.626	14.394
55	9.198	9.912	10.638	11.381	12.136	12.898	13.664	14.432
60	9.233	9.948	10.675	11.419	12.174	12.936	13.703	14.470
65	9.269	9.984	10.712	11.457	12.212	12.974	13.741	14.509
70	9.304	10.020	10.749	11.494	12.250	13.012	13.780	14.547
75	9.340	10.056	10.786	11.532	12.288	13.051	13.818	14.585
80	9.375	10.092	10.822	11.569	12.326	13.089	13.856	14.624
85	9.411	10.129	10.859	11.607	12.364	13.127	13.895	14.662
90	9.446	10.165	10.896	11.645	12.402	13.165	13.923	14.700
95	9.482	10.201	10.933	11.683	12.440	13.204	13.972	14.739
100	9.518	10.237	10.970	11.720	12.478	13.242	14.010	14.777
M V per °F	.00707	.00719	.00733	.00750	.00758	.00764	.00768	.00767

Deg. F.	2400°	2500°	2600°	2700°	2800°	2900°	3000°	
					Millivolts			
0	14.777	15.543	16.309	17.073	17.833	18.588	19.342	—
5	14.815	15.581	16.347	17.111	17.871	18.626	19.379	—
10	14.854	15.619	16.385	17.149	17.909	18.663	19.417	—
15	14.892	15.658	16.423	17.187	17.947	18.701	19.455	—
20	14.930	15.696	16.462	17.225	17.985	18.739	19.492	—
25	14.969	15.734	16.500	17.263	18.022	18.777	19.530	—
30	15.007	15.773	16.538	17.302	18.060	18.814	19.567	—
35	15.045	15.811	16.576	17.340	18.098	18.852	19.605	—
40	15.084	15.849	16.614	17.378	18.136	18.890	19.642	—
45	15.122	15.887	16.653	17.416	18.173	18.927	19.680	—
50	15.160	15.926	16.691	17.454	18.211	18.965	19.717	—
55	15.198	15.964	16.729	17.492	18.249	19.003	19.755	—
60	15.237	16.002	16.767	17.530	18.286	19.040	19.793	—
65	15.275	16.041	16.805	17.568	18.324	19.078	19.830	—
70	15.313	16.079	16.844	17.606	18.362	19.116	19.868	—
75	15.352	16.117	16.882	17.643	18.400	19.154	19.905	—
80	15.390	16.156	16.920	17.682	18.437	19.191	19.943	—
85	15.428	16.194	16.958	17.720	18.475	19.229	19.980	—
90	15.466	16.232	16.996	17.758	18.513	19.267	20.018	—
95	15.505	16.270	17.035	17.795	18.550	19.304	20.055	—
100	15.543	16.309	17.073	17.833	18.588	19.342	20.093	—
M V per °F	.00766	.00766	.00764	.00760	.00755	.00755	.00751	—

TABLE 9

CHROMEL VS. ALUMEL THERMOCOUPLE[1]
(Degrees Centigrade, Reference Junction 0°C)

Deg. C	−100°	−0°	0°	100°	200°	300°	400°	500°
				Millivolts				
0°	−3.49	0	0	4.10	8.13	12.21	16.39	20.64
2°	−3.55	− .08	.08	4.18	8.21	12.29	16.47	20.73
4°	−3.60	− .16	.16	4.26	8.29	12.37	16.55	20.81
6°	−3.66	− .23	.24	4.34	8.37	12.45	16.64	20.90
8°	−3.72	− .31	.32	4.42	8.45	12.53	16.73	20.98
10°	−3.78	− .39	.40	4.51	8.53	12.62	16.82	21.07
12°	−3.83	− .47	.48	4.59	8.61	12.70	16.90	21.15
14°	−3.89	− .54	.56	4.67	8.69	12.78	16.99	21.24
16°	−3.94	− .62	.64	4.75	8.77	12.86	17.07	21.32
18°	−4.00	− .69	.72	4.83	8.85	12.95	17.16	21.41
20°	−4.05	− .77	.80	4.92	8.93	13.04	17.24	21.49
22°	−4.10	− .84	.88	5.00	9.01	13.12	17.32	21.58
24°	−4.16	− .92	.96	5.08	9.09	13.20	17.41	21.66
26°	−4.21	− .99	1.04	5.16	9.17	13.28	17.49	21.75
28°	−4.27	−1.07	1.12	5.24	9.25	13.36	17.58	21.83
30°	−4.32	−1.14	1.20	5.33	9.34	13.45	17.66	21.92
32°	−4.37	−1.21	1.28	5.41	9.42	13.53	17.74	22.00
34°	−4.42	−1.28	1.36	5.49	9.50	13.61	17.83	22.09
36°	−4.47	−1.36	1.44	5.57	9.58	13.69	17.91	22.17
38°	−4.52	−1.43	1.52	5.65	9.66	13.78	18.00	22.26
40°	−4.57	−1.50	1.61	5.73	9.74	13.87	18.08	22.34
42°	−4.62	−1.57	1.69	5.81	9.82	13.95	18.16	22.43
44°	−4.67	−1.64	1.77	5.89	9.90	14.03	18.25	22.52
46°	−4.71	−1.72	1.85	5.97	9.98	14.11	18.33	22.60
48°	−4.76	−1.79	1.93	6.05	10.06	14.20	18.42	22.68
50°	−4.81	−1.86	2.02	6.13	10.15	14.29	18.50	22.77
52°	−4.85	−1.95	2.10	6.21	10.23	14.37	18.58	22.86
54°	−4.90	−2.00	2.18	6.29	10.31	14.45	18.66	22.94
56°	−4.94	−2.07	2.26	6.37	10.39	14.53	18.75	23.03
58°	−4.99	−2.14	2.34	6.45	10.47	14.62	18.84	23.11
60°	−5.03	−2.21	2.43	6.53	10.56	14.71	18.93	23.20
62°	−5.07	−2.28	2.51	6.61	10.64	14.79	19.02	23.28
64°	−5.11	−2.35	2.59	6.69	10.72	14.88	19.11	23.37
66°	−5.16	−2.41	2.67	6.77	10.80	14.96	19.20	23.45
68°	−5.20	−2.48	2.76	6.85	10.88	15.05	19.28	23.54
70°	−5.24	−2.55	2.85	6.93	10.97	15.13	19.36	23.62
72°	−5.28	−2.61	2.93	7.01	11.05	15.21	19.44	23.71
74°	−5.32	−2.68	3.01	7.09	11.13	15.30	19.53	23.79
76°	−5.35	−2.74	3.09	7.17	11.21	15.38	19.61	23.88
78°	−5.39	−2.81	3.17	7.25	11.29	15.47	19.70	23.96
80°	−5.43	−2.87	3.26	7.33	11.38	15.55	19.78	24.05
82°	−5.46	−2.93	3.34	7.41	11.46	15.63	19.87	24.14
84°	−5.50	−3.00	3.42	7.49	11.54	15.72	19.95	24.22
86°	−5.53	−3.06	3.50	7.57	11.62	15.80	20.04	24.31
88°	−5.57	−3.13	3.59	7.65	11.71	15.89	20.12	24.39
90°	−5.60	−3.19	3.68	7.73	11.80	15.97	20.21	24.48
92°	−5.63	−3.25	3.76	7.81	11.88	16.05	20.30	24.56
94°	−5.66	−3.31	3.84	7.89	11.96	16.14	20.38	24.65
96°	−5.69	−3.37	3.92	7.97	12.04	16.22	20.47	24.73
98°	−5.72	−3.43	4.01	8.05	12.12	16.31	20.55	24.82
100°	−5.75	−3.49	4.10	8.13	12.21	16.39	20.64	24.90
M V per °C			.041	.0403	.0408	.0413	.0425	.0426

[1] Leeds & Northrup Std. 21031 (values above 0°C).
See also W. F. Roeser, A. I. Dahl and G. J. Gowens, *J. Research Nat. Bur. Standards*, **14**, 239 (1935).

TABLE 9 (*Continued*)

CHROMEL VS. ALUMEL THERMOCOUPLE

Deg. C	600°	700°	800°	900°	1000°	1100°	1200°	1300°
					Millivolts			
0°	24.90	29.14	33.31	37.36	41.31	45.14	48.85	52.41
2°	24.99	29.22	33.39	37.44	41.39	45.22	48.93	52.48
4°	25.07	29.31	33.47	37.52	41.47	45.29	49.00	52.55
6°	25.16	29.39	33.55	37.60	41.55	45.37	49.07	52.62
8°	25.24	29.48	33.63	37.68	41.63	45.44	49.14	52.69
10°	25.33	29.56	33.71	37.76	41.70	45.52	49.21	52.75
12°	25.41	29.64	33.79	37.84	41.78	45.59	49.29	52.82
14°	25.50	29.73	33.87	37.92	41.86	45.67	49.36	52.89
16°	25.58	29.81	33.95	38.00	41.94	45.74	49.43	52.96
18°	25.67	29.90	34.03	38.08	42.01	45.82	49.50	53.03
20°	25.75	29.98	34.12	38.16	42.08	45.89	49.57	53.10
22°	25.84	30.06	34.20	38.24	42.16	45.97	49.65	53.17
24°	25.93	30.15	34.28	38.32	42.24	46.04	49.73	53.24
26°	26.01	30.23	34.36	38.40	42.32	46.12	49.80	53.31
28°	26.09	30.32	34.44	38.48	42.40	46.19	49.87	53.38
30°	26.18	30.40	34.53	38.56	42.47	46.27	49.94	53.45
32°	26.26	30.48	34.61	38.64	42.55	46.35	50.01	53.52
34°	26.35	30.57	34.69	38.72	42.62	46.43	50.08	53.59
36°	26.43	30.65	34.77	38.80	42.70	46.50	50.15	53.66
38°	26.52	30.74	34.85	38.88	42.78	46.57	50.22	53.73
40°	26.60	30.82	34.94	38.96	42.86	46.64	50.29	53.79
42°	26.69	30.90	35.02	39.04	42.94	46.71	50.37	53.86
44°	26.77	30.98	35.10	39.12	43.02	46.79	50.44	53.93
46°	26.86	31.06	35.18	39.20	43.10	46.86	50.51	54.00
48°	26.94	31.14	35.26	39.28	43.17	46.94	50.58	54.07
50°	27.03	31.23	35.35	39.35	43.24	47.01	50.65	54.13
52°	27.12	31.31	35.43	39.43	43.32	47.08	50.72	54.20
54°	27.20	31.40	35.51	39.51	43.39	47.16	50.79	54.27
56°	27.28	31.48	35.59	39.59	43.47	47.23	50.86	54.34
58°	27.37	31.57	35.67	39.67	43.54	47.31	50.93	54.41
60°	27.45	31.65	35.75	39.75	43.62	47.38	51.00	54.47
62°	27.53	31.73	35.83	39.83	43.70	47.45	51.08	54.54
64°	27.62	31.82	35.91	39.91	43.77	47.53	51.15	54.61
66°	27.70	31.90	35.99	39.99	43.85	47.60	51.22	54.68
68°	27.79	31.99	36.07	40.07	43.92	47.68	51.29	54.75
70°	27.87	32.07	36.16	40.14	44.00	47.75	51.36	54.81
72°	27.95	32.15	36.24	40.22	44.08	47.82	51.43	54.88
74°	28.04	32.23	36.32	40.30	44.15	47.90	51.50	54.95
76°	28.12	32.31	36.40	40.38	44.23	47.97	51.57	55.02
78°	28.21	32.39	36.48	40.46	44.30	48.05	51.64	55.09
80°	28.29	32.48	36.56	40.53	44.38	48.12	51.71	55.15
82°	28.38	32.56	36.64	40.61	44.46	48.20	51.78	55.22
84°	28.46	32.65	36.72	40.69	44.53	48.27	51.85	55.29
86°	28.55	32.73	36.80	40.77	44.61	48.34	51.92	55.36
88°	28.63	32.82	36.88	40.85	44.68	48.41	51.99	55.42
90°	28.72	32.90	36.96	40.92	44.76	48.48	52.06	55.48
92°	28.80	32.98	37.04	41.00	44.84	48.56	52.13	55.55
94°	28.89	33.06	37.12	41.08	44.91	48.64	52.20	55.62
96°	28.97	33.14	37.20	41.16	44.99	48.71	52.27	55.69
98°	29.06	33.22	37.28	41.24	45.06	48.78	52.34	55.75
100°	29.14	33.31	37.36	41.31	45.14	48.85	52.41	55.81
M V per °C	0.0424	.0417	.0405	.0395	.0383	.0371	.0356	.0340

TABLE 10

CHROMEL vs. ALUMEL THERMOCOUPLE[1]

(Degrees Fahrenheit, Reference Junction 32°F)

Deg. F	−200°	−100°	−0°	0°	100°	200°	300°
				Millivolts			
0°	−4.29	−2.65	−0.68	−0.68	1.52	3.82	6.09
5°	−4.36	−2.74	− .78	− .58	1.63	3.93	6.20
10°	−4.43	−2.83	− .89	− .47	1.74	4.05	6.31
15°	−4.50	−2.92	− .99	− .37	1.85	4.16	6.42
20°	−4.57	−3.01	−1.10	− .26	1.97	4.28	6.53
25°	−4.64	−3.10	−1.20	− .15	2.08	4.39	6.64
30°	−4.71	−3.19	−1.30	− .04	2.20	4.51	6.75
35°	−4.78	−3.27	−1.40	.07	2.31	4.62	6.86
40°	−4.84	−3.36	−1.50	.18	2.43	4.74	6.98
45°	−4.90	−3.44	−1.60	.29	2.54	4.85	7.09
50°	−4.96	−3.52	−1.70	.40	2.66	4.97	7.20
55°	−5.02	−3.60	−1.80	.51	2.77	5.08	7.31
60°	−5.08	−3.68	−1.90	.62	2.89	5.19	7.42
65°	−5.14	−3.76	−2.00	.73	3.00	5.30	7.53
70°	−5.19	−3.84	−2.09	.84	3.12	5.42	7.64
75°	−5.25	−3.92	−2.18	.95	3.24	5.53	7.75
80°	−5.30	−4.00	−2.28	1.06	3.36	5.64	7.87
85°	−5.36	−4.08	−2.37	1.17	3.48	5.75	7.98
90°	−5.41	−4.15	−2.47	1.29	3.59	5.87	8.09
95°	−5.46	−4.22	−2.56	1.40	3.70	5.98	8.20
100°	−5.51	−4.29	−2.65	1.52	3.82	6.09	8.31
M V per °F					.023	.0227	.0222

Deg. F	400°	500°	600°	700°	800°	900°	1000°
				Millivolts			
0°	8.31	10.56	12.85	15.18	17.52	19.88	22.25
5°	8.42	10.67	12.96	15.29	17.63	20.00	22.37
10°	8.53	10.79	13.08	15.41	17.75	20.12	22.49
15°	8.64	10.90	13.19	15.52	17.87	20.24	22.60
20°	8.76	11.02	13.31	15.64	17.99	20.36	22.72
25°	8.87	11.13	13.43	15.76	18.10	20.47	22.84
30°	8.98	11.25	13.55	15.88	18.22	20.59	22.96
35°	9.09	11.36	13.67	16.00	18.34	20.71	23.08
40°	9.20	11.47	13.78	16.11	18.46	20.83	23.20
45°	9.31	11.58	13.89	16.23	18.58	20.95	23.32
50°	9.43	11.70	14.01	16.35	18.70	21.07	23.43
55°	9.55	11.81	14.12	16.47	18.81	21.18	23.55
60°	9.66	11.93	14.24	16.58	18.93	21.30	23.67
65°	9.77	12.04	14.36	16.70	19.05	21.42	23.79
70°	9.88	12.16	14.48	16.82	19.17	21.54	23.91
75°	9.99	12.27	14.60	16.93	19.29	21.66	24.02
80°	10.11	12.39	14.71	17 05	19.41	21.78	24.14
85°	10.22	12.50	14.83	17.17	19.52	21.89	24.26
90°	10.33	12.62	14.94	17.29	19.64	22.01	24.38
95°	10.44	12.73	15.06	17.40	19.76	22.13	24.50
100°	10.56	12.85	15.18	17.52	19.88	22.25	24.62
M V per °F	.0225	.0229	.0233	.0234	.0236	.0237	.0237

[1] Leeds & Northrup Std. 21031 (values above 0°F).

See also W. F. Roeser, A. I. Dahl and G. J. Gowens, *J. Research Nat. Bur. Standards* **14**, 239 (1935).

TABLE 10 (*Continued*)
CHROMEL VS. ALUMEL THERMOCOUPLE

Deg. F	1100°	1200°	1300°	1400°	1500°	1600°	1700°
				Millivolts			
0°	24.62	26.98	29.33	31.65	33.94	36.20	38.43
5°	24.74	27.10	29.45	31.77	34.06	36.31	38.54
10°	24.85	27.21	29.56	31.88	34.17	36.42	38.65
15°	24.97	27.33	29.68	32.00	34.29	36.54	38.76
20°	25.09	27.45	29.79	32.11	34.40	36.65	38.87
25°	25.21	27.57	29.91	32.23	34.51	36.76	38.98
30°	25.33	27.68	30.02	32.34	34.62	36.87	39.09
35°	25.45	27.80	30.14	32.46	34.74	36.99	39.20
40°	25.57	27.92	30.26	32.57	34.85	37.10	39.31
45°	25.69	28.04	30.38	32.69	34.97	37.21	39.42
50°	25.80	28.15	30.49	32.80	35.08	37.32	39.53
55°	25.92	28.27	30.61	32.92	35.19	37.43	39.64
60°	26.04	28.39	30.72	33.03	35.30	37.54	39.75
65°	26.16	28.51	30.84	33.15	35.42	37.65	39.86
70°	26.27	28.62	30.96	33.26	35.53	37.76	39.96
75°	26.39	28.74	31.08	33.38	35.64	37.88	40.07
80°	26.51	28.86	31.19	33.49	35.75	37.99	40.18
85°	26.63	28.98	31.31	33.60	35.87	38.10	40.29
90°	26.74	29.09	31.42	33.71	35.98	38.21	40.40
95°	26.86	29.21	31.54	33.83	36.09	38.32	40.51
100°	26.98	29.33	31.65	33.94	36.20	38.43	40.62
M V per °F	.0236	.0235	.0232	.0229	.0226	.0223	.0219

Deg. F	1800°	1900°	2000°	2100°	2200°	2300°	2400°
				Millivolts			
0°	40.62	42.77	44.89	46.97	49.01	51.00	52.95
5°	40.73	42.88	45.00	47.08	49.11	51.10	53.05
10°	40.83	42.98	45.10	47.18	49.21	51.20	53.14
15°	40.94	43.09	45.20	47.28	49.31	51.30	53.24
20°	41.05	43.20	45.31	47.38	49.41	51.39	53.33
25°	41.16	43.31	45.41	47.49	49.51	51.49	53.43
30°	41.27	43.41	45.52	47.59	49.61	51.59	53.52
35°	41.38	43.52	45.62	47.69	49.71	51.69	53.62
40°	41.48	43.62	45.73	47.79	49.81	51.78	53.71
45°	41.59	43.73	45.83	47.89	49.91	51.88	53.81
50°	41.70	43.83	45.93	47.99	50.01	51.98	53.90
55°	41.81	43.94	46.04	48.10	50.11	52.08	54.00
60°	41.91	44.04	46.14	48.20	50.21	52.17	54.09
65°	42.02	44.15	46.25	48.30	50.31	52.27	54.19
70°	42.13	44.26	46.35	48.40	50.41	52.37	54.28
75°	42.24	44.37	46.46	48.51	50.51	52.47	54.38
80°	42.34	44.47	46.56	48.61	50.61	52.56	54.47
85°	42.45	44.58	46.66	48.71	50.71	52.66	54.57
90°	42.56	44.68	46.76	48.81	50.80	52.75	54.66
95°	42.67	44.79	46.87	48.91	50.90	52.85	54.76
100°	42.77	44.89	46.97	49.01	51.00	52.95	54.85
M V per °F	.0215	.0212	.0208	.0204	.0199	.0195	.0190

TABLE 11
COPPER VS. CONSTANTAN THERMOCOUPLE[1]
(Degrees Centigrade, Reference Junction 0°C)

Temperature (°C)	Electromotive force (mv.)	Temperature (°C)	Electromotive force (mv.)	Temperature (°C)	Electromotive force (mv.)
−200	−5.539	0	0.000	200	9.285
−190	−5.378	10	.389	210	9.820
−180	−5.204	20	.787	220	10.360
−170	−5.016	30	1.194	230	10.905
−160	−4.815	40	1.610	240	11.455
−150	−4.602	50	2.034	250	12.010
−140	−4.376	60	2.467	260	12.571
−130	−4.137	70	2.908	270	13.136
−120	−3.886	80	3.356	280	13.706
−110	−3.623	90	3.812	290	14.280
−100	−3.349	100	4.276	300	14.859
−90	−3.063	110	4.747	310	15.443
−80	−2.765	120	5.225	320	16.030
−70	−2.456	130	5.710	330	16.621
−60	−2.137	140	6.202	340	17.216
−50	−1.807	150	6.700	350	17.815
−40	−1.466	160	7.205	360	18.418
−30	−1.114	170	7.716	370	19.025
−20	−0.752	180	8.233	380	19.635
−10	−0.381	190	8.756	390	20.248
0	.000	200	9.285	400	20.865

[1] W. F. Roeser and A. I. Dahl, *J. Research Nat. Bur. Standards*, **20**, 337 (1938).

TABLE 12

COPPER VS. CONSTANTAN THERMOCOUPLE[1]
(Degrees Fahrenheit, Reference Junction 32°F)

Temperature (°F)	E m f (mv.)	Temperature (°F)	E m f (mv.)	Temperature (°F)	E m f (mv.)	Temperature (°F)	E m f (mv.)
−300	−5.283	0	−0.671	300	6.644	600	15.769
−290	−5.184	10	− .464	310	6.924	610	16.096
−280	−5.081	20	− .255	320	7.206	620	16.424
−270	−4.973	30	− .043	330	7.489	630	16.753
−260	−4.861	40	+ .172	340	7.774	640	17.084
−250	−4.745	50	.390	350	8.061	650	17.416
−240	−4.626	60	.610	360	8.350	660	17.749
−230	−4.503	70	.832	370	8.640	670	18.083
−220	−4.376	80	1.057	380	8.932	680	18.418
−210	−4.245	90	1.285	390	9.226	690	18.754
−200	−4.110	100	1.516	400	9.521	700	19.091
−190	−3.971	110	1.750	410	9.819	710	19.430
−180	−3.829	120	1.987	420	10.119	720	19.770
−170	−3.683	130	2.226	430	10.420	730	20.111
−160	−3.533	140	2.467	440	10.722	740	20.453
−150	−3.380	150	2.711	450	11.026	750	20.796
−140	−3.223	160	2.957	460	11.332		
−130	−3.062	170	3.206	470	11.639		
−120	−2.898	180	3.457	480	11.948		
−110	−2.731	190	3.710	490	12.259		
−100	−2.560	200	3.966	500	12.571		
− 90	−2.386	210	4.224	510	12.885		
− 80	−2.209	220	4.484	520	13.200		
− 70	−2.028	230	4.747	530	13.516		
− 60	−1.844	240	5.012	540	13.833		
− 50	−1.656	250	5.279	550	14.152		
− 40	−1.465	260	5.548	560	14.472		
− 30	−1.271	270	5.819	570	14.794		
− 20	−1.074	280	6.092	580	15.118		
− 10	−0.874	290	6.367	590	15.443		
0	− .671	300	6.644	600	15.769		

[1] W. F. Roeser and A. I. Dahl, *J. Research Nat. Bur. Standards*, **20,** 337 (1938).

TABLE 13

IRON vs. CONSTANTAN THERMOCOUPLE[1]
(Degrees Centigrade, Reference Junction 0°C)

Temperature (°C)	Emf (mv.)	Temperature (°C)	Emf (mv.)	Temperature (°C)	Emf (mv.)	Temperature (°C)	Emf (mv.)
		0	0.00	400	22.07	800	45.72
		10	0.52	410	22.62	810	46.37
		20	1.05	420	23.17	820	47.03
		30	1.58	430	23.72	830	47.69
		40	2.12	440	24.27	840	48.34
		50	2.66	450	24.82	850	49.00
		60	3.20	460	25.37	860	49.66
		70	3.75	470	25.92	870	50.32
		80	4.30	480	26.47	880	50.97
		90	4.85	490	27.03	890	51.63
		100	5.40	500	27.58	900	52.29
		110	5.95	510	28.14	910	52.88
		120	6.51	520	28.70	920	53.47
		130	7.07	530	29.26	930	54.06
		140	7.63	540	29.82	940	54.65
		150	8.19	550	30.39	950	55.25
		160	8.75	560	30.96	960	55.84
		170	9.31	570	31.53	970	56.43
		180	9.87	580	32.11	980	57.03
		190	10.43	590	32.69	990	57.63
−200	−8.27	200	10.99	600	33.27	1,000	58.22
−190	−8.02	210	11.56	610	33.86		
−180	−7.75	220	12.12	620	34.45		
−170	−7.46	230	12.68	630	35.04		
−160	−7.14	240	13.23	640	35.64		
−150	−6.80	250	13.79	650	36.24		
−140	−6.44	260	14.35	660	36.84		
−130	−6.06	270	14.90	670	37.45		
−120	−5.66	280	15.46	680	38.06		
−110	−5.25	290	16.01	690	38.68		
−100	−4.82	300	16.56	700	39.30		
− 90	−4.38	310	17.12	710	39.93		
− 80	−3.93	320	17.67	720	40.56		
− 70	−3.47	330	18.22	730	41.19		
− 60	−3.00	340	18.77	740	41.83		
− 50	−2.52	350	19.32	750	42.48		
− 40	−2.03	360	19.87	760	43.12		
− 30	−1.53	370	20.42	770	43.77		
− 20	−1.03	380	20.97	780	44.42		
− 10	−0.52	390	21.52	790	45.07		
0	0.00	400	22.07	800	45.72		

[1] W. F. Roeser and A. I. Dahl, *J. Research Nat. Bur. Standards*, **20,** 337 (1938).

TABLE 14

IRON VS. CONSTANTAN THERMOCOUPLE[1]
(Degrees Fahrenheit, Reference Junction 32°F)

Temperature (°F)	Electromotive force (mv.)	Temperature (°F)	Electromotive force (mv.)	Temperature (°F)	Electromotive force (mv.)	Temperature (°F)	Electromotive force (mv.)	Temperature (°F)	Electromotive force (mv.)
		0	−0.92	500	14.35	1,000	29.70	1,500	46.74
		10	− .63	510	14.65	1,010	30.01	1,510	47.10
		20	− .35	520	14.96	1,020	30.33	1,520	47.47
		30	− .06	530	15.27	1,030	30.64	1,530	47.83
		40	+ .23	540	15.58	1,040	30.96	1,540	48.20
		50	.52	550	15.89	1,050	31.28	1,550	48.56
		60	.82	560	16.20	1,060	31.60	1,560	48.93
		70	1.11	570	16.50	1,070	31.92	1,570	49.29
		80	1.41	580	16.81	1,080	32.24	1,580	49.66
		90	1.70	590	17.12	1,090	32.56	1,590	50.02
		100	2.00	600	17.43	1,100	32.88	1,600	50.39
		110	2.30	610	17.73	1,110	33.20	1,610	50.75
		120	2.60	620	18.04	1,120	33.53	1,620	51.12
		130	2.90	630	18.34	1,130	33.86	1,630	51.49
		140	3.20	640	18.65	1,140	34.18	1,640	51.85
		150	3.50	650	18.95	1,150	34.51	1,650	52.22
		160	3.81	660	19.26	1,160	34.84	1,660	52.55
		170	4.11	670	19.56	1,170	35.17	1,670	52.88
		180	4.42	680	19.87	1,180	35.50	1,680	53.21
		190	4.72	690	20.18	1,190	35.84	1,690	53.54
−300	−7.87	200	5.03	700	20.48	1,200	36.17	1,700	53.87
−290	−7.72	210	5.34	710	20.79	1,210	36.50	1,710	54.20
−280	−7.55	220	5.64	720	21.09	1,220	36.84	1,720	54.52
−270	−7.38	230	5.95	730	21.40	1,230	37.18	1,730	54.85
−260	−7.20	240	6.26	740	21.70	1,240	37.52	1,740	55.18
−250	−7.02	250	6.57	750	22.01	1,250	37.86	1,750	55.51
−240	−6.83	260	6.88	760	22.31	1,260	38.20	1,760	55.84
−230	−6.63	270	7.19	770	22.62	1,270	38.54	1,770	56.17
−220	−6.43	280	7.50	780	22.92	1,280	38.88	1,780	56.50
−210	−6.22	290	7.81	790	23.22	1,290	39.23	1,790	56.83
−200	−6.01	300	8.12	800	23.53	1,300	39.58	1,800	57.16
−190	−5.79	310	8.43	810	23.84	1,310	39.93		
−180	−5.57	320	8.75	820	24.14	1,320	40.28		
−170	−5.34	330	9.06	830	24.45	1,330	40.63		
−160	−5.11	340	9.37	840	24.75	1,340	40.98		
−150	−4.87	350	9.68	850	25.06	1,350	41.34		
−140	−4.63	360	10.00	860	25.37	1,360	41.69		
−130	−4.38	370	10.31	870	25.67	1,370	42.05		
−120	−4.13	380	10.62	880	25.98	1,380	42.40		
−110	−3.88	390	10.93	890	26.29	1,390	42.76		
−100	−3.63	400	11.24	900	26.59	1,400	43.12		
−90	−3.37	410	11.56	910	26.90	1,410	43.48		
−80	−3.11	420	11.87	920	27.21	1,420	43.84		
−70	−2.85	430	12.18	930	27.52	1,430	44.20		
−60	−2.58	440	12.49	940	27.83	1,440	44.56		
−50	−2.31	450	12.80	950	28.14	1,450	44.92		
−40	−2.04	460	13.11	960	28.45	1,460	45.28		
−30	−1.76	470	13.42	970	28.76	1,470	45.65		
−20	−1.48	480	13.73	980	29.07	1,480	46.01		
−10	−1.20	490	14.04	990	29.39	1,490	46.37		
0	−0.92	500	14.35	1,000	29.70	1,500	46.74		

[1] W. F. Roeser and A. I. Dahl, *J. Research Nat. Bur. Standards*, **20,** 337 (1938).

TABLE 15

THERMAL EMF OF IMPORTANT THERMOCOUPLE MATERIALS RELATIVE
TO PLATINUM

Temp. (°C)	Chromel P (mv.)	Alumel (mv.)	Copper (mv.)	Iron (mv.)	Constantan (mv.)
− 200	− 3.36	+ 2.39	− 0.19	− 2.92	+ 5.35
− 100	− 2.20	+ 1.29	− 0.37	− 1.84	+ 2.98
0	0	0	0	0	0
+ 100	+ 2.81	− 1.29	+ 0.76	+ 1.89	− 3.51
200	5.96	− 2.17	1.83	3.54	− 7.45
300	9.32	− 2.89	3.15	4.85	−11.71
400	12.75	− 3.64	4.68	5.88	−16.19
500	16.21	− 4.43	6.41	6.79	−20.79
600	19.62	− 5.28	8.34	7.80	−25.47
700	22.96	− 6.18	10.49	9.12	−30.18
800	26.23	− 7.08	12.84	10.86	−34.86
900	29.41	− 7.95	15.41	12.84	−39.45
1000	32.52	− 8.79	18.20	14.30	−43.92
1100	35.56	− 9.58			
1200	38.51	−10.34			
1300	41.35	−11.06			
1400	44.04	−11.77			

TABLE 16

THERMAL EMF OF SOME ALLOYS RELATIVE TO PLATINUM

Temp. (°C)	Man-ganin (mv.)	Gold-Chro-mium (mv.)	Copper-Beryl-lium (mv.)	Yellow brass (mv.)	Phospher bronze (mv.)	Solder 50Sn-50Pb (mv.)	Solder 96.5Sn-3.5Ag (mv.)
0	0	0	0	0	0	0	0
+100	+0.61	−0.17	+0.67	+0.60	+0.55	+0.46	+0.45
200	1.55	−0.32	1.62	1.49	1.34		
300	2.77	−0.44	2.81	2.58	2.34		
400	4.25	−0.55	4.19	3.85	3.50		
500	5.95	−0.63	......	5.30	4.81		
600	7.84	−0.66	......	6.96	6.30		

Temp. (°C)	18-8 Stainless steel (mv.)	Spring steel (mv.)	80Ni-20Cr (mv.)	60Ni-24Fe-16Cr (mv.)	Copper coin (95Cu-4Sn-1Zn) (mv.)	Nickel coin (75Cu-25Ni) (mv.)	Silver coin (90Ag-10Cu) (mv.)
0	0	0	0	0	0	0	0
+ 100	+0.44	+1.32	+ 1.14	+ 0.85	+0.60	− 2.76	+0.80
200	1.04	2.63	2.62	2.01	1.48	− 6.01	1.90
300	1.76	3.81	4.34	3.41	2.60	− 9.71	3.25
400	2.60	4.84	6.25	5.00	3.91	−13.78	4.81
500	3.56	5.80	8.31	6.76	5.44	−18.10	
600	4.67	6.86	10.53	8.68	·7.14	−22.59	8.64
700	5.93	......	12.91	10.78			
800	7.37	......	15.44	13.06			
900	8.99	......	18.11	15.50			
1000	......	......	20.91	18.10			

TABLE 17

ELECTRICAL RESISTIVITY AS A FUNCTION OF TEMPERATURE[1]

[At 0°C both the relative (Rt/Ro) and actual resistivity (microhm-cm) are given]

Temp. (°C)	Platinum (R_t/R_o)	Copper (R_t/R_o)	Nickel (R_t/R_o)	Iron (R_t/R_o)	Silver (R_t/R_o)	90% Pt-10% Rh (R_t/R_o)	87% Pt-13% Rh (R_t/R_o)
−200	0.177	0.117	.....	.....	0.176		
−100	0.599	0.557	.....	.....	0.596		
0	1.000	1.000	1.000	1.000	1.000	1.000	1.000
	(9.83)	(1.56)	(6.38)	(8.57)	(1.50)	(18.4)	(19.0)
+100	1.392	1.431	1.663	1.650	1.408	1.166	1.156
200	1.773	1.862	2.501	2.464	1.827	1.330	1.308
300	2.142	2.299	3.611	3.485	2.256	1.490	1.456
400	2.499	2.747	4.847	4.716	2.698	1.646	1.601
500	2.844	3.210	5.398	6.162	3.150	1.798	1.744
600	3.178	3.695	5.882	7.839	3.616	1.947	1.885
700	3.500	4.208	6.327	9.790	4.094	2.093	2.023
800	3.810	4.752	6.751	12.009	4.586	2.234	2.157
900	4.109	5.334	7.156	12.790	5.091	2.370	2.287
1000	4.396	5.960	7.542	13.070	.....	2.503	2.414
1100	4.671	.....	......	......	.....	2.633	2.538
1200	4.935	.....	.....	......	.....	2.761	2.660
1300	5.187	.....	.....	......	.....	2.887	2.780
1400	5.427	.....	.....	......	.....	3.011	2.898
1500	5.655	.....	.....	......	.....	3.133	3.014

[1] The values below 0°C, in most cases, have not been determined on the same samples as the values above 0°C.

TABLE 17 (*Continued*)

ELECTRICAL RESISTIVITY AS A FUNCTION OF TEMPERATURE

Temp. (°C)	80Ni-20Cr (R_t/R_o)	60Ni-24Fe-16Cr (R_t/R_o)	50Fe-30Ni-20Cr (R_t/R_o)	Chromel P (90Ni-10Cr) (R_t/R_o)	Alumel 95Ni-Bal Al Si and Mn (R_t/R_o)	Constantan (55 Cu-45Ni) (R_t/R_o)	Manganin (R_t/R_o)
0	1.000 (107.6)	1.000 (111.6)	1.000 (99.0)	1.000 (70.0)	1.000 (28.1)	1.000 (48.9)	1.000 (48.2)
100	1.021	1.025	1.037	1.041	1.239	0.999	1.002
200	1.041	1.048	1.073	1.086	1.428	0.996	0.996
300	1.056	1.071	1.107	1.134	1.537	0.994	0.991
400	1.068	1.092	1.137	1.187	1.637	0.994	0.983
500	1.073	1.108	1.163	1.222	1.726	1.007	
600	1.071	1.115	1.185	1.248	1.814	1.024	
700	1.067	1.119	1.204	1.275	1.899	1.040	
800	1.066	1.127	1.221	1.304	1.982	1.056	
900	1.071	1.138	1.237	1.334	2.066	1.074	
1000	1.077	1.149	1.251	1.365	2.150	1.092	
1100	1.083	.....	.....	1.397	2.234	1.110	
1200	.....	.....	.....	1.430	2.318		

TABLE 18
SPECTRAL EMISSIVITY OF MATERIALS, SURFACE UNOXIDIZED

Element	$\epsilon_{0.65\mu}$		Element	$\epsilon_{0.65\mu}$	
	Solid	Liquid		Solid	Liquid
Beryllium..........	0.61	0.61	Thorium..........	0.36	0.40
Carbon............	0.80–0.93		Titanium..........	0.63	0.65
Chromium.........	0.34	0.39	Tungsten..........	0.43	
Cobalt............	0.36	0.37	Uranium..........	0.54	0.34
Columbium........	0.37	0.40	Vanadium.........	0.35	0.32
Copper...........	0.10	0.15	Yttrium...........	0.35	0.35
Erbium...........	0.55	0.38	Zirconium.........	0.32	0.30
Gold.............	0.14	0.22	Steel.............	0.35	0.37
Iridium...........	0.30		Cast Iron.........	0.37	0.40
Iron..............	0.35	0.37	Constantan.......	0.35	
Manganese........	0.59	0.59	Monel............	0.37	
Molybdenum.......	0.37	0.40	Chromel P		
Nickel............	0.36	0.37	(90Ni-10Cr)	0.35	
Palladium.........	0.33	0.37	80Ni-20Cr.........	0.35	
Platinum..........	0.30	0.38	60Ni-24Fe-16Cr....	0.36	
Rhodium..........	0.24	0.30	Alumel		
Silver.............	0.07	0.07	(95Ni; Bal. Al,		
Tantalum..........	0.49		Mn, Si)	0.37	
			90Pt-10Rh... ...	0.27	

TABLE 19

Spectral Emissivity of Oxides

The emissivity of oxides and oxidized metals depends to a large extent upon the roughness of the surface. In general, higher values of emissivity are obtained on the rougher surfaces.

Material	$\epsilon_{0.65\mu}$ Range of observed values	$\epsilon_{0.65\mu}$ Probable value for the oxide formed on smooth metal
Aluminum oxide	0.22 to 0.40	0.30
Beryllium oxide	0.07 to 0.37	0.35
Cerium oxide	0.58 to 0.80	
Chromium oxide	0.60 to 0.80	0.70
Cobalt oxide		0.75
Columbium oxide	0.55 to 0.71	0.70
Copper oxide	0.60 to 0.80	0.70
Iron oxide	0.63 to 0.98	0.70
Magnesium oxide	0.10 to 0.43	0.20
Nickel oxide	0.85 to 0.96	0.90
Thorium oxide	0.20 to 0.57	0.50
Tin oxide	0.32 to 0.60	
Titanium oxide		0.50
Uranium oxide		0.30
Vanadium oxide		0.70
Yttrium oxide		0.60
Zirconium oxide	0.18 to 0.43	0.40
Alumel (oxidized)		0.87
Cast Iron (oxidized)		0.70
Chromel P (90Ni-10Cr) (oxidized)		0.87
80Ni-20Cr (oxidized)		0.90
60Ni-24Fe-16Cr (oxidized)		0.83
55Fe-37.5Cr-7.5Al (oxidized)		0.78
70Fe-23Cr-5Al-2Co (oxidized)		0.75
Constantan (55Cu-45Ni) (oxidized)		0.84
Carbon Steel (oxidized)		0.80
Stainless Steel (18-8) (oxidized)		0.85
Porcelain	0.25 to 0.50	

TABLE 20

TOTAL EMISSIVITY OF METALS, SURFACE UNOXIDIZED

Material	ϵ_t					
	25°C	100°C	500°C	1000°C	1500°C	2000°C
Aluminum...........	0.022	0.028	0.060			
Bismuth............	0.048	0.061				
Carbon.............	0.81	0.81	0.79			
Chromium..........	.....	0.08				
Cobalt.............	.....	.....	0.13	0.23		
Columbium.........	.....	.....	.....	....	0.19	0.24
				(Liquid 0.15)		
Copper.............	.....	0.02	.....			
Gold...............	.....	0.02	0.03			
Iron...............	.....	0.05				
Lead...............	.....	0.05				
Mercury...........	0.10	0.12				
Molybdenum.......	.....	.....	.....	0.13	0.19	0.24
Nickel.............	0.045	0.06	0.12	0.19		
Platinum...........	0.037	0.047	0.096	0.152	0.191	
Silver..............	.....	0.02	0.035			
Tantalum..........	.....	.....	.....	.....	0.21	0.26
Tin................	0.043	0.05				
Tungsten...	0.024	0.032	0.071	0.15	0.23	0.28
Zinc...............	(0.05 at 300°C.)					
Brass..............	0.035	0.035				
Cast iron..........	.....	0.21		(Liquid 0.29)		
Steel..............	.....	0.08		(Liquid 0.28)		

TABLE 21

TOTAL EMISSIVITY OF MISCELLANEOUS MATERIALS

(Most values are uncertain by 10 to 30 per cent.   In many cases value depends on particle size)

Material	Temp. (°C)	ϵ_t
Aluminum (oxidized)	200 600	0.11 0.19
Brass (oxidized)	200 600	0.61 0.59
Calorized copper	100 500	0.26 0.26
Calorized copper (oxidized)	200 600	0.18 0.19
Calorized steel (oxidized)	200 600	0.52 0.57
Cast iron (strongly oxidized)	40 250	0.95 0.95
Cast iron (oxidized)	200 600	0.64 0.78
Copper (oxidized)	200 1000	0.6 0.6
Fire brick	1000	0.75
[1]Glass, smooth	20	.937
Gold enamel	100	0.37
[1]Hoar frost (.1 to. 2mm. thick)	0	.985
Iron (oxidized)	100 500 1200	0.74 0.84 0.89
Iron (rusted)	25	0.65
Lead (oxidized)	200	0.63
Monel (oxidized)	200 600	0.43 0.43
Nickel (oxidized)	200 1200	0.37 0.85
[1]Plaster, rough lime	10–90	.91
Silica brick	1000 1100	0.80 0.85
Steel (oxidized)	25 200 600	0.80 0.79 0.79
Steel plate (rough)	40 400	0.94 0.97
[1]Water [1]Wet ice	20 0	.965 .966
Wrought iron (dull oxidized)	25 350	0.94 0.94
20Ni-25Cr-55Fe (oxidized)	200 500	0.90 0.97
60Ni-12Cr-28Fe (oxidized)	270 560	0.89 0.82
80Ni-20C (oxidized)	100 600 1300	0.87 0.87 0.89

[1] H. W. McAdams, *Heat Transmission*, Table I, "from Hottel."   New York: McGraw-Hill, 1933, p. 383.

TABLE 22

TRUE TEMPERATURES CORRESPONDING TO VARIOUS EMISSIVITIES AND
VARIOUS TEMPERATURES OBSERVED WITH AN OPTICAL PYROMETER

(Temperatures, in °C, are for $\lambda = 0.65\mu$ and $c_2 = 1.432$ cm deg)

Spectral emis-sivity	Observed temperature in headings, true temperature in the body of the table										
	.700	800	900	1000	1100	1200	1300	1400	1600	1800	2000
0.05	848	983	1123	1266	1415	1569	1728	1849	2240	2614	3017
0.10	810	935	1064	1195	1330	1468	1609	1754	2056	2373	2708
0.15	789	909	1032	1157	1284	1414	1546	1682	1960	2250	2552
0.20	774	891	1010	1130	1253	1378	1504	1633	1897	2170	2453
0.25	763	878	993	1111	1230	1350	1473	1597	1850	2111	2379
0.30	755	867	980	1095	1211	1329	1448	1568	1814	2065	2322
0.35	747	858	969	1082	1196	1311	1427	1545	1783	2027	2276
0.40	741	850	960	1071	1183	1296	1410	1525	1758	1996	2237
0.45	736	843	952	1062	1172	1283	1395	1508	1736	1968	2204
0.50	731	837	945	1053	1162	1272	1382	1493	1717	1945	2175
0.55	726	832	939	1046	1153	1261	1370	1480	1700	1923	2149
0.60	722	827	933	1039	1145	1252	1360	1467	1685	1905	2126
0.65	719	823	927	1032	1138	1244	1350	1457	1671	1888	2106
0.70	716	819	923	1027	1131	1236	1341	1447	1659	1872	2087
0.75	712	815	917	1021	1125	1229	1333	1437	1647	1858	2069
0.80	710	812	914	1017	1119	1222	1325	1429	1636	1844	2054
0.85	707	809	910	1012	1114	1216	1318	1421	1626	1832	2039
0.90	704	805	907	1008	1109	1210	1312	1413	1617	1821	2025
0.95	702	803	903	1004	1104	1205	1306	1407	1608	1810	2012
1.00	700	800	900	1000	1100	1200	1300	1400	1600	1800	2000

TABLE 22 (*Continued*)

TRUE TEMPERATURES CORRESPONDING TO VARIOUS VALUES OF TOTAL
EMISSIVITY AND VARIOUS BRIGHTNESS TEMPERATURES

(All temperatures in °C)

Total emis-sivity	Observed temperature in headings, true temperature in body of table										
	100	200	300	400	600	800	1000	1200	1400	1600	1800
0.05	422	686	916	1137	1567	1993	2317	2841	3264	3687	4110
0.10	316	536	728	913	1275	1632	1989	2345	2701	3057	3413
0.15	264	460	633	799	1126	1449	1771	2093	2415	2736	3058
0.20	231	410	571	725	1029	1330	1629	1929	2228	2527	2827
0.25	207	375	526	672	958	1243	1526	1809	2093	2376	2658
0.30	189	347	491	630	904	1175	1446	1717	1987	2258	2528
0.35	175	325	463	596	860	1121	1381	1642	1902	2162	2422
0.40	164	307	439	568	823	1075	1327	1579	1830	2082	2333
0.45	154	291	419	544	791	1036	1281	1525	1769	2014	2258
0.50	146	278	402	523	763	1002	1240	1478	1716	1954	2192
0.55	138	266	387	505	739	972	1204	1437	1669	1902	2134
0.60	132	255	373	489	718	945	1173	1400	1628	1855	2082
0.65	126	246	361	474	698	921	1144	1367	1590	1813	2036
0.70	121	238	350	461	680	900	1119	1337	1556	1775	1993
0.75	117	230	340	448	664	880	1095	1310	1525	1740	1955
0.80	113	223	331	437	649	861	1073	1284	1496	1707	1919
0.85	109	217	322	427	636	844	1053	1261	1469	1678	1886
0.90	106	211	314	417	623	828	1034	1239	1445	1650	1855
0.95	103	205	307	408	611	814	1016	1219	1422	1624	1827
1.00	100	200	300	400	600	800	1000	1200	1400	1600	1800

TABLE 23

Properties of Tungsten

(The values of ϵ_c, T_c, and $T_{0.65\mu}$ have been calculated from the spectral emissivities $\epsilon_{0.65\mu}$ and $\epsilon_{0.467\mu}$)

True temperature (T °K)	Relative resistance (R_T/R_{273})	Normal brightness (New candles per cm²)	Spectral emissivity		Color emissivity (ϵ_c)	Total emissivity ϵ_t	Brightness temperature $T_{0.65\mu}$	Color temperature T_c
			$\epsilon_{0.65\mu}$	$\epsilon_{0.467\mu}$				
300	1.12	....	0.472	0.505	.....	0.032		
400	1.58	....	....	....	.....	.042		
500	2.07	....	....	....	.....	.053		
600	2.58	....	....	....	.....	.064		
700	3.11	....	....	....	.....	.076		
800	3.65	....	....	....	.....	.088		
900	4.21	....	....	....	.....	.101		
1000	4.78	0.0001	.458	.486	0.395	.114	966	1007
1100	5.36	0.001	.456	.484	.392	.128	1059	1108
1200	5.95	0.006	.454	.482	.390	.143	1151	1210
1300	6.55	0.029	.452	.480	.387	.158	1242	1312
1400	7.16	0.11	.450	.478	.385	.175	1332	1414
1500	7.78	0.33	.448	.476	.382	.192	1422	1516
1600	8.41	0.92	.446	.475	.380	.207	1511	1619
1700	9.04	2.3	.444	.473	.377	.222	1599	1722
1800	9.69	5.1	.442	.472	.374	.236	1687	1825
1900	10.34	10.4	.440	.470	.371	.249	1774	1928
2000	11.00	20.0	.438	.469	.368	.260	1861	2032
2100	11.65	36	.436	.467	.365	.270	1946	2136
2200	12.33	61	.434	.466	.362	.279	2031	2241
2300	13.01	101	.432	.464	.359	.288	2115	2345
2400	13.69	157	.430	.463	.356	.296	2198	2451
2500	14.38	240	.428	.462	.353	.303	2280	2556
2600	15.08	350	.426	.460	.349	.311	2362	2662
2700	15.78	500	.424	.459	.346	.318	2443	2769
2800	16.48	690	.422	.458	.343	.323	2523	2876
2900	17.19	950	.420	.456	.340	.329	2602	2984
3000	17.90	1260	.418	.455	.336	.334	2681	3092
3100	18.62	1650	.416	.454	.333	.337	2759	3200
3200	19.35	2100	.414	.452	.330	.341	2837	3310
3300	20.08	2700	.412	.451	.326	.344	2913	3420
3400	20.82	3400	.410	.450	.323	.348	2989	3530
3500	21.56	4200	.408	.449	.320	.351	3063	3642
3600	22.30	5200	.406	.447	.317	.354	3137	3754

TABLE 24

SATURATED WATER VAPOR

(Showing pressure P and density d of aqueous vapor saturated at temperature t; or showing boiling point t of water and density d of steam corresponding to a pressure P)

t, °C	P, mm of mercury	d, gm/cm³	t, °C	P, mm of mercury	d, gm/cm³
−10	2.0	2.2×10^{-6}	80.0	355.1	293.8×10^{-6}
− 9	2.1	2.4	85.0	433.5	354.1
− 8	2.3	2.6	90.0	525.8	424.1
− 7	2.6	2.8	91.0	546.1	439.5
− 6	2.8	3.0	92.0	567.1	455.2
− 5	3.0	3.3	93.0	588.7	471.3
− 4	3.3	3.5	94.0	611.0	487.8
− 3	3.6	3.8	95.0	634.0	505
− 2	3.9	4.1	96.0	657.7	523
− 1	4.2	4.5	96.5	669.8	
0	4.6	4.9	97.0	682.1	541
1	4.9	5.2	97.5	694.5	
2	5.3	5.6	98.0	707.3	560
3	5.7	5.9	98.2	712.5	
4	6.1	6.4	98.4	717.6	
5	6.5	6.8	98.6	722.8	
6	7.0	7.3	98.8	728.0	
7	7.5	7.8	99.0	733.3	579
8	8.0	8.3	99.2	738.6	
9	8.6	8.8	99.4	743.9	
10	9.2	9.4	99.6	749.3	
11	9.8	10.0	99.8	754.7	
12	10.5	10.7	100.0	760.0	598
13	11.2	11.4	100.2	765.5	
14	12.0	12.1	100.4	770.9	
15	12.8	12.8	100.6	776.4	
16	13.6	13.6	100.8	781.9	
17	14.5	14.5	101	787.5	618
18	15.5	15.4	102	815.9	639
19	16.5	16.3	103	845.1	661
20	17.6	17.3	104	875.1	683
21	18.7	18.3	105	906.1	705
22	19.8	19.4	106	937.9	728
23	21.1	20.6	107	970.6	751
24	22.4	21.8	108	1,004.3	776
25	23.8	23.0	109	1,038.8	801
26	25.2	24.4	110	1,074.5	827
27	26.8	25.8	112	1,148.7	880
28	28.4	27.2	114	1,227.1	936
29	30.1	28.8	116	1,309.8	995
30	31.8	30.4	118	1,397.0	1,057
35	42.0	39.6	120	1,489	1,122
40	55.1	51.1	125	1,740	1,299
45	71.7	65.6	130	2,026	1,498
50	92.3	83.2	135	2,348	1,721
55	117.8	104.6	140	2,710	1,968
60	149.2	130.5	150	3,569	2,550
65	187.4	161.5	160	4,633	3,265
70	233.5	198.4	175	6,689	4,621
75	289.0	242.1	200	11,650	7,840

TABLE 25
TRIGONOMETRIC FUNCTIONS

Radians	Degrees	Sines	Cosines	Tangents	Cotangents		
.0000	0	.0000	1.0000	.0000	∝	90	1.5708
.0175	1	.0175	.9998	.0175	57.29	89	1.5533
.0349	2	.0349	.9994	.0349	28.64	88	1.5359
.0524	3	.0523	.9986	.0524	19.08	87	1.5184
.0698	4	.0698	.9976	.0699	14.30	86	1.5010
.0873	5	.0872	.9962	.0875	11.430	85	1.4835
.1047	6	.1045	.9945	.1051	9.514	84	1.4661
.1222	7	.1219	.9925	.1228	8.144	83	1.4486
.1396	8	.1392	.9903	.1405	7.115	82	1.4312
.1571	9	.1564	.9877	.1584	6.314	81	1.4137
.1745	10	.1736	.9848	.1763	5.671	80	1.3963
.1920	11	.1908	.9816	.1944	5.145	79	1.3788
.2094	12	.2079	.9781	.2126	4.705	78	1.3614
.2269	13	.2250	.9744	.2309	4.332	77	1.3439
.2443	14	.2419	.9703	.2493	4.011	76	1.3265
.2618	15	.2588	.9659	.2679	3.732	75	1.3090
.2793	16	.2756	.9613	.2867	3.487	74	1.2915
.2967	17	.2924	.9563	.3057	3.271	73	1.2741
.3142	18	.3090	.9511	.3249	3.078	72	1.2566
.3316	19	.3256	.9455	.3443	2.904	71	1.2392
.3491	20	.3420	.9397	.3640	2.748	70	1.2217
.3665	21	.3584	.9336	.3839	2.605	69	1.2043
.3840	22	.3746	.9272	.4040	2.475	68	1.1868
.4014	23	.3907	.9205	.4245	2.356	67	1.1694
.4189	24	.4067	.9135	.4452	2.246	66	1.1519
.4363	25	.4226	.9063	.4663	2.144	65	1.1345
.4538	26	.4384	.8988	.4877	2.050	64	1.1170
.4712	27	.4540	.8910	.5095	1.963	63	1.0996
.4887	28	.4695	.8829	.5317	1.881	62	1.0821
.5061	29	.4848	.8746	.5543	1.804	61	1.0647
.5236	30	.5000	.8660	.5774	1.732	60	1.0472
.5411	31	.5150	.8572	.6009	1.664	59	1.0297
.5585	32	.5299	.8480	.6249	1.600	58	1.0123
.5760	33	.5446	.8387	.6494	1.540	57	0.9948
.5934	34	.5592	.8290	.6745	1.483	56	0.9774
.6109	35	.5736	.8192	.7002	1.428	55	0.9599
.6283	36	.5878	.8090	.7265	1.376	54	0.9425
.6458	37	.6018	.7986	.7536	1.327	53	0.9250
.6632	38	.6157	.7880	.7813	1.280	52	0.9076
.6807	39	.6293	.7771	.8098	1.235	51	0.8901
.6981	40	.6428	.7660	.8391	1.192	50	0.8727
.7156	41	.6561	.7547	.8693	1.150	49	0.8552
.7330	42	.6691	.7431	.9004	1.111	48	0.8378
.7505	43	.6820	.7314	.9325	1.072	47	0.8203
.7679	44	.6947	.7193	.9657	1.036	46	0.8029
.7854	45	.7071	.7071	1.0000	1.000	45	0.7854
		Cosines	Sines	Cotangents	Tangents	Degrees	Radians

TABLE 26

LOGARITHMS TO THE BASE e

These two pages give the natural (hyperbolic, or Napierian) logarithms of numbers between 1 and 10, correct to four places. Moving the decimal point n places to the right (or left) in the number is equivalent to adding n times 2.3026 (or n times 3.6974) to the logarithm.

1	**2.3026**	1	**0.6974–3**
2	4.6052	2	0.3948–5
3	6.9078	3	0.0922–7
4	9.2103	4	0.7897–10
5	11.5129	5	0.4871–12
6	13.8155	6	0.1845–14
7	16.1181	7	0.8819–17
8	18.4207	8	0.5793–19
9	20.7233	9	0 2767–21

	0	1	2	3	4	5	6	7	8	9	10	Tenths of the Tabular Difference 1 2 3 4 5
1.0	0.0000	0100	0198	0296	0392	0488	0583	0677	0770	0862	0.0953	10 19 29 38 48
1.1	0953	1044	1133	1222	1310	1398	1484	1570	1655	1740	1823	9 17 26 35 44
1.2	1823	1906	1989	2070	2151	2231	2311	2390	2469	2546	2624	8 16 24 32 40
1.3	2624	2700	2776	2852	2927	3001	3075	3148	3221	3293	3365	7 15 22 30 37
1.4	3365	3436	3507	3577	3646	3716	3784	3853	3920	3988	4055	7 14 21 28 34
1.5	4055	4121	4187	4253	4318	4383	4447	4511	4574	4637	4700	6 13 19 26 32
1.6	4700	4762	4824	4886	4947	5008	5068	5128	5188	5247	5306	6 12 18 24 30
1.7	5306	5365	5423	5481	5539	5596	5653	5710	5766	5822	5878	6 11 17 23 29
1.8	5878	5933	5988	6043	6098	6152	6206	6259	6313	6366	6419	5 11 16 22 27
1.9	6419	6471	6523	6575	6627	6678	6729	6780	6831	6881	0.6931	5 10 15 21 26
2.0	0.6931	6981	7031	7080	7129	7178	7227	7275	7324	7372	7419	5 10 15 20 24
2.1	7419	7467	7514	7561	7608	7655	7701	7747	7793	7839	7885	5 9 14 19 23
2.2	7885	7930	7975	8020	8065	8109	8154	8198	8242	8286	8329	4 9 13 18 22
2.3	8329	8372	8416	8459	8502	8544	8587	8629	8671	8713	8755	4 9 13 17 21
2.4	8755	8796	8838	8879	8920	8961	9002	9042	9083	9123	9163	4 8 12 16 20
2.5	9163	9203	9243	9282	9322	9361	9400	9439	9478	9517	9555	4 8 12 16 20
2.6	9555	9594	9632	9670	9708	9746	9783	9821	9858	9895	0.9933	4 8 11 15 19
2.7	0.9933	9969	0006	0043	0080	0116	0152	0188	0225	0260	1.0296	4 7 11 15 18
2.8	1.0296	0332	0367	0403	0438	0473	0508	0543	0578	0613	0647	4 7 11 14 18
2.9	0647	0682	0716	0750	0784	0818	0852	0886	0919	0953	1.0986	3 7 10 14 17
3.0	1.0986	1019	1053	1086	1119	1151	1184	1217	1249	1282	1314	3 7 10 13 16
3.1	1314	1346	1378	1410	1442	1474	1506	1537	1569	1600	1632	3 6 10 13 16
3.2	1632	1663	1694	1725	1756	1787	1817	1848	1878	1909	1939	3 6 9 12 15
3.3	1939	1969	2000	2030	2060	2090	2119	2149	2179	2208	2238	3 6 9 12 15
3.4	2238	2267	2296	2326	2355	2384	2413	2442	2470	2499	2528	3 6 9 12 14
3.5	2528	2556	2585	2613	2641	2669	2698	2726	2754	2782	2809	3 6 8 11 14
3.6	2809	2837	2865	2892	2920	2947	2975	3002	3029	3056	3083	3 5 8 11 14
3.7	3083	3110	3137	3164	3191	3218	3244	3271	3297	3324	3350	3 5 8 11 13
3.8	3350	3376	3403	3429	3455	3481	3507	3533	3558	3584	3610	3 5 8 10 13
3.9	3610	3635	3661	3686	3712	3737	3762	3788	3813	3838	1.3863	3 5 8 10 13
4.0	1.3863	3888	3913	3938	3962	3987	4012	4036	4061	4085	4110	2 5 7 10 12
4.1	4110	4134	4159	4183	4207	4231	4255	4279	4303	4327	4351	2 5 7 10 12
4.2	4351	4375	4398	4422	4446	4469	4493	4516	4540	4563	4586	2 5 7 9 12
4.3	4586	4609	4633	4656	4679	4702	4725	4748	4770	4793	4816	2 5 7 9 11
4.4	4816	4839	4861	4884	4907	4929	4951	4974	4996	5019	5041	2 4 7 9 11
4.5	5041	5063	5085	5107	5129	5151	5173	5195	5217	5239	5261	2 4 7 9 11
4.6	5261	5282	5304	5326	5347	5369	5390	5412	5433	5454	5476	2 4 6 9 11
4.7	5476	5497	5518	5539	5560	5581	5602	5623	5644	5665	5686	2 4 6 8 11
4.8	5686	5707	5728	5748	5769	5790	5810	5831	5851	5872	5892	2 4 6 8 10
4.9	5892	5913	5933	5953	5974	5994	6014	6034	6054	6074	1.6094	2 4 6 8 10

TABLE 26 (Continued)

Log_e (Base $e = 2.718284$)

	0	1	2	3	4	5	6	7	8	9	10	Tenths of the Tabular Difference 1 2 3 4 5
5.0	1.6094	6114	6134	6154	6174	6194	6214	6233	6253	6273	6292	2 4 6 8 10
5.1	6292	6312	6332	6351	6371	6390	6409	6429	6448	6467	6487	2 4 6 8 10
5.2	6487	6506	6525	6544	6563	6582	6601	6620	6639	6658	6677	2 4 6 8 10
5.3	6677	6696	6715	6734	6752	6771	6790	6808	6827	6845	6864	2 4 6 7 9
5.4	6864	6882	6901	6919	6938	6956	6974	6993	7011	7029	7047	2 4 6 7 9
5.5	7047	7066	7084	7102	7120	7138	7156	7174	7192	7210	7228	2 4 5 7 9
5.6	7228	7246	7263	7281	7299	7317	7334	7352	7370	7387	7405	2 4 5 7 9
5.7	7405	7422	7440	7457	7475	7492	7509	7527	7544	7561	7579	2 3 5 7 9
5.8	7579	7596	7613	7630	7647	7664	7681	7699	7716	7733	7750	2 3 5 7 9
5.9	7750	7766	7783	7800	7817	7834	7851	7867	7884	7901	1.7918	2 3 5 7 8
6.0	1.7918	7934	7951	7967	7984	8001	8017	8034	8050	8066	8083	2 3 5 7 8
6.1	8083	8099	8116	8132	8148	8165	8181	8197	8213	8229	8245	2 3 5 7 8
6.2	8245	8262	8278	8294	8310	8326	8342	8358	8374	8390	8405	2 3 5 6 8
6.3	8405	8421	8437	8453	8469	8485	8500	8516	8532	8547	8563	2 3 5 6 8
6.4	8563	8579	8594	8610	8625	8641	8656	8672	8687	8703	8718	2 3 5 6 8
6.5	8718	8733	8749	8764	8779	8795	8810	8825	8840	8856	8871	2 3 5 6 8
6.6	8871	8886	8901	8916	8931	8946	8961	8976	8991	9006	9021	2 3 5 6 8
6.7	9021	9036	9051	9066	9081	9095	9110	9125	9140	9155	9169	1 3 4 6 7
6.8	9169	9184	9199	9213	9228	9242	9257	9272	9286	9301	9315	1 3 4 6 7
6.9	9315	9330	9344	9359	9373	9387	9402	9416	9430	9445	1.9459	1 3 4 6 7
7.0	1.9459	9473	9488	9502	9516	9530	9544	9559	9573	9587	9601	1 3 4 6 7
7.1	9601	9615	9629	9643	9657	9671	9685	9699	9713	9727	9741	1 3 4 6 7
7.2	9741	9755	9769	9782	9796	9810	9824	9838	9851	9865	1.9879	1 3 4 6 7
7.3	1.9879	9892	9906	9920	9933	9947	9961	9974	9988	∫0001	2.0015	1 3 4 5 7
7.4	2.0015	0028	0042	0055	0069	0082	0096	0109	0122	0136	0149	1 3 4 5 7
7.5	0149	0162	0176	0189	0202	0215	0229	0242	0255	0268	0281	1 3 4 5 7
7.6	0281	0295	0308	0321	0334	0347	0360	0373	0386	0399	0412	1 3 4 5 7
7.7	0412	0425	0438	0451	0464	0477	0490	0503	0516	0528	0541	1 3 4 5 6
7.8	0541	0554	0567	0580	0592	0605	0618	0631	0643	0656	0669	1 3 4 5 6
7.9	0669	0681	0694	0707	0719	0732	0744	0757	0769	0782	2.0794	1 3 4 5 6
8.0	2.0794	0807	0819	0832	0844	0857	0869	0882	0894	0906	0919	1 2 4 5 6
8.1	0919	0931	0943	0956	0968	0980	0992	1005	1017	1029	1041	1 2 4 5 6
8.2	1041	1054	1066	1078	1090	1102	1114	1126	1138	1150	1163	1 2 4 5 6
8.3	1163	1175	1187	1199	1211	1223	1235	1247	1258	1270	1282	1 2 4 5 6
8.4	1282	1294	1306	1318	1330	1342	1353	1365	1377	1389	1401	1 2 4 5 6
8.5	1401	1412	1424	1436	1448	1459	1471	1483	1494	1506	1518	1 2 4 5 6
8.6	1518	1529	1541	1552	1564	1576	1587	1599	1610	1622	1633	1 2 3 5 6
8.7	1633	1645	1656	1668	1679	1691	1702	1713	1725	1736	1748	1 2 3 5 6
8.8	1748	1759	1770	1782	1793	1804	1815	1827	1838	1849	1861	1 2 3 5 6
8.9	1861	1872	1883	1894	1905	1917	1928	1939	1950	1961	2.1972	1 2 3 4 6
9.0	2.1972	1983	1994	2006	2017	2028	2039	2050	2061	2072	2083	1 2 3 4 6
9.1	2083	2094	2105	2116	2127	2138	2148	2159	2170	2181	2192	1 2 3 4 5
9.2	2192	2203	2214	2225	2235	2246	2257	2268	2279	2289	2300	1 2 3 4 5
9.3	2300	2311	2322	2332	2343	2354	2364	2375	2386	2396	2407	1 2 3 4 5
9.4	2407	2418	2428	2439	2450	2460	2471	2481	2492	2502	2513	1 2 3 4 5
9.5	2513	2523	2534	2544	2555	2565	2576	2586	2597	2607	2618	1 2 3 4 5
9.6	2618	2628	2638	2649	2659	2670	2680	2690	2701	2711	2721	1 2 3 4 5
9.7	2721	2732	2742	2752	2762	2773	2783	2793	2803	2814	2824	1 2 3.4 5
9.8	2824	2834	2844	2854	2865	2875	2885	2895	2905	2915	2925	1 2 3 4 5
9.9	2925	2935	2946	2956	2966	2976	2986	2996	3006	3016	2.3026	1 2 3 4 5

TABLE 27

Logarithms to the Base 10

Only the mantissa (or fractional part) of the logarithm is given. Each mantissa should be preceded by a decimal point and the proper characteristic.

100–500

N	0	1	2	3	4	5	6	7	8	9
10	0000	0043	0086	0128	0170	0212	0253	0294	0334	0374
11	0414	0453	0492	0531	0569	0607	0645	0682	0719	0755
12	0792	0828	0864	0899	0934	0969	1004	1038	1072	1106
13	1139	1173	1206	1239	1271	1303	1335	1367	1399	1430
14	1461	1492	1523	1553	1584	1614	1644	1673	1703	1732
15	1761	1790	1818	1847	1875	1903	1931	1959	1987	2014
16	2041	2068	2095	2122	2148	2175	2201	2227	2253	2279
17	2304	2330	2355	2380	2405	2430	2455	2480	2504	2529
18	2553	2577	2601	2625	2648	2672	2695	2718	2742	2765
19	2788	2810	2833	2856	2878	2900	2923	2945	2967	2989
20	3010	3032	3054	3075	3096	3118	3139	3160	3181	3201
21	3222	3243	3263	3284	3304	3324	3345	3365	3385	3404
22	3424	3444	3464	3483	3502	3522	3541	3560	3579	3598
23	3617	3636	3655	3674	3692	3711	3729	3747	3766	3784
24	3802	3820	3838	3856	2874	3892	3909	3927	3945	3962
25	3979	3997	4014	4031	4048	4065	4082	4099	4116	4133
26	4150	4166	4183	4200	4216	4232	4249	4265	4281	4298
27	4314	4330	4346	4362	4378	4393	4409	4425	4440	4456
28	4472	4487	4502	4518	4533	4548	4564	4579	4594	4609
29	4624	4639	4654	4669	4683	4698	4713	4728	4742	4757
30	4771	4786	4800	4814	4829	4843	4857	4871	4886	4900
31	4914	4928	4942	4955	4969	4983	4997	5011	5024	5038
32	5051	5065	5079	5092	5105	5119	5132	5145	5159	5172
33	5185	5198	5211	5224	4237	5250	5263	5276	5289	5302
34	5315	5328	5340	5353	5366	5378	5391	5403	5416	5428
35	5441	5453	5465	5478	5490	5502	5514	5527	5539	5551
36	5563	5575	5587	5599	5611	5623	5635	5647	5658	5670
37	5682	5694	5705	5717	5729	5740	5752	5763	5775	5786
38	5798	5809	5821	5832	5843	5855	5866	5877	5888	5899
39	5911	5922	5933	5944	5955	5966	5977	5988	5999	6010
40	6021	6031	6042	6053	6064	6075	6085	6096	6107	6117
41	6128	6138	6149	6160	6170	6180	6191	6201	6212	6222
42	6232	6243	6253	6263	6274	6284	6294	6304	6314	6325
43	6335	6345	6355	6365	6375	6385	6395	6405	6415	6425
44	6435	6444	6454	6464	6474	6484	6493	6503	6513	6522
45	6532	6542	6551	6561	6571	6580	6590	6599	6609	6618
46	6628	6637	6646	6656	6665	6675	6684	6693	6702	6712
47	6721	6730	6739	6749	6758	6767	6776	6785	6794	6803
48	6812	6821	6830	6839	6848	6857	6866	6875	6884	6893
49	6902	6911	6920	6928	6937	6946	6955	6964	6972	6981
50	6990	6998	7007	7016	7024	7033	7042	7050	7059	7067
N	0	1	2	3	4	5	6	7	8	9

100–500

TABLE 27 (*Continued*)
LOGARITHMS TO THE BASE 10
500–1000

N	0	1	2	3	4	5	6	7	8	9
50	6990	6998	7007	7016	7024	7033	7042	7050	7059	7067
51	7076	7084	7093	7101	7110	7118	7126	7135	7143	7152
52	7160	6168	7177	7185	7193	7202	7210	7218	7226	7235
53	7243	7251	7259	7267	7275	7284	7292	7300	7308	7316
54	7324	7332	7340	7348	7356	7364	7372	7380	7388	7396
55	7404	7412	7419	7427	7435	7443	7451	7459	7466	7474
56	7482	7490	7497	7505	7513	7520	7528	7536	7543	7551
57	7559	7566	7574	7582	7589	7597	7604	7612	7619	7627
58	7634	7642	7649	7657	7664	7672	7679	7686	7694	7701
59	7709	7716	7723	7731	7738	7745	7752	7760	7767	7774
60	7782	7789	7796	7803	7810	7818	7825	7832	7839	7846
61	7853	7860	7868	7875	7882	7889	7896	7903	7910	7917
62	7924	7931	7938	7945	7952	7959	7966	7973	7980	7987
63	7993	8000	8007	8014	8021	8028	8035	8041	8048	8055
64	8062	8069	8075	8082	8089	8096	8102	8109	8116	8122
65	8129	8136	8142	8149	8156	8162	8169	8176	8182	8189
66	8195	8202	8209	8215	8222	8228	8235	8241	8248	8254
67	8261	8267	8274	8280	8287	8293	8299	8306	8312	8319
68	8325	8331	8338	8344	8351	8357	8363	8370	8376	8382
69	8388	8395	8401	8407	8414	8420	8426	3432	8439	8445
70	8451	8457	8463	8470	8476	8482	8488	8494	8500	8506
71	8513	8519	8525	8531	8537	8543	8549	8555	8561	8567
72	8573	8579	8585	8591	8597	8603	8609	8615	8621	8627
73	8633	8639	8645	8651	8657	8663	8669	8675	8681	8686
74	8692	8698	8704	8710	8716	8722	8727	8733	8739	8745
75	8751	8756	8762	8768	8774	8779	8785	8791	8797	8802
76	8808	8814	8820	8825	8831	8837	8842	8848	8854	8859
77	8865	8871	8876	8882	8887	8893	8899	8904	8910	8915
78	8921	8927	8932	8938	8943	8949	8954	8960	8965	8971
79	8976	8982	8987	8993	8998	9004	9009	9015	9020	9025
80	9031	9036	9042	9047	9053	9058	9063	9069	9074	9079
81	9085	9090	9096	9101	9106	9112	9117	9122	9128	9133
82	9138	9143	9149	9154	9159	9165	9170	9175	9180	9186
83	9191	9196	9201	9206	9212	9217	9222	9227	9232	9238
84	9240	9248	9253	9258	9263	9269	9274	9279	9284	9289
85	9294	9299	9304	9309	9315	9320	9325	9330	9335	9340
86	9345	9350	9355	9360	9365	9370	9375	9380	9385	9390
87	9395	9400	9405	9410	9415	9420	9425	9430	9435	9440
88	9445	9450	9455	9460	9465	9469	9474	9479	3884	9489
89	9494	9499	9504	9509	9513	9518	9523	9528	9533	9538
90	9542	9547	9552	9557	9562	9566	9571	9576	9581	9586
91	9590	9595	9600	9605	9609	9614	9619	9624	9628	9633
92	9638	9643	9647	9652	9657	9661	9666	9671	9675	9680
93	9685	9689	9694	9699	9703	9708	9713	9717	9722	9727
94	9731	9736	9741	9745	9750	9754	9759	9763	9768	9773
95	9777	9782	9786	9791	9795	9800	9805	9809	9814	9818
96	9823	9827	9832	9836	9841	9845	9850	9854	9859	9863
97	9868	9872	9877	9881	9886	9890	9894	9899	9903	9908
98	9912	9917	9921	9926	9930	9934	9939	9943	9948	9952
99	9956	9961	9965	9969	9974	9978	9983	9987	9991	9996
100	0000	0004	0009	0013	0017	0022	0026	0030	0035	0039
U	0	1	2	3	4	5	6	7	8	9

500–1000

Index

||||||||||||||||||||||